Instructor's Resource Manual
to accompany

Medical Law and Ethics

Third Edition

Bonnie F. Fremgen, Ph.D.

PEARSON

Prentice
Hall

Upper Saddle River, New Jersey 07458

Copyright © 2009, 2006, 2002 by Pearson Education, Inc., Upper Saddle River, New Jersey 07458.
All rights reserved. Printed in the United States of America. This publication is protected by Copyright and permission should be obtained from the publisher prior to any prohibited reproduction, storage in a retrieval system, or transmission in any form or by any means, electronic, mechanical, photocopying, recording, or likewise. For information regarding permission(s), write to: Rights and Permissions Department.

Pearson Prentice Hall™ is a trademark of Pearson Education, Inc.
Pearson® is a registered trademark of Pearson plc
Prentice Hall® is a registered trademark of Pearson Education, Inc.

Pearson Education, Ltd., London
Pearson Education Singapore, Pte. Ltd.
Pearson Education, Canada, Inc.
Pearson Education–Japan
Pearson Education Australia PTY, Limited

Pearson Education North Asia, Ltd., Hong Kong
Pearson Educación de Mexico, S.A. de C.V.
Pearson Education Malaysia, Pte. Ltd.
Pearson Education, Upper Saddle River, New Jersey

10 9 8 7 6 5 4 3 2 1

ISBN-13 978-0-13-515066-5
ISBN-10   0-13-515066-3

Contents

Preface

Thank you for adopting *Medical Law and Ethics, 3/e.* Answers to the textbook questions are provided, and additional questions are included that can be used to determine students' comprehension of the material.

The study of law, and particularly ethics, is not always black and white. The discussion questions, exercises, and cases used within the textbook are meant to stimulate the student's awareness of this subject. They are not meant to offer definitive answers in all situations. The students do not have to memorize the case names or legal citations. All the cases are based on real situations that either the author or the legal community have observed. However, not all the cases ended up in court.

By selecting *Medical Law and Ethics, 3/e* as your textbook you have given yourself access to a wide variety of excellent text-specific instructional tools. In the pages of this preface that follow, I will introduce you to these resources.

Instructor's Resource Manual

The goal of this manual is to help you synthesize all of the resources you now have at your disposal in connection with your adoption of *Medical Law and Ethics, 3/e.* The manual is designed not only to aid your course preparation, but also to help you truly shine in the classroom.

Each chapter includes the following features:

Short Case
Learning Objectives
Glossary
Introduction
Med Tips
Points to Ponder
Discussion Questions
Practice Exercises
   Matching Questions
   Multiple-Choice Questions
   Fill-in-the-Blanks Questions
Put It Into Practice
Web Hunt
Case Study
Bibliography

Learning Objectives

Objectives that can be used by the student as a review are included for every chapter.

Glossary

The major glossary terms used in the chapter are listed alphabetically at the beginning of each chapter. Glossary terms are printed in bold the first time they are defined in the text. There is a complete glossary at the end of the book.

Short Case

A brief case is included at the beginning of each chapter to stimulate discussion as the student begins to read the chapter material. After reading the chapter, the students can then go back to the beginning case to determine if their original case answers have changed.

Introduction

A brief introduction discusses the major topic of each chapter.

Med Tips

These helpful hints and useful information are placed at strategic points throughout the narrative to stimulate the student's interest in the topic.

Points to Ponder

Several thought-provoking questions are included at the end of each chapter. These are meant to stimulate classroom discussion and promote critical thinking. The Points to Ponder do not always have clear solutions, since ethical questions do not always have a clear right or wrong answer. The author has purposely not added the "right answer" to these since they are only meant as discussion questions.

Discussion Questions

End-of-chapter discussion questions are included to serve as a wrap-up to test the student's comprehension of the chapter material.

Practice Exercises

A variety of matching and multiple-choice questions are included to test the student's understanding of the chapter material. The questions are meant to include a wide-range of average to moderately difficult questions. Instructors may wish to adjust the questions to the level of learning of their own student populations. The individual instructor is the best judge of his or her students' ability.

Matching Questions

The ten matching questions found at the end of each chapter are given to test the student's understanding of vocabulary used within the chapter.

Multiple-Choice Questions

The ten multiple-choice questions are similar to those questions found on certification exams.

Fill-in-the-Blanks Questions

These ten questions are meant to reinforce the glossary terms.

Put It Into Practice

This brief exercise found at the end of each chapter increases the student's understanding of the topic by seeking information that is found outside of the classroom setting. In some cases, the student is asked to interview a practicing healthcare professional to discuss current ethical dilemmas and situations.

In order not to overwhelm or frustrate students, the instructor may wish to assign the exercise to just one or two students and then have them report their findings back to the class. The entire class can then submit a brief written report on the topic. Many office managers are happy to help students with class assignments since they are helping to train the next generation of healthcare professionals. Student responses to this exercise will vary.

Web Hunt

This Internet activity is meant to increase the student's awareness of the usefulness of the Internet in medical practice. Using an Internet address, given at the end of each chapter, the student searches for solutions to an exercise or question that is related to topics discussed within the chapter. Student responses to this exercise will vary according to their interpretation of the Web site information.

Case Study

The case studies given at the end of each chapter are taken from real-life situations. Students may question the importance of including cases that seem to be simplistic, such as stealing textbooks from the books store (Chapter 1) or "reading" a patient's EKG results when the physician is unavailable (Chapter 5). However, these situations have happened, and continue to happen, even though it seems to be common sense not to do this.

For some cases, the student may need to refer to a medical dictionary for assistance with terminology. Possible solutions to the cases are included in the instructor's resource manual. However, the instructor may add additional solutions by drawing upon personal experience.

Bibliography

A list of current references is included that can be used by the instructor or student to gain additional information about the topics discussed within the chapter.

Other components of this manual include:

- Test questions that measure student mastery of pertinent objectives are provided in a variety of formats for use in quizzes and examinations. An electronic version of the test bank can be found in the Instructor's Media Library.
- Worksheets and tests provide you with a comprehensive list of unique assignment options directly correlated to the chapter content.

Instructor's Resource CD-ROM

The Instructor's Resource CD-ROM (0-13-515067-1) is available upon adoption and gives you access to a number of powerful tools in electronic format.

- A 625-question test bank allows instructors to design customized quizzes and exams using our award-winning TestGen 7.0 test-building engine. The Test-Gen wizard steps you through the creation of a simple test with drag-and-drop or point-and-click transfer. You can select test questions either manually or randomly and use online spellchecking and other tools to quickly polish your test content and presentation. You can save your test in a variety of formats both locally and on a network, print up to 25 variations of a single test, and publish your tests in an online course. For more information go to **www.prenhall.com/testgen.**
- A PowerPoint lecture package contains key discussion points, along with color images for each chapter. This feature provides dynamic, fully designed, integrated lectures that are ready to use and allow instructors to customize the materials to meet their specific course needs. These ready-made lectures will save you time and ease the transition into your use of *Medical Law and Ethics.*
- A sample curriculum, which includes the following features for each chapter:
  - Lesson Overview provides a short summary of the essential content covered within the chapter.
  - Detailed Lesson Plans provide teaching stategies that will meet the needs of students with various learning styles.
- An electronic version of this Instructor's Resource Manual in PDF and Word formats.

Other Components of the Teaching and Learning Package

OneKey is Prentice Hall's online course system. Those instructors wishing to facilitate online courses will be able to access a premium online course management option, which is available in WebCT, Blackboard, or CourseCompass formats. OneKey is an integrated online resource that brings a wide array of supplemental resources together in one convenient place for both students and faculty. OneKey features everything you and your students need for out-of-class work, conveniently organized to match your syllabus. OneKey's online course management solution features interactive modules, text and image PowerPoints, animations, videos, and more. OneKey also provides course management tools so faculty can customize course content, build online tests, create assignments, enter grades, post announcements, communicate with students, and much more. Testing materials, gradebooks, and other instructor resources are available in a separate section that can be accessed by instructors only. OneKey content is available in three different platforms. A nationally hosted version is available in the reliable, easy-to-use CourseCompass platform. The same content is also available for download to locally hosted versions of Black-Board and WebCT. Please contact your Pearson Prentice Hall Sales Representative for a demonstration or go online to **www.prenhall.com/onekey.**

Sample Syllabus

The following sample syllabi use the textbook to teach either a sixteen-week course or a ten-week course.

Sample Syllabus (16 weeks, 48 hours)

Week 1	Introduction to Medical Law, Ethics, and Bioethics	Chapter 1
Week 2	The Legal System	Chapter 2
Week 3	The Legal System	Chapter 2
Week 4	Importance of the Legal System for the Physician	Chapter 3
Week 5	Medical Practice and Allied Health Professionals	Chapter 4
Week 6	The Physician–Patient Relationship	Chapter 5
Week 7	Professional Liability and Medical Malpractice	Chapter 6
Week 8	Professional Liability and Medical Malpractice	Chapter 6
Week 9	Public Duties of the Physician	Chapter 7
Week 10	Workplace Law and Ethics	Chapter 8
Week 11	The Medical Record	Chapter 9
Week 12	Confidentiality in Medical Practice	Chapter 10
Week 13	Ethical and Bioethical Issues in Medicine	Chapter 11
Week 14	Ethical Issues Relating to Life	Chapter 12
Week 15	Death and Dying	Chapter 13
Week 16	Review	

Final Examination

Sample Syllabus (10 weeks, 40 hours)

Week 1	Introduction to Medical Law, Ethics, and Bioethics	Chapter 1
Week 2	The Legal System	Chapter 2
Week 3	Importance of the Legal System for the Physician	Chapter 3
	Medical Practice and Allied Health Professionals	Chapter 4
Week 4	The Physician–Patient Relationship	Chapter 5
Week 5	Professional Liability and Medical Malpractice	Chapter 6
Week 6	Public Duties of the Physician	Chapter 7
Week 7	Workplace Law and Ethics	Chapter 8
Week 8	The Medical Record	Chapter 9
	Confidentiality in Medical Practice	Chapter 10
Week 9	Ethical and Bioethical Issues in Medicine	Chapter 11
Week 10	Ethical Issues Relating to Life	Chapter 12
	Death and Dying	Chapter 13

Final Examination

Introduction to Medical Law, Ethics, and Bioethics

CHAPTER SYNOPSIS

The study of medical ethics, or applied ethics, is necessary for healthcare professionals who often face dilemmas that are not experienced by the general population. The fast-paced growth of medical technology has made the study of ethics even more relevant. The study of bioethics, or biomedical ethics, refers to moral dilemmas due to advances in medicine and medical research. Since medical law and ethics are often interrelated, students need to have a clear understanding of both in order to protect themselves, their employer, and the patient. This chapter includes the similarities and differences between ethics, bioethics, and the law. The student is also presented with an easy-to-understand and easy-to-use three-step model for determining if an action might be unethical. The study of ethics includes many questions for which there is no one right answer. The student must become comfortable discussing and debating these issues.

Chapter Lecture Outline	Instructor's Notes

I. Introduction: Interrelatedness of Medical Law, Ethics, and Bioethics
  A. Individuals cannot practice medicine without an understanding.
  B. Applied ethics—It is the practical application of moral standards that concern benefiting the patient.
  C. Medical practitioners must adhere to certain ethical standards and codes of conduct.
  D. Medical ethics is moral conduct based on principles regulating the behavior of health care professionals.
  E. Bioethics refers to moral dilemmas and issues that are a result of advances in medicine and medical research.
II. Why Study Law, Ethics, and Bioethics?
  A. We all believe we know right from wrong.
  B. We do not always make the "right" or correct ethical decisions.
  C. It is important to know the law.
  D. Understanding the law will help protect you and your employer from being sued.
III. Medical Law
  A. Laws—Rules or actions prescribed by a government authority that have a binding legal force.
  B. The law provides a yardstick to measure behavior.
  C. The law punishes certain behaviors in a consistent manner.
  D. Many people believe a behavior is wrong only if the law forbids it.	

Chapter Lecture Outline	Instructor's Notes

IV. Ethics—Several Categories
    A. Utilitarianism—An ethical theory based on the principle of the greatest good for the greatest number.
    B. Rights-Based or Natural Rights-Based Ethics—Emphasis is on individual rights.
    C. Duty-Based Ethics—Focuses on performing one's duty.
    D. Virtue-Based Ethics—Based on character traits, such as integrity, that are morally valued.
        1. Virtues are good habits.
        2. Also known as "seeking the good life."
        3. Aristotle.
    E. Principles or Values That Drive Ethical Behavior
        1. Beneficence.
        2. Fidelity.
        3. Gentleness.
        4. Honesty.
        5. Humility.
        6. Justice.
        7. Perseverance.
        8. Responsibility.
        9. Sanctity of life.
        10. Tolerance.
        11. Work.
    F. Interpersonal Ethics
        1. Definition: The expectation that people will be treated with respect.
        2. Respect.
        3. Integrity.
        4. Honesty.
        5. Fairness.
        6. Empathy.
        7. Sympathy.
        8. Compassion.
        9. Loyalty.
        10. Privacy.
        11. Due process.
        12. Freedom from sexual harassment.
        13. Comparable worth.
 V. Models for Examining Ethical Dilemmas
    A. Three-step ethics model.
    B. Seven-step decision model.
    C. Dr. Bernard Lo's Clinical Model.
VI. Bioethics
    A. Principle of autonomy.
    B. Principle of beneficence.
VII. What Ethics Is Not
    A. Ethics is not just about how you feel.
    B. Ethics is not the same as "feelings."

Chapter Lecture Outline	Instructor's Notes
C. Ethics is not an emotional response. D. Ethics is not just about religious beliefs. VIII. The Role of Ethics Committees IX. Quality Assurance Programs X. Medical Etiquette	

LEARNING OBJECTIVES

(Student answers may vary.)

1. Define the glossary terms.

   Amoral   a lack of or indifference to moral standards.

   Applied ethics   the practical application of moral standards to the conduct of individuals involved in organizations.

   Bioethicists   persons who specialize in the field of bioethics.

   Bioethics   also called biomedical ethics; the moral dilemmas and issues of advanced medicine and medical research.

   Comparable worth   also known as pay equity, the theory that extends equal pay requirements to all persons doing equal work.

   Cost/benefit analysis   also called utilitarianism, an ethical approach in which the benefit of the decision should outweigh all costs.

   Due process   the entitlement of employees of the government and public companies to have certain procedures followed when they believe their rights are in jeopardy.

   Empathy   the ability to understand the feelings of another person without actually experiencing the pain or distress that person is going through.

   Ethics   the branch of philosophy relating to morals or moral principles.

   Fidelity   loyalty and faithfulness to others.

   Integrity   the unwavering adherence to one's principles; dedication to maintaining high standards.

   Laws   rules or actions prescribed by a governmental authority that have a binding legal force.

   Litigious   excessively inclined to sue.

   Medical etiquette   standards of professional behavior that physicians use for conduct with other physicians.

   Medical ethics   moral conduct based on principles regulating the behavior of healthcare professionals.

   Medical practice acts   laws established in all fifty states that define the practice of medicine as well as requirements and methods for licensure in a particular state.

   Precedent   a ruling of an earlier case that is then applied to subsequent cases.

   Principle of autonomy   right to make decisions about one's own life.

   Principle of beneficence   in doing good, we must not harm patients while we are trying to help them.

Principle of nonmaleficence   means "First do no harm."

Quality assurance   gathering and evaluating information about the **services** provided as well as the results achieved and comparing this information with an accepted standard.

Statutes   laws enacted by state and federal legislatures.

Sympathy   pity for someone else.

Tolerance   respect for those whose opinions, practices, race, religion, and nationality differ from our own.

Utilitarianism   an ethical theory based on the principle of the greatest good for the greatest number.

2. Describe the similarities and differences between laws and ethics.
   Student responses may include:

   Similarities
   * Both use reason and logic.
   * Both demonstrate a concern for the welfare of people.
   * Both provide a yardstick by which to measure our actions.

   Differences
   * Laws are considered to be a binding legal force; ethics are not regulated by law as a binding legal force.
   * Some illegal actions may be ethical.
   * Some unethical practices may be legal.

3. Discuss the reasons for studying law, ethics, and bioethics.
   * Without a moral structure for one's actions, people would be free to pursue their own self-Interests.
   * Without some constraints and limitations on our actions, only the interests of the strong might prevail.
   * The words *justice* and *injustice* might have little meaning.
   * In times of crisis, people do not always make the correct ethical decisions.
   * An understanding of the law will protect both the healthcare worker and the physician/employer.

4. Describe how to apply the three decision-making models discussed in this chapter. The three-step ethical model tells us to ask three questions when faced with an ethical dilemma:
   * Is the action legal?
   * Is the action balanced?
   * How will doing this action make me feel?

   If you can answer "yes" to the first two questions, and "good" to the third question, then the action is most likely an ethical one. The instructor might have the students apply this model to personal ethical dilemmas such as lying on a resume, cheating in class, showing up late for work, and taking a book from the bookstore without paying for it.

   The seven-step model uses a fact-gathering technique to assist with decision making. The instructor may wish to have students use this model when examining the cases at the end of each chapter. Since their answers may vary somewhat, it would be beneficial to have them work in teams.

   Dr. Lo's Clinical Model is useful in a clinical setting such as a hospital. The instructor may wish to have the student role-play the parts of healthcare team members: physician, nurse, medical student, social worker, and patient. They might examine an ethical dilemma such as the Mickey Mantle liver transplant case. Even though not all of the students will be working in a clinical setting, it is beneficial for them to experience this problem-solving method.

5. Explain why ethics is not just about the sincerity of one's beliefs, emotions, or religious viewpoints.

   People come from a multitude of backgrounds, both social and ethnic. Ethics is based on concepts of good and bad, right and wrong, just and unjust, fair and unfair. It is not enough to have a "feeling" that something is wrong. One should be able to determine why it is wrong.

THE CASE OF MARGUERITE M. AND THE ANGIOGRAM

Marguerite M., an 89-year-old widow, was admitted into the cardiac intensive care unit in Chicago's Memorial Hospital at 3:00 A.M. on a Sunday morning with a massive heart attack (myocardial infarction). Her internist, Dr. K., who is a close family friend, has ordered an angiogram to determine the status of Marguerite's infarction (heart attack). Dr. K. has found that the angiogram and resulting treatment needs to be done within the first six hours after an infarction in order to be effective. The procedure is going to be done as soon as the on-call surgical team can set up the angiography room. The radiologist, who lives thirty minutes from the hospital, must also be in the hospital before the procedure can begin. At 4:30 A.M. the team is ready to have Marguerite, who is barely conscious, transferred from the intensive care unit (ICU) to the surgical suite.

Coincidentally, at 4:30 A.M., Sarah W., an unconscious 45-year-old woman is brought in by ambulance with a massive heart attack. The emergency room (ER) physicians, after conferring with her physician by phone, conclude that she will need a balloon angiography to save her life. When they call the surgical department to have the on-call angiography team brought in, they are told that the room is already set up for Dr. K.'s patient. They do not have another team or surgical room for Sarah. A decision is made that Sarah, who needs the balloon angiography in order to survive, will receive the procedure.

Dr. K. is called at home and told that his patient, Marguerite, will not be able to have the angiogram. The hospital is going to use the angiography team for Sarah, since she is younger than Marguerite and has a better chance for recovery. Unfortunately, it took longer than expected to stabilize Sarah before and after the procedure, and the six-hour "window" when the procedure, could be performed on Marguerite passed. Sarah survived, made a full recovery, and returned to her family. Marguerite expired (died) the following morning.

Case Questions

NOTE: Students will not have studied ethics long enough to know the process for analyzing a situation such as this. However, this case can produce some thought-provoking discussion. Instructors may wish to revisit this case later in the course to determine if the students are better equipped to look in-depth at the ethical issues.

1. Do you believe that this case presents a legal or an ethical problem or both?

   There could be both a legal and an ethical problem depending upon the wishes of the patient and her family. If Marguerite's family insisted that she receive the angiogram (and potential angioplasty) since she was in the hospital first, and then the treatment was given to Sarah instead, there might be a resulting lawsuit. Anyone can sue anyone else. However, the hospital acted in good faith that Sarah had a better chance for survival.

2. What do you believe should be the criteria for a physician to use when having to choose between a solution that will benefit one patient at the expense of another?

   Many physicians use ethical problem-solving models such as the seven-step model or Dr. Lo's Clinical Model that are discussed in the textbook. Generally, the overall health of the patient and his or her ability to survive are considered, as well as the patient's age. The patient's wealth, religion, or racial background should never be taken into consideration.

3. How can Dr. K. justify this decision when speaking to the family of Marguerite M.?

   This is a true case. Dr. K explained the situation about Sarah, her age, and her critical need for an immediate angioplasty. He said that, if possible, there might still be time to perform a procedure on Marguerite after Sarah's was complete. Marguerite's family agreed since they believed that Dr. K. was honest with them. The family did not sue Dr. K. or the hospital when their mother expired the next morning.

POINTS TO PONDER (FROM TEXTBOOK)

The instructor may wish to have the class discuss these issues during the first class and then bring up these same issues for discussion again toward the end of the course. Students should then be able to examine the issues in greater depth with a better understanding of the ethical issues involved. Note that student answers may vary.

1. Should an alcoholic patient, who may die of liver disease, be eligible for an organ transplant?

2. Should a suicidal patient be allowed to refuse a tube feeding?

3. Should prisoners be eligible to receive expensive medical therapies for illnesses?

4. Is assisting with suicide ever ethically justified?

5. Should medical personnel suggest other treatment modes or suggest that the patient request a consultation with another physician?

6. Under what circumstances should you report a colleague or physician who is physically, psychologically, or pharmacologically impaired?

7. Is experimentation on human subjects ever justified?

8. When, if ever, should you disclose a patient's medical condition to the family?

9. Should parents be allowed to refuse medical treatment, such as chemotherapy, for their infant?

10. Should you protect your friend by telling him that his lover has tested positive for AIDS?

REVIEW QUESTIONS (FROM TEXTBOOK)
Discussion Questions

1. Discuss the difference between the terms *legal* and *moral*.

   Legal refers to those issues and statements that are governed and controlled by laws. *Moral* refers to the difference between right and wrong.

2. Give an example for each of the following: a medical ethics dilemma, a bioethics situation, and a medical-legal problem.

Responses will vary but might include the following:

Medical ethics dilemma: euthanasia
Bioethics situation: who should receive a scarce resource such as a heart or liver?
Medical-legal problem: practicing medicine without a license

3. Determine if the ten questions under Points to Ponder are ethical or legal issues, or both.

Responses will vary but might include the following:

1. Could be both. The alcoholic patient may believe that it is discriminatory (a legal issue) to deny him or her access to a scarce resource such as a liver.
2. Both. The court may have to appoint a *guardian ad litem* to represent the patient's best interests. This guardian may then petition the court to intervene and require that the patient accept a feeding tube.
3. Both. Since prisoners are in jail or prison, they are part of the legal system.
4. Both. This is an ethical dilemma for most people. Many believe that it is ethical to assist a terminally ill patient with suicide. However, this is illegal in most states.
5. Both. The patient's physician is the only person who can suggest treatment modes and refer patients. It is considered to be practicing medicine if a healthcare professional performs a physician's duties.
6. Both. An impaired physician must ultimately be reported to the state medical licensing authority. A healthcare professional who has knowledge of a physician's impairment must report it to his or her immediate supervisor.
7. Both. Controlled experimentation in order to determine the usefulness of treatments and medications is permitted as part of medical research. Therapeutic research is discussed further in Chapter 11. Human experimentation such as that conducted by Hitler during World War II is immoral and unethical.
8. Both. A patient's medical condition cannot be disclosed to anyone without the patient's permission. Such disclosure constitutes a violation of confidentiality, and the patient may file a lawsuit. However, if the patient is not competent to understand the diagnosis, then there are legal measures the family can take, such as acquiring power of attorney, in order to handle the patient's affairs. In that case, the physician can convey the condition to the family.
9. Both. This is both a legal and ethical dilemma, since infants cannot speak for themselves regarding care and treatment. The courts have become involved in such cases concerning minor children.
10. Both. This would be a violation of the patient's confidentiality. The decision to disclose such information falls within the scope of practice for the physician. He or she may have to tell the patient's partner about the positive AIDS test if the patient refuses to do so.

4. Describe five ethical situations that you may face in the profession you intend to follow.

Responses will vary but might include

- Unethical treatment of employees.
- Unethical treatment of patients.
- Taking drug samples from a physician's office.
- Falsifying medical records.
- Examining patient records of neighbors and friends.
- Giving medical advice outside the scope of one's practice.

Matching

Column A

1. bioethics
2. ethics
3. applied ethics
4. laws
5. medical ethics

6. utilitarianism
7. rights-based ethics
8. three-step ethics model

9. R/O
10. gut feeling

Column B

e. moral dilemmas due to recent advances in medicine
i. branch of philosophy
f. practical application of moral standards
c. binding rules determined by an authority
h. moral conduct to regulate behavior of medical professionals
d. greatest good for the greatest number
a. justice-based
j. Kenneth Blanchard and Norman Vincent Peale's approach to ethics
g. rule out a diagnosis
b. decision based on emotion

Multiple Choice

1. A problem that occurs when using a duty-based approach to ethics is
   a. the primary emphasis on a person's individual rights
   b. determining the greatest good for the greatest number
   c. the conflicting opinions regarding what our responsibility is
   d. remembering the three-step model approach to solving ethical dilemmas
   e. understanding the difference between what is fair and unfair

   Answer: c

2. Moral issues that occur as a result of modern medical technology are covered under what specific discipline?
   a. law
   b. medicine
   c. philosophy
   d. bioethics
   e. none of the above

   Answer: d

3. When trying to solve an ethical dilemma, it is necessary to
   a. do what everyone else is doing
   b. use logic to determine the solution
   c. do what we are told to do by others
   d. base the decision on religious beliefs only
   e. allow our emotions and feelings to guide us

   Answer: b

4. The three-step approach to solving ethical dilemmas is based on
   a. asking ourselves how our decision would make us feel if we had to explain our actions to a loved one
   b. asking ourselves if the intended action is legal
   c. asking ourselves if the intended action results in a balanced decision
   d. a and b only
   e. a, b, and c

   Answer: e

5. A utilitarian approach to solving ethical dilemmas might be used when
    a. allocating a limited supply of donor organs
    b. trying to find a just decision in which everyone will benefit
    c. finding a decision based on a sense of duty toward another person
    d. making sure that no one will "fall through the cracks" and not receive access to care
    e. none of the above

    Answer: a

6. An illegal act is almost always
    a. hidden
    b. unethical
    c. performed with the full knowledge of the healthcare worker
    d. obvious
    e. all of the above

    Answer: b

7. A practical application of ethics is
    a. philosophy
    b. the law
    c. illegal
    d. applied ethics
    e. b and d

    Answer: d

8. An employee who is entitled to a fair hearing in the case of a dismissal from a job is an example of
    a. duty-based ethics
    b. utilitarianism
    c. rights-based ethics
    d. justice-based ethics
    e. c and d

    Answer: e

9. Laws that affect the medical profession
    a. often overlap with ethics
    b. have a binding force
    c. are always fair to all persons
    d. are determined by a governmental authority
    e. a, b, and d

    Answer: e

10. Modern laws
    a. may allow some unethical acts such as lying on job applications
    b. are interpreted by some people to require no ethical responsibility beyond what the law requires
    c. are not used as a type of yardstick for group behavior
    d. a and b only
    e. a, b, and c

    Answer: d

Fill in the Blanks

1. <u>Laws</u> are rules or actions prescribed by an authority that have a legal binding force.
2. Statutes established in all fifty states that apply to the way that medicine is practiced in that state are <u>medical practice acts.</u>
3. An unwavering adherence to one's principles is known as <u>integrity.</u>
4. Feeling sorry or pitying a person is <u>sympathy.</u>
5. Having the ability to understand the feelings of others without actually experiencing their pain or suffering is <u>empathy.</u>
6. <u>Quality assurance</u> is the gathering and evaluating of information about the services provided in a hospital or other medical organization.
7. In our current <u>litigious</u> society people are excessively prone to sue medical practitioners.
8. When a person lacks or is indifferent to moral standards, he or she is considered to be <u>amoral.</u>
9. The branch of philosophy that is related to morals, moral principles, and moral judgments is known as <u>ethics.</u>
10. The right to make decisions about one's own life is the principle of <u>autonomy.</u>

PUT IT INTO PRACTICE

Talk to someone who is currently working in the medical field that you are working in or plan to enter. Ask him or her for a definition of medical ethics. Then compare it with the textbook definition. Does it match? Discuss with that person an ethical dilemma that he or she has faced and handled.

Teaching note: Students should not have any difficulty finding a friend or acquaintance who is in a medical field such as nursing, medical assisting, physician assistant, pharmacy, physical therapy, or medicine. This exercise may only require a brief telephone conversation. The instructor might ask a student to invite a medical professional to class to further explore the question, "What is medical ethics?"

WEB HUNT

Search the Web site of the Joint Commission on Accreditation of Health Care Organizations (*www.jcaho.org*). Using either the heading "For the General Public" or "Quality Check," enter the name of a health care institution in your area and determine its quality rating, according to JCAHO.

Teaching note: The instructor may wish to include additional components to the search, such as "Provide a description of what function JCAHO performs as described on its Web site."

CASE STUDY

Your friend shows you some books he took from the bookstore without paying for them. When you question him about it, he says, "Sure, I took them. But I'm no different than anybody else around here. That's how we all manage to get through school on limited funds. I'll be a better medical professional because of all the knowledge I gain from these books."

1. Do you agree or disagree with his rationalization? Why or why not?

   Student responses will vary, but should clearly state that rationalizations for unethical behavior are always wrong.

2. What do you say to him?

   The student should be comfortable in the belief that this behavior is stealing. Students should be able to make statements that can indicate to their friends that this behavior is wrong.

3. What ethical principles discussed in this chapter helped you with your answer?

   Responses will vary.

SUPPLEMENTAL QUESTIONS

Chapter Review

Cover the terms in the left-hand column with a piece of paper. Read the statement and fill in the blank with the answer before uncovering the correct response.

applied law/Ethics	The practical application of moral standards that concern benefiting the patient is called _____ ethics. Many people believe that something is unethical only if the _____ forbids it. _____ is that branch of philosophy related to morals.
Utilitarianism number consequences ends	_____ is an ethical theory based on the principle of the greatest good for the greatest _____. This is considered a _____-based ethical theory that assumes that the _____ justifies the means or methods of achieving the ends.
freedom responsibility virtue	A rights-based ethical theory is based on the premise of an individual's _____. Duty-based ethics is based on a person's _____ to another person. The final ethical virtue theory discussed in the chapter is _____-based.
Due VII	_____ process means that all employees are entitled to have certain procedures followed when they believe their rights are in jeopardy. Sexual harassment in the workplace is defined under Title _____ of the Amended Civil Rights Act of 1964.
worth	Comparable _____ is also known as pay equity and is based on the premise that all persons should receive equal pay for doing equal work.

Multiple Choice

Select the one best response to the following questions.

1. Utilitarianism is an ethical theory based on the principle of
   a. performing one's duty to various persons and institutions
   b. the greatest good for the greatest number of people
   c. adhering to laws enforced by government authorities
   d. a person's individual rights
   e. a and c only

   Answer: b

2. Bioethics refers to
   a. moral dilemmas and issues that are a result of advances in medicine
   b. ethics focused only on individual rights
   c. moral conduct based on emotions regulating the behavior of healthcare professionals
   d. b and c only
   e. a, b, and c

   Answer: a

3. Ethics is based solely on
   a. how you feel
   b. your emotions
   c. sincerity of your beliefs
   d. religious viewpoints
   e. none of the above

   Answer: e

4. The three-step model or approach to solving ethical dilemmas includes
   a. assessing how the action will make us feel
   b. concluding that the action is legal
   c. associating the problem with religious beliefs
   d. a and b only
   e. a, b, and c

   Answer: d

5. The statement, "I feel capital punishment is wrong," is
   a. sufficient to make an ethical decision because it is a sincere statement
   b. insufficient to make an ethical decision because it does not state why it is wrong
   c. sufficient to make an ethical decision because it is based on a religious belief
   d. insufficient to make an ethical decision because it does not address medical law
   e. sufficient to make an ethical decision because ethics is based on personal choice

   Answer: b

6. Ethical standards that apply to the medical profession are set by
   a. professional organizations
   b. individual medical professionals
   c. a congressional oversight committee
   d. patient committees
   e. none of the above

   Answer: a

7. The ethical theory that places the primary emphasis on a person's individual rights is
   a. utilitarianism
   b. rights-based
   c. duty-based
   d. philosophy
   e. justice-based

   Answer: b

8. Medical law addresses legal rights and obligations that
   a. affect patients
   b. protect the rights of individuals
   c. protect the rights of health care professionals
   d. a and b only
   e. a, b, and c

   Answer: e

9. The nation's Medicare system, in which all persons over the age of 65 receive healthcare benefits, is an example of which ethical theory?
   a. duty-based
   b. philosophy
   c. utilitarianism
   d. justice-based
   e. rights-based

   Answer: c

10. According to the three-step ethical model, a dilemma is ethical if
    a. it is illegal
    b. there is an imbalance
    c. the answer to "How does it make me feel?" is a strong "Good."
    d. one person benefits more than another
    e. all of the above

    Answer: c

True/False Questions

1. Ethics will be best determined by a "gut" reaction of what is right or wrong. (false)

2. There is often confusion about the right thing to do relating to critical decisions in healthcare. (true)

3. What is illegal is almost always unethical. (true)

4. Some laws are rarely enforced. (true)

5. Subjectivism regarding ethical decisions is always a good option. (false)

6. The right to due process means that every U.S. citizen is entitled to receive healthcare. (false)

7. The most cost-efficient ethical theory is considered to be utilitarianism. (true)

8. Seeking the good life, or virtue ethics, was proposed by Aristotle. (true)

9. An action is generally considered unethical if it makes a person feel uncomfortable about doing it. (true)

10. Loyalty to one's employer means overlooking the occasional mistake. (false)

Short Answer Questions

1. What are four categories of ethics?
   a. utilitarianism
   b. rights-based
   c. duty-based
   d. virtue-based

2. What are the three steps of the Blanchard-Peale model?
   a. Is it legal?
   b. Is it balanced?
   c. How does it make me feel?

3. When, generally, do people believe an action is wrong or unethical?
   a. It causes emotional or physical harm to someone.
   b. It goes against one's deepest beliefs.
   c. It makes a person feel guilty or uncomfortable about a particular action.
   d. It breaks the law or traditions of their society.
   e. It violates the rights of another person.

4. What is bioethics?

   Bioethics refers to moral dilemmas and issues resulting from advances in medicine and medical research.

5. What can a medical professional study to assist in making a sound decision?
   a. law
   b. ethics
   c. bioethics

6. The expectation of each person in the workplace is that he or she will be treated ethically with what seven characteristics?
   a. respect
   b. integrity
   c. honesty
   d. fairness
   e. empathy
   f. compassion
   g. loyalty

7. What are some of the most common items that are considered unprofessional conduct by state medical practice acts?
   a. impaired ability to practice medicine due to addiction or mental illness
   b. conviction of a felony
   c. insufficient record keeping
   d. allowing an unlicensed person to practice medicine
   e. physical abuse of patients

8. What is the difference between sympathy and empathy?

   Sympathy is feeling sorry, or pity, for someone else.
   Empathy is the ability to understand another person's feeling without actually experiencing the pain or distress that the other person is going through. Patients react better to empathy than to sympathy.

9. What is an example of honesty in medical practice?

   Answers will vary but might include:
   a. admitting an error
   b. pointing out a discrepancy in a physician's order

10. What is gender harassment?

   Gender harassment consists of a person of one gender (male or female) exerting power over another person of the opposite gender.

TEACHING STRATEGIES

1. Invite a director of human resources to speak to the class about employment issues such as comparable worth, sexual harassment, due process, and confidentiality.
2. Divide the class into three teams (Team I, II, and III). Using the Blanchard-Peale three-step ethics model, have the class discuss the eleven questions in the Points to Ponder in this chapter. Have Team I only address the first ethical model question (Is it legal?), Team II the second question (Is it balanced?), and Team III the third question (How does it make me feel?).
3. Have each student bring in a newspaper article that discusses a medical ethics case. Ask the student to summarize the article for the class and to offer an opinion on whether the case is a legal, ethical, or bioethical one. The instructor may wish to have the class use the seven-step decision model to examine one of the best newspaper articles.
4. Have the students write and submit a fictional story about someone in their field of practice who commits an unethical act that threatens the practice he or she works for. The students should focus on the internal struggle that takes place within that person as well as the effect that the unethical action has on his or her career.
5. Have the students prepare flash cards for the key terms (glossary) with term on one side of the card and the definition on the other. Using a partner, have the students test each other on the terms.

The Legal System

CHAPTER SYNOPSIS

In order to fully appreciate the study of medical law and ethics, the student must have a basic understanding of the U.S. legal system. This can be a complicated system to understand unless broken into its basic components. This chapter discusses the legal system, including the concept of checks and balances, sources of the law, classification of laws, and the trial process, including testifying in court.

Chapter Lecture Outline	Instructor's Notes

I. The Legal System
  A. Two fundamental processes
    1. Federal system—Power is divided between central (federal) government and smaller governments.
    2. Checks and balances—Designed by the framers of the Constitution so that no single branch of government could control the entire government, and so that each branch of government is scrutinized by other branches of government.
  B. All powers not specifically delegated to federal government by the Constitution are retained by states.
  C. Legislative branch—Congress
    1. Law-making body.
    2. Confirms Presidential appointments to the courts.
    3. Can pass law to override judicial decision.
II. Sources of Law
  A. Constitutional law—Rights, privileges, or immunities secured and protected for each citizen by the U.S. Constitution or by state constitutions.
  B. Statutory and regulatory law—Statutes are laws enacted by state or federal legislatures.
  C. Common law—Case law that is based on decisions made by judges.
    1. Precedent—A ruling on an earlier case that is then applied to subsequent cases.
    2. Stare decisis—"Let the decision stand."
    3. Many old case decisions still influence today's medical practitioners.	

Chapter Lecture Outline	**Instructor's Notes**

III. Classification of Laws
   A. Civil (Private) law—Concerns relationships between individuals or between individuals and the government that are not criminal.
      1. Tort Law—Division of law that covers acts that result in harm to others.
         a. Intentional torts
            i. Assault—Threat of bodily harm.
            ii. Battery—Actual bodily harm.
            iii. False imprisonment—Violation of personal liberty.
            iv. Defamation of character—Damage to a person's reputation.
            v. Fraud—Deceitful practice.
            vi. Invasion of privacy—Break in confidentiality, unauthorized publicity of information.
         b. Unintentional torts—Such as negligence, occur when the patient is injured as a result of the healthcare professional's not exercising the ordinary standard of care.
      2. Contract Law
         a. Expressed contract—An oral or written agreement.
            i. Most agreements, including oral agreements, are enforceable.
            ii. Specific state and federal laws relate to the medical profession.
         b. Consideration—Something of value.
         c. Implied contract—An agreement that is made through inference by signs, inaction, or silence.
         d. Breach of contract—Either party fails to comply with the terms of the agreement.
         e. Abandonment—Withdrawing medical care from a patient without providing sufficient notice to the patient.
            i. Sending a letter by certified mail is the best method physicians can use to protect themselves from a charge of abandonment.
            ii. Termination of contract should be made in writing by the physician.
   B. Public Law: Criminal Law
      1. Criminal case—Government brings a lawsuit against an individual or group.
      2. Administrative law—Regulations set by government agencies.
      3. Felony—A serious crime that carries a punishment of death or imprisonment for more than one year.
      4. Misdemeanors—Less serious than felonies, punishable by fine or imprisonment of up to one year.
IV. The Court System
   A. Two court systems—Federal and state.
   B. Jurisdiction—Power to hear a case.
   C. The federal court system has jurisdiction when one of the following is present:
      1. The dispute relates to federal law or the U.S. Constitution.
      2. The U.S. government is one of the parties involved in the dispute.

Chapter Lecture Outline	Instructor's Notes

      3. Citizens from different states are involved in the dispute, and the case involves over $75,000.

      4. Citizens of another country are involved in the dispute, and the case involved over $75,000.

      5. The dispute occurred on or in international waters.

  D. The court system has three levels:

      1. District (municipal).

      2. Court of Appeals (circuit court).

      3. U.S. Supreme Court.

  E. The case must go from lower to higher levels

  F. Small claims court.

  G. Probate court—Estate court.

V. The Trial Process

  A. The grand jury—A group of private citizens selected to hear evidence about a criminal case to determine if the case has enough merit to be heard in court.

  B. The procedure

      1. Litigation—A dispute resulting in one party suing another.

      2. Plaintiff—A person or group bringing suit against another person or group.

      3. Defendant—A person or group sued civilly or prosecuted criminally in a court of law.

      4. Waive—Give up the right to something.

  C. Course of typical trial

      1. Judge or jury.

      2. Opening statements.

      3. Plaintiff—Questioning of witnesses.

      4. Cross-examination of witnesses by defendant.

      5. Defendant—presents own witnesses.

      6. Cross-examination of witnesses by plaintiff.

      7. Closing arguments or comments.

      8. Decision making by jury or judge.

      9. Appeals process.

  D. Subpoena—Court Order

      1. Deposition—Oral testimony.

      2. A subpoena must be hand delivered.

  E. Expert Witness

      1. An expert witness has special education, training, or experience in a given area and testifies in a court of law for a fee.

      2. An expert witness does not testify about the actual facts of the case.

  F. Testifying in Court

LEARNING OBJECTIVES

(Student answers may vary.)

1. Define the glossary terms.

   Administrative law   a branch of law that covers regulations set by government agencies.

   Assault   "imminent apprehension of bodily harm."

   Battery   requires bodily harm and unlawful touching (touching without consent of patient).

   Beyond a reasonable doubt   evidence that is almost an absolute certainty that a person did commit a crime.

   Breach   neglect of an understanding between two parties; failing to perform a legal duty.

   Breach of contract   the failure, without legal excuse, to perform any promise or to carry out any of the terms of an agreement; failure to perform a contractual duty.

   Case law   also called common law; case law is based on decisions made by judges.

   Checks and balances   designed by the framers of the Constitution so that no one branch of government would have more power than another and so that each branch of government is scrutinized by other branches of government.

   Civil law   concerns relationships that are not criminal, either between individuals or individuals and the government.

   Class action lawsuit   lawsuit filed by one or more people on behalf of a larger group of people who are all affected by the same situation.

   Closing argument   closing speech or summary made by the attorneys for the plaintiff and the defendant.

   Common law   also called case law; common law is based on decisions made by judges.

   Competent   capable of making a decision without mental confusion due to drugs, alcohol, or other reasons.

   Consideration   in contract law, consideration is something of value given as part of the agreement.

   Constitutional law   the inviolable rights, privileges, or immunities secured and protected for each citizen by the Constitution of the United States or by the constitution of each state.

   Contract law   that division of law that includes enforceable promises and agreements between two or more persons to do or not do a particular thing.

   Criminal case   one in which court action is brought by the government against a person or groups of people accused of committing a crime, resulting in a fine or imprisonment if found guilty.

   Criminal laws   set up to protect the public from the harmful acts of others.

   Defamation of character   making false and/or malicious statements about another person; includes libel and slander if the plaintiff can prove damages.

Defendant   person or group of people sued civilly or prosecuted criminally in a court of law.

Deposition   oral testimony that is made before a public officer of the court to be used in a lawsuit.

Discovery   the legal process by which facts are discovered before a trial.

Embezzlement   the illegal appropriation of property, usually money, by a person entrusted with its possession.

Expert witness   a medical practitioner or other expert who, through education, training, or experience, has special knowledge about a subject and gives testimony about a subject in court, usually for a fee. They do not testify about the facts of the case.

Expressed contract   an agreement that is entered into orally or in writing and that clearly states all the terms.

Felony   a serious crime that carries a punishment of death or imprisonment for more than one year. Examples are murder, rape, robbery, and practicing medicine without a license.

Fraudulent   deceitful.

Implied contract   an agreement that is made through inference by signs, inaction, or silence.

Indictment   a written charge presented to the court by the grand jury against a defendant.

Jurisdiction   the power to hear a case.

Libel   any publication in print, writing, pictures, or signs that injures the reputation of another person.

Litigation   a dispute that has resulted in one party suing another.

Misdemeanors   less-serious offenses than felonies; punishable by fines or imprisonment of up to one year. These include traffic violations and disturbing the peace.

Plaintiff   a person or group of people suing another person or groups of people; a person who instigates the lawsuit.

Preponderance of evidence   evidence more likely than not that the incident occurred.

Prosecutor   a person who brings a criminal suit on behalf of the government.

Regulations   rules or laws made by agencies.

Slander   speaking false and malicious words concerning another person, which brings injury to his or her reputation.

Stare decisis   Latin phrase meaning "let the decision stand."

Statutes   laws enacted by state and federal legislatures.

Subpoena   court order for a person or documents to appear.

Subpoena duces tecum   Latin phrase meaning "under penalty, take with you"; a court order requiring a witness to appear in court and to bring certain records or other material to a trial or a deposition.

Summary judgment   judge's ruling to end a lawsuit without a trial based on a matter of law presented in pleadings.

Tort   a wrongful act, defined by the law, that is committed against another person or property that results in harm; a civil wrong.

Tort law   that division of law that covers acts that result in harm to another.

Unintentional torts   such as negligence, occur when the patient is injured as a result of the healthcare professional's not exercising the ordinary standard of care.

Waive   give up the right to something.

2. Discuss why an understanding of the legal profession is necessary for the healthcare professional.

The advanced state of medical technology creates new legal, ethical, moral, and financial problems for the consumer and healthcare professional. Patients are now more aware of their legal rights than in the past. The outcome of court cases has had a great impact on the way that healthcare professionals practice their business.

3. Describe the sources of law.

There are four sources of law: constitutional, statutory, regulatory, and common or case law.

Constitutional law is based on the U.S. Constitution and the constitutions of the individual states. The Constitution defines the power of the government to act and sets limits on the government's power.

Statutory laws are made by legislative bodies such as Congress or the state legislatures. The bills that are passed by these legislative bodies are called statutes.

Regulatory law is made by agencies such as the Food and Drug Administration.

Common or case law is established from a court decision. This law may explain or interpret other sources of law—for example, when a case explains what a federal regulation means.

4. Describe the steps for a bill to become a law.

Statutes begin as bills submitted by legislators at the state or federal level. The bill is first introduced into one of the two houses of Congress: the Senate or the House of Representatives. It goes on to a committee in either the Senate or the House for discussion and consideration. After a hearing about the bill, the committee sends a report with a recommendation of pass or fail, and the bill goes back to the house in which it originated. A vote takes place in that house. If the bill passes, it becomes an act. The act is then sent to the other house, where it goes through the same steps as it did as a bill. The act can be amended in the second house, but the amended version has to be considered and passed in the first house in its new form. After it passes there, the heads of the Senate and the House of Representatives sign it. The act is then sent to the President for a federal act or to the governor for a state act for final signature. It becomes a law if it is signed by the chief executive and not vetoed within ten days. A presidential veto can be overridden by a two-thirds majority of both houses of Congress.

5. Discuss the difference between civil law and criminal law, explaining the areas covered by each.

Civil law concerns relationships between individuals or between individuals and the government. Civil law cases include divorce, child custody, auto accidents, slander, libel, and trespassing.

Criminal laws are set up to protect the public as a whole from the harmful acts of others. The purpose of this branch of law is to define socially intolerable conduct that is punishable by law. With this type of law, the government (usually the individual state) brings the suit against a person or group of people accused of committing a crime. If convicted, the person may receive a fine, prison term, or both. These crimes may involve the borders of the United States, as would the transport of illegal drugs. Also included under criminal law are the crimes of murder, robbery, burglary, larceny, rape, sodomy, arson, and practicing medicine without a license.

6. List six intentional torts and give examples of each.
   (Student examples may vary.)

   1. Assault: Threatening to hold a patient down on an exam table while a procedure for which the patient has not granted consent is performed.
   2. Battery: Performing a surgical procedure, such as an appendectomy during an abdominal operation for a hysterectomy, without the patient's consent.
   3. False imprisonment: Refusing to allow a patient to leave a medical office or hospital when he or she requests to leave.
   4. Defamation of character: Making a negative statement about another physician's ability.
   5. Fraud: Promising to cure a patient.
   6. Invasion of privacy: Allowing a patient's test results or medical condition to become known without the patient's permission.

7. List examples of criminal actions that relate to the healthcare worker.
   - Practicing medicine without a license.
   - Illegal drug sale and abuse.
   - Rape of a patient or employee.

8. Discuss the difference between a felony and a misdemeanor.

   A felony is a serious crime that carries a punishment of death or imprisonment for more than one year.

   A misdemeanor is a less serious offense, punishable by fine or imprisonment of up to one year.

9. Describe the types of courts in the legal system.

   The two court systems are the state and federal courts. The federal court system tries cases relating to federal law when the government is one of the parties; when citizens of different states are involved in a dispute; when citizens of another country are involved in a dispute with a U.S. citizen and the case involves over $75,000; and, when the actual dispute occurred on or in international waters. The state court is set up with a structure similar to the federal court system but tries cases that relate to citizens and companies within that particular state.

10. Explain the trial process.

    Litigation occurs when two parties cannot resolve a dispute by themselves. The plaintiff brings the action into litigation and sues the defendant in a court of law. Note that not all lawsuits end up in court. Many cases, if not most, are settled outside of the court. If the parties cannot settle their dispute, a trial is held. The court case can be tried before a judge only or before a judge and jury of the defendant's peers. If a jury is requested, then six to twelve people are selected from among a large pool of potential jurors.

The trial begins with opening statements made by the attorneys for each side of the case. The plaintiff's attorney then questions the first witness. This witness can be cross-examined by the defendant's attorney. After the plaintiff's witnesses are examined and cross-examined, the defendant's attorney presents witnesses for their side of the case, and the plaintiff's attorney may cross-examine the defense witnesses. When this process is completed, both sides "rest their case."

A request may be made by an attorney for a summary judgment to take place in a civil lawsuit. A summary judgment is a decision made by the court (judge) in response to a motion that declares there is no necessity for a trial since neither the defendant nor the plaintiff is entitled to win based on existing law.

Attorneys make closing speeches (arguments) or summaries for each side. In a jury trial, the judge instructs the jury on the points of law that affect the case. The jury deliberates in private and comes to a conclusion, or verdict. If there is no jury, then the judge makes the decision based on evidence presented in the case.

In a civil case, the defendant, if found guilty, will be ordered to pay the plaintiff a monetary award. If found guilty in a criminal case, the defendant will receive a fine and/or prison sentence.

11. Discuss why an expert witness might be used during a lawsuit.

    An expert witness is a person called as a witness in a case where the subject matter is beyond the general knowledge of most people in the court or on the jury. The testimony should assist the jury or judge in determining the accuracy of the facts in the case.

THE CASE OF JACOB AND THE DISEASED LEG

Jacob is an outstanding quarterback on his high school football team who has been offered a college scholarship when he graduates. Unfortunately, Jacob was injured during a late summer practice just before his senior year. He suffered a compound fracture of the fibula bone in his lower leg. Since the fracture broke through his skin, he required a surgical repair to align or set the bone and close the skin. Dr. M., an orthopedic surgeon, kept Jacob in the hospital for three days and ordered intravenous antibiotics to be administered. When he was discharged from the hospital, Jacob was told to come in for an office visit once a week for six weeks.

At six weeks Jacob's parents took him in to the surgeon's office for his cast removal, and except for a slightly inflamed and draining area around his stitches, Jacob's broken bone seemed to be healing. After his cast was removed, Jacob was told to wait for a few minutes while the surgeon went across the hall to check on another patient. Dr. M. removed his gloves, washed his hands in Jacob's exam room, and then went across the hall to examine another patient, Sarah K. The doors between the exam rooms were left open and Jacob's parents could see and hear Dr. M. examine Sarah's infected leg. They could tell that Dr. M. did not replace his gloves. He told Sarah that he was glad to see that her osteomyelitis (a serious bone infection) was almost better, and he told her to come back in another week. Dr. M. then came back into Jacob's room, still without gloves, and examined Jacob's leg more carefully. He was concerned about the inflammation around the incision site and told the parents to keep the area clean and dry. He wrote Jacob a prescription for an oral antibiotic and said he could start to put a little weight on his leg. When Jacob came back the following week, his leg was grossly infected with a large abscess. Jacob had to have further surgery to drain the abscess. The pathology report of tissue specimens from Jacob's leg determined that he had developed osteomyelitis. This infection took several months to heal. The delay in his recovery meant that Jacob was unable to play football that fall and lost his chance at a college scholarship. Jacob's parents asked Dr. M. to provide them with the results of the tissue test. They then sued Dr. M. for negligence.

Case Questions

1. What obvious mistake did Dr. M. make?

   Students should immediately note that Dr. M. did not put on sterile (or even clean gloves) each time he examined a patient. Dr. M. did not close the doors between the two exam rooms, but this should not be the "mistake" that students dwell on.

2. Did Jacob or his parents contribute in any way to his condition?

   It is hard to imagine the Jacob did not notice any discomfort or pain from his inflamed incision site before his cast was removed at six weeks. However, a young patient is not always cognizant of what type of discomfort he or she should be looking for after a broken leg. Jacob's parents did notice that Dr. M. did not put gloves on after returning from Sarah's exam and before he examined Jacob's leg. They did not speak up at that time. However, many patients and their families are intimidated by physicians and surgeons and fail to speak up. If his parents kept his incision clear and dry, as requested, and administered his antibiotics correctly, then they, apparently, did all they could to assist in his recovery.

3. What could all of the involved parties have done to prevent this situation from occurring?

   Dr. M. should have provided clear written and verbal instructions to Jacob and his parents regarding what symptoms to look out for while he had his cast in place (i.e., fever, pain, and unusually warm toes, feet and leg. Itching around the incision site is usually a good sign that healing is taking place.) The parents could have asked Dr. M. to wash is hands and put on fresh gloves before touching their son.

   These are suggested solutions to the case. Instructors may be able to add many more options based on their own experiences.

POINTS TO PONDER (FROM TEXTBOOK)

Teaching note: These questions are meant to stimulate classroom discussion. Some questions, such as "Can I be sued if I unintentionally leave a patient record with a diagnosis of AIDS within sight of another patient?" have clear answers: Students must realize that even if an action is unintentional, they can still be sued. However, other questions, such as "Can I restrain a person against his or her will if I know it is for his or her own good?" are not as clear. Students may discuss what is the greater good in this case—allowing a person the freedom of a lack of restraint or protecting the person and risking a charge of false imprisonment. The student answers may vary to all of these questions.

1. Why do I have to know how a bill becomes a law?

2. Why is common law important?

3. How can I avoid a lawsuit?

4. Can I restrain a person against his or her will if I know it is for his or her own good?

5. Can I be sued if I make a statement to a patient about a mistake a physician has made?

6. What should I do if I see a physician or other healthcare employee make an error?

7. Can I be sued if I unintentionally leave a patient record with a diagnosis of AIDS within sight of another patient?

8. What do I do if I am subpoenaed?

REVIEW QUESTIONS (FROM TEXTBOOK)
Discussion Questions

1. Discuss the significance of common laws for the healthcare professional.

   Common law, or case law, is based on precedent that was set by an earlier case when it was tried. This previous case established a law based on a court decision. Common law defines the legal obligation that a healthcare professional has to use reasonable care in treating a patient.

2. Explain what is meant by the statement, "It is easier to prevent negligence than it is to defend it."

   Negligence is the failure to perform professional duties to an accepted standard of care. It is difficult to defend why a person did not do something that was required of him or her. Preventing negligence means that medical professionals must perform those responsibilities they were trained to perform within their scope of practice.

3. Differentiate between common law and statutory law.

   Common law is based on a precedent that was set when a similar case was tried and a law was established by a court decision.
   Statutory law is law passed by a legislative body at the state or federal level. Statutes also create agencies, such as the Food and Drug Administration, that can pass rules governing particular aspects of concern, such as the sale of food or drugs.

4. Explain what the numbering system in public law means.

   A public law is designated by the initials P.L. The five or six digits that follow indicate the Congress that passed the law (the first two or three digits) and which piece of legislation this law was in that Congress (the last three digits).

5. Discuss what is meant by the term *abandonment* and describe ways that this claim can be avoided.

   Abandonment is withdrawing medical care from a patient without providing sufficient notice to the patient. A physician must give sufficient notice before withdrawing care so that the patient has time to find another physician. One of the best means of avoiding the charge of abandonment is for the physician to send a letter to the patient by certified mail severing the relationship.

6. What is meant by *burden of proof*?

   Burden of proof means that the responsibility for proving that the defendant is guilty of an action falls on the plaintiff who brought about the action or lawsuit.

7. What is a subpoena and who can accept it?

   A subpoena is a written command from the court for a person or documents to appear in court. A subpoena must be hand-delivered, or served, to the person who is being requested to appear in court. This is the person named on the subpoena. An assistant cannot accept a subpoena on behalf of a physician without his or her knowledge; otherwise the subpoena is considered "not served." However, a physician may delegate this responsibility to an assistant. [Note that this practice is not encouraged since the physician can then deny that he or she actually received the subpoena.]

Matching

Column A	Column B
1. breach	f. failure
2. deposition	i. oral testimony to be used in court
3. plaintiff	g. person who sues another party
4. defendant	b. person who is being sued
5. felony	j. serious crime such as practicing medicine without a license
6. misdemeanor	h. less serious crime such as a traffic violation
7. waive	c. give up the right to something
8. tort	d. law that covers harm to another person
9. subpoena	a. order for person or documents to appear in court
10. precedent	e. earlier ruling applied to present case

Multiple Choice

1. Sources of law include all of the following except
   a. regulatory law
   b. executive law
   c. statutory law
   d. common law
   e. constitutional law

   Answer: b

2. *Subpoena duces tecum* means
   a. "let the master answer."
   b. "under penalty, take with you."
   c. "let the decision stand."
   d. "the thing speaks for itself."
   e. "the thing has been decided."

   Answer: b

3. *Stare decisis* means
   a. "let the master answer."
   b. "under penalty, take with you."
   c. statutory law has been invoked
   d. constitutional law has been invoked
   e. "let the decision stand."

   Answer: e

4. Administrative law covers all of the following except
   a. health department regulations
   b. licensing of prescription drugs
   c. Internal Revenue Service regulations
   d. fraud
   e. all of the above are covered under administrative law

   Answer: e

5. The person who brings the action into litigation is called a(n)
   a. attorney
   b. plaintiff
   c. defendant
   d. judge
   e. jury

   Answer: b

6. A court order that requires a witness to appear in court with certain records is called a
   a. deposition
   b. discovery
   c. *subpoena duces tecum*
   d. *res judicata*
   e. waiver

   Answer: c

7. The common law of the past that is based on a decision made by judges is called
   a. civil law
   b. constitutional law
   c. case law
   d. criminal law
   e. statutory law

   Answer: c

8. The threat of doing bodily harm to another person—stating, for example, "If you won't allow us to continue this procedure, we will have to tie your hands"—is
   a. assault
   b. battery
   c. fraud
   d. invasion of privacy
   e. all of the above

   Answer: a

9. Standard of care refers to the care that
   a. a reasonable person would use
   b. is ordinary care
   c. a prudent person would use
   d. healthcare professionals in all specialties must practice
   e. all of the above

   Answer: e

10. Removing one's clothing in order to allow the physician to perform a physical examination is a(n)
    a. invasion of privacy
    b. defamation of character
    c. implied contract
    d. abandonment
    e. none of the above is correct

    Answer: c

Fill in the Blanks

1. A judge's ruling to end a lawsuit without a trial, based on a matter of law and pleadings, is called a <u>summary judgment</u>.
2. A lawsuit filed on behalf of a large group of people who are all affected by the same situation is a called a <u>class action</u> suit.
3. A <u>preponderance</u> of evidence shows that more likely than not an incident occurred.
4. Evidence that determines with almost absolute certainty that a person did commit a crime is said to be <u>beyond a reasonable</u> doubt.
5. Law that covers wrongful acts that result in harm to another person is <u>tort</u> law.
6. Formal written statements given to the court are called <u>pleadings</u>.
7. In many cases, civil lawsuits are settled <u>outside</u> a courtroom.
8. An imminent apprehension of bodily harm can be considered to be the tort of <u>assault</u>.
9. A violation of the personal liberty of another person through unlawful restraint is called <u>false imprisonment</u>.
10. Negligence is considered to be an <u>unintentional</u> tort.

PUT IT INTO PRACTICE

Give an example of a violation of each of the six torts mentioned in this chapter (assault, battery, false imprisonment, defamation of character, fraud, and invasion of privacy) as it might affect your particular area of medical specialization.

Teaching note: The instructor may wish to divide the class into six teams and have each team present (or act out) one of the six torts for the rest of the class.

WEB HUNT

1. Search the website of the National Institutes of Health (*www.nih.gov*). What types of information and services does this site offer?
2. Search the website *www.findlaw.com* and click on Medical Malpractice. Read the article "Lessons Learned the Hard Way: Medical Malpractice." Summarize the six examples of successful medical malpractice claims discussed in that article.

Teaching note: The website *www.findlaw.com* is a very useful tool for students to find out more about the law. Students can research a Supreme Court case by doing a full text search at the Website *www.findlaw.com/casecode/supreme.html.*

CASE STUDY

Adam Green is an orderly in the Midwest Nursing Home. His supervisor, Nora Malone, has asked him to supervise the dining room while 20 residents eat their evening meal. Bill Heckler is an 80-year-old resident who is very alert. He tells Adam that he doesn't like the meal that's being served, and he wants to leave the dining room and go back to his own room. Adam is quite busy, since he has to watch the behavior of several patients who are confused. He's concerned that patients might choke on their food or otherwise harm themselves. Adam becomes impatient with Bill and tells him that he cannot leave the room until everyone is finished eating. Adam then locks the dining room door. Bill complains to the nursing home administrator that he was unlawfully detained. He then hires an attorney, who brings forth a charge of false imprisonment.

Case Questions

1. Was Adam's action justified?

   The action may have been justified in light of the circumstances, but he still cannot take the action of locking a door so that a competent patient cannot leave.

2. In your opinion, was this a case of false imprisonment?

   The student should view this as a case of false imprisonment.

3. What could Adam have done to defuse the situation?

   He should have used his communication skills to have Bill wait until he was able to accompany Bill to his room. He might offer Bill other food instead of what was served. He might ask Bill to help him by talking to some of the other patients.

4. Do the nursing home administrator and Nora Malone have any legal responsibility for Adam's action?

   Yes, under the doctrine of *respondeat superior,* they are responsible for the actions of their employees. In addition, the nursing home appears to be short-staffed, since Adam is the only person caring for twenty residents.

5. What would a "reasonable and prudent" person do in the same circumstances?

   This person would call for some help from another staff member either to assist with Bill or to care for the other residents while Adam cared for Bill.

SUPPLEMENTAL QUESTIONS

Chapter Review

Cover the terms in the left-hand column with a piece of paper. Read the statement and fill in the blank with the answer before uncovering the correct response.

Federalism checks and balances states	The two fundamental principles under which the U.S. system of government was founded are _____ and _____ _____ _____. All powers that have not been specifically delegated to the federal government by the Constitution are retained by the _____.
Congress judges/federal courts	The legislative branch of government, or lawmaking body, is called _____. The judicial branch consists of _____ and _____ _____.

executive/president   The _____ branch consists of the _____.

common

torts

assault

Law based on the precedent set by other cases is called _____ law. Acts that result in harm to another person are called _____. Threatening to harm a person without actually touching the person is called _____.

fraud

A deceitful practice such as making a false claim is called _____.

standard of care

expressed

implied

The degree of care that a person of ordinary prudence would exercise in the same or similar circumstance is called _____ _____ _____. An agreement entered into orally or in writing is an _____ contract. A contract that is shown through inference by signs is called an _____ contract.

criminal

plaintiff

deposition

Income tax evasion, sexual misconduct, and violation of the narcotics laws by a healthcare professional all fall under the category of _____ law. The person bringing forward the litigation is called the _____. A person's statement taken as a record for the court is called a _____.

Multiple Choice

Select the one best response to the following questions.

1. Constitutional law
    a. addresses the relationship between individuals and the government
    b. addresses the relationship between individuals and private entities
    c. is superceded by statutory and regulatory law
    d. defines and sets limits on the government's power
    e. a and d only

    Answer: e

2. Which of the following is *not* a step in the process of a bill becoming law?
    a. the bill goes to a committee for discussion and consideration
    b. the chief executive signs the bill
    c. the bill is approved as "constitutional" by the courts and submitted to the House
    d. both the Speaker of the House of Representatives and the vice president of the Senate sign the bill
    e. after the bill passes in one house, it becomes an act and is submitted to the other house

    Answer: c

3. Rules and laws made by agencies are defined as
    a. regulatory law
    b. executive law
    c. statutory law
    d. common law
    e. constitutional law

    Answer: a

4. Common law is established by
   a. statutes
   b. a judge
   c. the constitution
   d. a previous court decision
   e. b and d

   Answer: e

5. Reasons for premature termination of a medical contract include all of the following except
   a. the patient is competent
   b. failure to pay for the service
   c. failure to follow instructions
   d. missed appointments
   e. the patient states that he or she is seeking the care of another physician

   Answer: a

6. In the U.S. legal system, the burden of proof is placed upon
   a. the defendant
   b. the judge
   c. the jury
   d. the plaintiff
   e. none of the above

   Answer: d

7. An oral testimony that is made before a public officer of the court to be used in a lawsuit is a
   a. deposition
   b. consideration
   c. precedent
   d. breach
   e. confession

   Answer: a

8. Consideration, under contract law, is defined as
   a. the legal process by which facts are discovered before a trial
   b. a possible out-of-court agreement
   c. laws enacted by state and federal legislation
   d. something of value given as part of the agreement
   e. a dispute that has resulted in one party suing another

   Answer: d

9. When a patient rolls up his sleeve to have his blood pressure taken, he is demonstrating
   a. discovery
   b. precedent
   c. implied contract
   d. *stare decisis*
   e. a tort

   Answer: c

10. If called to testify in court, one should
    a. not memorize his or her testimony ahead of time
    b. not answer questions he or she does not understand
    c. always tell the truth
    d. be professional
    e. all of the above

    Answer: e

True/False Questions

1. Administrative law is that branch of public law that covers regulations set by government agencies. (true)

2. Checks and balances were set up by the government to regulate the banking industry. (false)

3. Federal law is administered in the same way in all fifty states. (true)

4. When applying case law, the facts in the new case must be the same as those in which the precedent was established. (true)

5. For a tort of assault to be present, it is sufficient for the patient to only fear that he or she will be hurt. (true)

6. Slander is placing statements in writing that injure the reputation of a person. (false)

7. To prevent embezzlement, it is always wise to have only one person in a medical office handle the money (receive payments, issue receipts, audit the account, and deposit the money). (false)

8. Standard of care is the type of healthcare that a "reasonable person" would provide. (true)

9. Consideration must have both an offer to do something and the acceptance of the offer. (true)

10. Physicians cannot be sued if they have promised to cure patients and then, through no fault of their own, have failed to do so. (false)

Short Answer Questions

1. Why is there a system of checks and balances within our branches of government?

   To make sure that no one branch of government (legislative, judicial, or executive) has too much power.

2. What are the four sources of law?
   a. constitutional law
   b. statutory law
   c. regulatory law
   d. common or case law

3. What are the two main classifications of law?
   a. civil
   b. criminal

4. What is contract law?

   Contract law is that branch of law that includes enforceable promises and agreements between two or more persons to do, or not do, a particular action.

5. What are six categories of private or civil law?
   a. tort
   b. contract
   c. property
   d. inheritance
   e. family
   f. corporate

6. What are six classifications of intentional torts?
   a. assault
   b. battery
   c. false imprisonment
   d. defamation of character
   e. fraud
   f. invasion of privacy

7. What is an example of an unintentional tort?

   Negligence that occurs, for example, when a patient is injured as a result of the healthcare professional's not exercising the ordinary standard of care.

8. What are two examples of defamation of character?
   a. slander
   b. libel

9. What are some reasons a physician may wish to terminate a medical contract of care for a patient?
   a. failure to follow instructions
   b. missed appointments
   c. failure to pay for services
   d. the patient is seeking the care of another physician

10. What are the two categories of torts?
    a. intentional
    b. unintentional (accidental)

TEACHING STRATEGIES

1. Have a small group of students write a scenario in which the patient's privacy appears to have been violated. They should write the scenario so that it seems the medical professional did not know that he or she was violating the patient's privacy and very little harm seems to have resulted from the incident. Form two teams of debaters—four students on each team—to debate whether this scenario is an example of intentional or unintentional tort. A class discussion should follow the debate.

2. Instruct each student to write a certified letter to a fictitious psychiatric patient who has neglected to keep his appointments. It appears, too, that the patient is no longer being compliant with the prescribed medication regime, because medication refills have not been requested. The letter should be written in such a way that a claim of abandonment could never be lodged against the treating psychiatrist. The letters should then be displayed for all the other students to read.

3. Divide the class into groups of three, and ask each group to write a scenario in which a medical professional commits malpractice. The scenarios should then be presented to the class as a whole, and the class should arrive at a consensus as to the one scenario they think best to portray. "Actors" should then be selected to represent the judge, prosecuting attorney, defense attorney, defendant,

plaintiff, and witnesses. The remainder of the class should serve as the jury. A class discussion on the verdict should follow the role-playing.

4. Instruct each student to bring in a recent newspaper article describing an illegal action or the trial of a tort case. Have the students work in groups of four to discuss their articles and determine the following: the type of tort, the verdict, and the sentence.

5. Invite a physician into the classroom to discuss various ways in which he or she protects against litigation, such as in charges of abandonment by the patient.

6. Divide the class into six teams and have each team present (or act out) one of the six torts for the rest of the class.

7. Have the students prepare flash cards for the key terms (glossary).

3

Importance of the Legal System for the Physician

CHAPTER SYNOPSIS

Even though only a small number of malpractice cases actually end up in court, it is nevertheless important for the student to understand how the law impacts upon his or her physician/employer. The licensing requirements are important to remember, since the actions of healthcare personnel can have a direct impact upon a physician's reputation and medical license.

Chapter Lecture Outline	Instructor's Notes

I. Medical Practice Acts
  A. Revoked—Taken away, as in revoked license.
  B. Reciprocity—The cooperation of one state in granting a license to practice medicine to a physician already licensed in another state.
  C. These may vary from state to state but generally have the following in common:
    1. Establish the baseline for the practice of medicine in the state.
    2. Determine the prerequisites for licensure.
    3. Forbid the practice of medicine without a license.
    4. Specify the conditions for license renewal, suspension, and revocation.
II. Licensure of the Physician
  A. Examination—Each state offers its own exam.
  B. Endorsement—An approval or sanction.
  C. Reciprocity—The cooperation of one state in granting a license to practice medicine to a physician already licensed in another state.
  D. Registration
    1. Physicians must pay a fee.
    2. Renewal or re-registration occurs annually or biannually.
    3. Physicians are required to complete 75 hours of continuing medical education (CME) units in a three-year period.
  E. Revocation and suspension of license—A state may revoke or suspend a physician's license for cases of severe misconduct.
III. Licensure and Certification of Allied Health Professionals
  A. Licensure and certification are two different things.
  B. A physician can be certified in a specialty area.	

Chapter Lecture Outline	Instructor's Notes

C. Certification indicates that an allied health professional has met certain standards, but is not licensed.

D. A physician cannot practice medicine without a license.

IV. Accreditation—A voluntary process in which an agency is requested to officially review and authorize healthcare institutions and educational programs.

V. Standard of Care

  A. The ordinary skill and care that medical practitioners use and that is commonly used by other medical practitioners in the same locality when caring for patients.

  B. The standard of care for particular professionals has changed somewhat over the years.

  C. Physicians are not obligated to treat everyone, except in the case of an emergency.

    1. Once a physician accepts a patient for treatment, he or she has entered into a contract.

    2. The law does not require a physician to use extraordinary skill. It only requires reasonable, ordinary care and skill. The physician is expected to perform the same acts that a "reasonable and prudent" physician would perform (Prudent Person Rule).

    3. Physicians are expected to exhaust all resources available to them when treating patients and not to expose patients to undue risk.

VI. Confidentiality

  A. Confidentiality refers to keeping private all information about a person (patient) and not disclosing it to a third party without the patient's written consent.

  B. Medical Patient Rights Act—Federal law

    1. Information given to a physician by a patient should be communicated on a need-to-know basis.

    2. Medical practitioners should be especially careful about discussing in public anything relating to a patient.

VII. Statute of Limitations

  A. Statute of limitations is the period of time that a patient has to file a lawsuit.

  B. Discovery rule—Legal theory that provides that the statute of limitations begins to run at the time the injury is discovered or when a patient should have known of the injury.

  C. *Guardian ad litem* ("court appointed")—Legal term for an adult who will act in court on behalf of a child in litigation.

VIII. Good Samaritan Laws

  A. Good Samaritan laws are state laws that help protect healthcare personnel from liability during emergency care to an accident victim.

  B. No one is required to provide aid in an emergency (except in Vermont).

    1. Responder is only required to act within the limits of acquired skill and training.

    2. Trained professionals are not under legal obligations, but do have an ethical obligation in an emergency.

Chapter Lecture Outline	Instructor's Notes
IX. *Respondeat Superior* A. "Let the master answer" means the employer is responsible for the actions of the employees. B. Duties can be delegated, but not responsibility. C. Employees have a duty to interpret and carry out orders. D. Employers have a duty to provide a safe work environment. E. Insurance and employer liability—Bonding insurance to cover employees who handle financial statements, records, and cash. F. Scope of practice—Every employee must work within the scope of practice for his or her particular discipline. X. Risk Management—A practice used to control or minimize the incidence of problem behavior that might result in injury to patients and employees.	

LEARNING OBJECTIVES

(Student answers may vary.)

1. Define all glossary terms.

Discovery rule   legal theory that provides that the statute of limitations begins to run at the time the injury is discovered or when the patient should have known of the injury.

Endorsement   an approval or sanction.

Good Samaritan laws   state laws that help protect healthcare professionals from liability while giving emergency care to accident victims.

Guardian ad litem   court-appointed guardian to represent a minor or unborn child in litigation.

Medical practice acts   laws established in all fifty states that define the practice of medicine as well as requirements and methods for licensure in a particular state.

Prudent person rule   also called the reasonable person standard, requires the healthcare professional to provide the information that a prudent, reasonable person would want before making a decision about treatment or refusal of treatment.

Reciprocity   the cooperation of one state in granting a license to practice medicine to a physician already licensed in another state. Reciprocity can be applied to other licensed professionals, such as nurses and pharmacists.

Respondeat superior   Latin phrase meaning "let the master answer" means the employer is responsible for the actions of the employee.

Revoked   take away, as in revoke a license.

Risk management   a practice to minimize the incidence of problem behavior that might result in injury to the patient and liability for the organization.

Standard of care   the ordinary skill and care that medical practitioners use and that is commonly used by other medical practitioners in the same locality when caring for patients; what another medical professional would consider appropriate care in similar circumstances.

Statute of limitations   the period of time that a patient has to file a lawsuit.

2. List the four basic characteristics of state medical practice acts.
    * Establish the baseline for the practice of medicine in that state.
    * Determine the prerequisites for licensure.
    * Forbid the practice of medicine without a license.
    * Specify the conditions for license renewal, suspension, and revocation.

3. Describe the three methods by which a state grants a license to practice medicine.
    * Examination: Each state offers its own examination for licensure.
    * Endorsement: This is an approval or sanction granting a license by endorsement to applicants who have successfully passed the National Board of Medical Examination.
    * Reciprocity: A license to practice medicine may be granted by a state that accepts a medical license granted by another state.

4. Discuss conduct that may result in a physician's loss of license to practice medicine.

    Conduct that could result in the loss of a physician's license includes Medicare/Medicaid fraud, rape, murder, larceny, narcotics conviction, and the inappropriate use of drugs and alcohol.

5. Identify the difference between licensure and certification.

    A license is granted by a state or federal entity. This provides the legal right for a professional, such as a physician, to practice.

    Certification is granted by a certification board and means that a person has met the special requirements, such as additional education and training, of the certifying board.

6. Discuss what the term *standard of care* means for a physician and what it means for someone in your profession.

    Responses will vary depending on the student's profession. Standard of care, as it relates to the physician, is the ordinary skill and care that medical practitioners use and that is commonly used by other medical practitioners in the same locality when caring for patients. It is the care that another professional would find appropriate in similar circumstances.

7. Describe the importance of the discovery rule as it relates to the statute of limitations.

    The discovery rule is the legal theory that provides that the statute of limitations begins to run at the time the injury is discovered or when the patient should have known of the injury.

8. Discuss the importance of the phrase *respondeat superior* as it relates to the physician.

    This translates to "let the master answer." It means that the employer (physician) is responsible for the actions of the employee.

THE CASE OF EMILY A. AND THE HERNIA REPAIR

Emily has been admitted for a two-day hospital stay for the repair of an umbilical hernia and cholecystectomy (gall bladder removal) under a general anesthesia. Her recovery from the surgical repair is uneventful except that she develops a cough. The cough keeps Emily awake all night after the surgery. She tells the nurses taking care of her about the cough, but they seem to think it is not serious and nothing is done other than taking Emily's temperature, which is normal. Emily is discharged, and her coughing becomes much more frequent once she is home. She develops pain around her hernia incision every time she coughs, and the surgical site has become inflamed. Emily still does not have a temperature. She calls her surgeon on the fourth day after surgery to explain her condition. He tells her that he doesn't treat internal medicine problems. He suggests that she call her internist. Emily calls her internist who is out of town. Emily takes some cough medicine that she finds in her medicine cabinet. Ten days after surgery Emily is readmitted to the hospital with a diagnosis of pneumonia.

Case Questions

1. What could have been done to prevent Emily from "falling through the cracks" of the healthcare system?

   The nurses should have called the surgeon even if Emily did not have a temperature. A cough after a hernia repair can damage the repair. Her surgeon had a responsibility to care for Emily during her recovery period. In addition, the internist who was "covering" for Emily's doctor when he was out of town should have treated her.

   Emily could have been more insistent that her surgeon pay attention to her complaint of a cough. She could have asked her hospital nurses to inform her surgeon about her cough. Also, she could have asked to speak to the physician who was "covering" the cases while her internist was out of town. Many patients are not aware that they can prod healthcare professionals to listen to them.

2. What does abandonment of a patient mean?

   Abandonment is the withdrawal of medical care from a patient without providing sufficient notice to the patient. Emily was separated, or abandoned, from both her surgeon and her physician when they did not respond to her request for assistance. She did not receive follow-up care from either one of them. However, in the strictest sense of the term *abandonment*, both physicians might declare that it was Emily's fault since she did not insist that they listen to her.

3. Is Emily at fault in any way?

   Emily is apparently not an informed consumer since she did not call her surgeon until the fourth day after surgery. However, the student should remember that Emily was hospitalized for the first two days and the next two days after that were probably spent recovering from an anesthetic as well as from the surgical procedure. Patients do not always call their physicians as quickly as they should. As healthcare professionals who are aware of this fact, it is our responsibility to properly educate patients about when to call their physicians once they do go home.

   However, the main responsibility does remain with the surgeon, the internist, and the nurses who agree to care for the patient. When patients undergo an anesthetic and a surgical procedure, they become dependent upon healthcare professionals to care for them.

POINTS TO PONDER (from textbook)

Teaching notes: Students should be aware that anyone can institute a lawsuit against anyone else. Even though, in principle, the student is protected by doctrines such as *respondeat superior* and by laws such as the statute of limitations and the Good

Samaritan laws, they can still be sued. In some cases, they are liable if they have caused injury to the patient, but in many cases, lawsuits without merit are not even tried in court. These issues are not meant to frighten students, but to alert them to the necessity for careful medical practice.

1. If a patient who suffers from cirrhosis tells me in confidence that she has started drinking again, what should I do?

2. Does *respondeat superior* mean that I am fully protected from a lawsuit? Why or why not?

3. Does the medical practice act in my state allow a registered nurse to prescribe birth control pills for patients? Why or why not?

4. Is it really beneficial for me to become a licensed or certified member of my profession? Why or why not?

5. Am I expected to maintain the same standard of care for patients that my physician/employer is held to?

6. Am I protected by Good Samaritan laws if I perform CPR on a patient in a hospital emergency room waiting area and the patient dies?

7. Am I protected from a lawsuit if I have reported a medical emergency to my supervisor that I did not believe I was capable of handling?

8. If an injury occurred four years ago, am I protected from a lawsuit if the statute of limitations is two years in my state?

REVIEW QUESTIONS (from textbook)
Discussion Questions

1. You have been asked to discuss the importance of the legal system for the physician at your next staff meeting. Draft an outline of what your talk would include.

   Responses will vary but should include information concerning licensure, suspension of license, practicing medicine without a license, standard of care, confidentiality, statute of limitations, discovery rule, *guardian ad litem,* Good Samaritan laws, *respondeat superior,* employees' duties to carry out orders, and employers' duties to employees.

2. You have a patient collapse on the floor in your department (office) and you must administer CPR. If the patient is injured when you administer CPR, are you protected from a malpractice suit under the Good Samaritan laws?

   The Good Samaritan laws protect medical personnel who administer emergency care <u>outside</u> of their work environment.

3. Describe the process Dr. Williams might use to become licensed to practice medicine when she moves from Chicago to New York.

   Dr. Williams would apply, in writing, to the New York state medical licensing board for reciprocity, which would allow her to practice in New York.

4. Describe what *reasonable and prudent* means as it relates to standard of care.

   Reasonable and prudent refers to the care that a normal healthcare professional would administer in similar circumstances.

Matching

Column A	Column B
1. endorsement	g. sanction
2. *guardian ad litem*	d. court-appointed representative
3. revoked	h. medical license taken away
4. *respondeat superior*	c. "let the master answer"
5. statute of limitations	f. period of time that a patient has to file a lawsuit
6. discovery rule	a. begins at the time the injury is noticed or should have been noticed
7. reciprocity	j. one state granting a license to a physician in another state
8. standard of care	b. ordinary skill that medical practitioners use
9. Good Samaritan law	e. law to protect the healthcare professional
10. nonrenewal of license	i. practicing medicine without a license

Multiple Choice

1. According to the Medical Patient's Rights Act, patient information
   a. may be given over the telephone without the patient's consent
   b. must be communicated on a need-to-know basis
   c. can always be given out to another physician
   d. other than test results, cannot be given out to a relative
   e. can never be given out to a third party

   Answer: b

2. The term for a court-appointed person to represent a minor or unborn child in litigation is
   a. *respondeat superior*
   b. advance directive
   c. *guardian ad litem*
   d. durable power of attorney
   e. living will

   Answer: c

3. Standard of care refers to
   a. ordinary skill
   b. type of care given to patients by other practitioners in the same locality
   c. only the care given by the physician
   d. a, b, and c
   e. a and b only

   Answer: e

4. The statute of limitations varies somewhat from state to state but is typically
   a. ten years
   b. five years
   c. one to three years
   d. there is no limitation
   e. none of the above

   Answer: c

5. *Respondeat superior* means that
   a. a healthcare employee can act independently of the employer
   b. the healthcare employee is never found negligent by the courts
   c. the employer is liable for the actions of the employee
   d. healthcare employees have a duty to carry out the orders of their employers without question
   e. all of the above

   Answer: c

6. A process by which a physician in one state is granted a license to practice medicine in another state is
   a. endorsement
   b. reciprocity
   c. statute of limitations
   d. revocation
   e. suspension

   Answer: b

7. Patient's rights to have their personal privacy respected and their medical records handled with confidentiality are covered in the
   a. statute of limitations
   b. rule of discovery
   c. FLEX Act
   d. Medical Patients Rights Act
   e. Good Samaritan laws

   Answer: d

8. The prudent person rule refers to
   a. the needs of a medical assistant
   b. the information that a reasonable person would need
   c. the type of employee that a physician would wish to hire in his or her office
   d. the credentials of a malpractice attorney
   e. none of the above is correct

   Answer: b

9. When a physician places an ambiguous order, the healthcare professional
   a. has a duty to carry out the order
   b. can decline to carry out the order
   c. should immediately notify the physician
   d. b and c only
   e. none of the above is correct

   Answer: d

10. Both physicians and employees are
    a. liable in a lawsuit
    b. have the same responsibility to protect patient's confidentiality
    c. operate under a standard of care
    d. must be trained to perform a procedure before attempting it
    e. all of the above

    Answer: e

Fill in the Blanks

1. The discovery rule is a legal theory that provides that the statute of limitations begins to "run" at the time the injury is discovered or when the patient should have known about the injury.
2. The law that protects healthcare professionals from liability while giving emergency care to accident victims is called the Good Samaritan law.
3. A *guardian ad litem* is a court-appointed person to represent a minor or unborn child in litigation.
4. The prudent person rule is also called the reasonable person standard.
5. The practice that minimizes the incidence of problem behavior that might result in injury to the patient and liability for the organization is called risk management.
6. To take away or recall a medical license is to revoke it.
7. The ordinary skill and care that medical practitioners use and that is commonly used by other medical practitioners in the same locality when caring for patients is called standard of care.
8. An employer is liable for the actions of the employee within the scope of employment according to the principle of *respondeat superior.*
9. JCAHO provides accreditation to hospitals and other healthcare institutions that have met certain standards and criteria.
10. Granting a state license to practice medicine to a physician already licensed in another state is called reciprocity.

PUT IT INTO PRACTICE

Search the newspapers in your area for an article relating to a medical malpractice or medical ethics issue. Discuss whether the standard of care was violated in the situation discussed in your newspaper.

WEB HUNT

1. Search the website of the American Health Lawyers Association (*www.health-lawyers.org.* Discuss what type of information this site offers to physicians.
2. Using a search engine, search the law relating to Good Samaritan laws in your state.

CASE STUDY

You are drawing a specimen of blood on Emma Helm, who says she doesn't like having blood drawn. In fact, she tells you that the sight of blood makes her "queasy." You attempt to make her feel relaxed by quietly talking to her as you help her into a chair. While you are taking her blood specimen, she faints and hits her head against the side of a cabinet.

Case Questions

1. Are you liable for Emma's injury? Why or why not?

   You are liable because you did not use the same skill or provide the same standard of care that someone else in your position would. In addition, your employer also has liability under *respondeat superior.*

2. If you are not liable, do you know who is?

   Under the doctrine of *respondeat superior,* the employer/physician is ultimately responsible for injuries that are caused by his or her employees. The physician/employer does not have to be present in order to be liable for the injury.

3. Is Emma Helm at fault for her accident? Why or why not?

   She warned you that she doesn't like having this procedure done. She even warned you that the sight of blood makes her queasy. She could have insisted that she lie down for the procedure, but this may not have even occurred to her. Emma apparently did all that she could to warn the person performing the phlebotomy about the danger.

4. What might you do to prevent this type of injury from happening?

   Always listen to the patient! Assume that a patient may faint from a procedure such as this. Therefore, have the patient lie down unless the patient refuses and then document the refusal.

SUPPLEMENTAL QUESTIONS

Chapter Review

Cover the terms in the left-hand column with a piece of paper. Read the statement and fill in the blank with the answer before uncovering the correct response.

board of examiners — The _____ _____ _____ in each state grants a license to practice medicine. Licensure may be granted in one of three ways. _____ is approval or sanction. The practice of cooperation by which a state grants a license to a physician already licensed in another state is known as _____. The final way a license is granted is through _____. _____ _____ _____ refers to the ordinary skill and care that medical practitioners must use.

Endorsement

reciprocity
examination/
   Standard of care

risk — Physicians are expected not to expose their patients to undue _____. Physicians who violate this standard are liable for _____.
negligence

Confidentiality — _____ refers to keeping private all information about a person and not disclosing it to a third party without _____ consent. According to the _____ _____ _____ Act, a law passed by Congress, all patients have the right to have their personal privacy respected and their medical records handled with confidentiality.

written/Medical
Patients Rights

statute of limitations — The _____ _____ _____ does not always start "running" at the time of treatment, but begins when the problem is discovered or should have been discovered. This is known as the _____ rule. A patient
discovery

guardian	under 18 can either sue through the _____ *ad litem* or wait until turning 18.
Good Samaritan	State laws that help to protect healthcare professionals from liability while giving emergency care to an accident victim are called _____ _____ laws. Those professionals who do offer aid in good faith, without
gross	_____ negligence, are protected by these laws.
respondeat	An employer is liable for the acts of the employee within the scope of employment, referred to as _____
superior	_____. Under this doctrine, when the physician delegates duties to other healthcare professionals and they perform them incorrectly, the liability rests on the
physician/employee	_____. However, the _____ may also be named in the lawsuit.

Multiple Choice

Select the one best response to the following questions.

1. The process by which a physician is licensed through approval or sanction is
   a. reciprocity
   b. registration
   c. endorsement
   d. examination
   e. *guardian ad litem*

   Answer: c

2. Inappropriate use of drugs or alcohol is an example of a(n)
   a. unprofessional conduct
   b. reciprocity
   c. endorsement
   d. *respondeat superior*
   e. discovery rule

   Answer: a

3. The law requires a physician to
   a. use extraordinary skill
   b. treat everyone
   c. be certified by the American Medical Association
   d. perform the same acts that a "reasonable and prudent" physician would
   e. all of the above

   Answer: d

4. The Medical Patients Rights Act protects the privacy of
   a. the patient's history
   b. the fact that the person is a patient
   c. test results
   d. a and c
   e. a, b, and c

   Answer: e

5. The statute of limitations starts running
   a. but does not apply to medical practitioners
   b. when the problem is discovered or should have been discovered
   c. one to three years after the treatment, depending on the state
   d. on a case-by-case basis
   e. at the time of treatment

   Answer: b

6. An employee's duties include
   a. clarifying physician orders when they are ambiguous or erroneous
   b. having a knowledge of basic information concerning procedures that are likely to be used
   c. interpreting and carrying out the orders of his or her physician/employer
   d. declining to carry out a procedure that seems dangerous for the patient
   e. all of the above

   Answer: e

7. To renew a license, a physician must
   a. complete 75 hours of continuing medical education
   b. retake the state examination
   c. pay a fee
   d. a and c only
   e. a, b, and c

   Answer: d

8. Laws that help to protect healthcare professionals from liability while giving emergency care to an accident victim are known as
   a. Medical Patients Rights Acts
   b. FLEX Acts
   c. Good Samaritan laws
   d. discovery rule
   e. *respondeat superior.*

   Answer: c

9. The practice of one states granting a license to a physician who is already licensed in another state is known as
   a. registration
   b. reciprocity
   c. endorsement
   d. examination
   e. goodwill

   Answer: b

10. A state may revoke a physician's license for
    a. unprofessional conduct
    b. personal incapacity to perform one's duties
    c. severe misconduct
    d. commission of a crime
    e. all of the above

    Answer: e

True/False Questions

1. The prudent person rule is a federal law that protects the healthcare professional who provides emergency care from liability. (false)

2. *Respondeat superior* means "let the decision stand." (false)

3. Reciprocity occurs when one state grants a physician a license to practice medicine if he or she is already licensed in another state. (true)

4. Medical practice acts define the penalties for practicing medicine without a license. (true)

5. USMLE is a single licensing examination for medical school graduates that will allow them to practice medicine. (true)

6. JCAHO is a licensing organization that provides examinations for registered nurse licensure. (false)

7. Physicians, by the very nature of their calling, are obligated to treat everyone. (false)

8. The Medical Patients Rights Act provides the right for the patient to own his or her medical record. (false)

9. When a statute of limitations is "tolled," it means that it starts to run. (false)

10. Good Samaritan laws protect the healthcare worker who accidentally causes an injury to a patient while performing his or her normal duties at work. (false)

Short Answer Questions

1. What are the four basic characteristics of the state medical practice acts?
   a. establish the baseline for the practice of medicine in that state
   b. determine the prerequisites for licensure
   c. forbid the practice of medicine without a license
   d. specify the conditions for license renewal, suspension, and revocation

2. What are the three methods by which a state grants a license to practice medicine?
   a. endorsement
   b. reciprocity
   c. registration

3. Why do Good Samaritan laws exist in most states?

   Good Samaritan laws exist in most states to encourage physicians and other healthcare professionals to offer aid in an emergency situation. Those professionals who do offer aid in good faith, without gross negligence, are protected.

4. What are the duties of a healthcare employee?
   a. interpret and carry out the orders of his or her employer
   b. know basic information concerning procedures and drugs that are likely to be used
   c. clarify physician's orders when they are ambiguous or erroneous
   d. decline to carry out any procedure or administer any drug that appears dangerous to the patient

5. What is the discovery rule?

   The statute of limitations begins to run at the time a problem is discovered or should have been discovered.

6. Under the doctrine of *respondeat superior,* who is liable for a health professional's actions?

   The employer is liable.

7. What are the requirements, in addition to passing a written and oral examination, that most states impose on applicants who wish to become licensed physicians?

   The applicant must:
   a. provide proof that he or she has completed the professional education as required by his or her state
   b. provide proof of the successful completion in an approved internship/residency program
   c. provide proof of any past convictions, history of drug or alcohol abuse
   d. have obtained the age of majority, generally 21 years old
   e. be of good moral character
   f. be a resident of that state.

8. What are some of the reasons that a physician's license to practice medicine may be revoked?
   a. unprofessional conduct such as use of drugs or alcohol, gross immorality, and falsifying records
   b. commission of a crime such as Medicare and Medicaid fraud, rape, murder, larceny, and narcotics conviction
   c. mental or physical incapacity to perform one's duties

9. What does standard of care refer to?

   This is the level of expertise that is commonly used by other medical practitioners, such as physicians, nurses, and medical assistants, in the same locality and medical specialty when caring for patients.

10. What is the purpose of risk management?

    To identify behaviors and practices in an organization that could result in injury for patients and employees and, ultimately, liability for the organization.

TEACHING STRATEGIES

Have the students role-play the following situations (students should assume the roles of the healthcare professionals, attorneys, and patients):

a. A patient asks a medical receptionist to give her the results of her recent HIV test over the telephone. How does the receptionist respond?
b. An employee calls out loudly to a patient in the reception room and asks her for the date of her last menstrual period. How does the employee's supervisor, who hears this conversation, respond?
c. A nurse's next-door neighbor is a lawyer. He tells the nurse that he is going to subpoena the medical records of one of her employer's patients. What does the nurse say to the neighbor? To her employer/physician? To the patient?
d. As the student is traveling home from work on a train, a woman becomes unconscious. What does the student do, if anything?
e. Dr. Williams asks you to do a procedure that you are unsure about. Ordinarily this procedure is within the scope of practice in your particular medical discipline, but you have not had much experience doing it. You do not want to lose your job. What do you do? What do you say to your employer?

    f. Have students describe to the class the action they plan on taking in an emergency situation. How will the Good Samaritan laws influence their decision?

    g. Get students involved with this material by conducting a "kangaroo court" or mock trial involving the *Cline v. Lund* case described in Chapter 3. Have them discuss the issue of an employee's duty to carry out orders.

    h. Have students prepare flash cards for key words (glossary) in this chapter.

4

Medical Practice and Allied Health Professionals

CHAPTER SYNOPSIS

Today's healthcare students are entering an ever-changing professional work environment. They need to understand the impact of managed care on their own career as well as on their patient's lives. This chapter concentrates on managed care, the various types of physicians' medical practices, and the descriptions of allied health professionals they will be working with. The ethics of managed care is emphasized.

Chapter Lecture Outline	Instructor's Notes

I. Today's Healthcare Environment
  A. Healthcare has undergone major changes during the past fifteen years.
    1. The growth rate of the older adult population is just one of the developments that caused a rapid expansion of the healthcare system.
    2. Insurance companies have significantly impacted the way healthcare is delivered.
    3. Advances in medicine, such as heart and kidney transplants and mobile mammogram units, have caused a rapid expansion of the healthcare system.
    4. Emerging managed care plans have also significantly impacted the way healthcare is delivered.
  B. Managed Care Organization (MCO)—Three types of managed care plans.
    1. Health Maintenance Organization (HMO)—A type of managed care plan that offers a wide range of healthcare services to plan members for a predetermined fee per member by a limited group of providers.
    2. Preferred Provider Organization (PPO)—A managed care concept in which the patient must use a medical provider who is under contract with the insurer for an agreed-upon fee in order to receive co-payment from the insurer.
    3. Exclusive Provider Organization (EPO)—A type of managed care that combines the concepts of HMO and PPO.
  C. Federal Assistance Programs
    1. Medicare—Federal program that provides healthcare for elderly and disabled persons.	

Chapter Lecture Outline	Instructor's Notes

2. Medicaid—Implemented by the individual states; provides financial assistance for certain categories of the poor and indigent.
      3. Diagnostic Related Groups (DRGs)—A health payment system that classifies each Medicare patient by illness.
    D. Ethical Considerations of Managed Care
      1. Concern that the wealthy may receive better healthcare than the poor.
      2. Concern for a "bait-and-switch" approach used by an MCO that lures the patient into joining a managed care plan only to realize that only minimal services are provided.
      3. Concern that patient's interests are sacrificed to the "bottom line" on the financial statements.
 II. Types of Medical Practice
    A. Solo practice—A medical practice in which the physician works alone.
    B. Partnership—A legal agreement in which physicians share in the business operations of a medical practice and become responsible for the actions of the other partners.
    C. Associate practice—A legal agreement in which physicians agree to share a facility and staff, but do not, as a rule, share legal responsibility for the actions of each other.
    D. Group practice—Three or more physicians who share the same facility and practice medicine together.
    E. Professional corporation—A type of medical practice, as established by law, that is managed by a board of directors.
III. The Ethics of Fee Splitting—A physician offering to pay another physician for references is illegal.
IV. Medical Specialty Boards
    A. Currently, twenty-three specialty boards are covered by the American Board of Medical Specialists.
    B. The majority of physicians work in specialty fields such as anesthesiology, psychiatry, or a surgical specialty.
    C. The specialty boards seek to improve the quality of medical care and treatment by encouraging physicians to further their education and training.
    D. The board evaluates the qualifications of candidates who apply for and pass an examination.
 V. Medical and Surgical Specialties
    A. American College of Surgeons
    B. American College of Physicians
VI. Allied Health Professionals
    A. Certified Medical Assistant (CMA)
    B. Certified Medical Transcriptionist (CMT)
    C. Dental Assistant
    D. Electrocardiograph Technologist
    E. Emergency Medical Technician (EMT)
    F. Laboratory or Medical Technologist
    G. Licensed Practical Nurse	

Chapter Lecture Outline	Instructor's Notes
H. Medical Records Technician (ART) I. Nurse Practitioner (NP) J. Occupational Therapist (OT) K. Pharmacist L. Pharmacy Technician M. Phlebotomist N. Physical Therapist (PT) O. Physician Assistant (PA) P. Registered Nurse (RN) Q. Respiratory Therapist (RT) R. Social Worker S. Surgical Technician T. Ultrasound Technician (AART) U. X-ray Technologist	

LEARNING OBJECTIVES

(Student answers may vary.)

1. Define all glossary terms.

Associate practice   a legal agreement in which physicians agree to share a facility and staff but do not, as a rule, share responsibility for the legal actions of each other.

Capitation rate   a fixed monthly fee paid by an HMO to healthcare providers for providing medical services to patients who are members of that HMO.

Conscience clause   legislation or regulation stating that hospitals and healthcare professionals are not required to assist with such procedures as abortion and sterilization.

Co-payment   an agreed-upon fee paid by the insured for certain medical services, usually $10 to $20.

Corporation   a type of medical practice, as established by law, that is managed by a board of directors.

Diagnostic Related Groups (DRGs)   designations used to identify reimbursement per condition in a hospital; used for Medicare patients.

Exclusive Provider Organization (EPO)   a type of managed care that combines the concepts of HMO and PPO.

Fee splitting   an agreement to pay a fee to another physician or agency for the referral of patients; this is illegal in some states and is considered an unethical medical practice.

Fixed-payment plan   a payment plan for medical bills that offers subscribers (members) complete medical care in return for a fixed monthly fee.

Franchise   a business run by an individual to whom a franchisor grants the exclusive right to market a product or service in a certain market area.

Franchisees   persons or companies that hold a franchise.

Gatekeeper the person, such as a primary care physician, or entity, such as an insurance company, that approves patient referrals to other physicians or services.

Group practice three or more physicians who share the same facility and practice medicine together.

Health Maintenance Organization (HMO) a type of managed care plan that offers a range of healthcare services to plan members for a predetermined fee per member by a limited group of providers.

Indigent a person without funds.

Managed Care Organization (MCO) a type of medical plan that pays for and manages the medical care a patient receives.

Medicaid a federal program implemented by the individual states that provides financial assistance to states for insuring certain categories of the poor and indigent.

Medicare federal program that provides healthcare coverage for persons over 65 years of age as well as for disabled persons or those who suffer from kidney disease or other debilitating ailments.

Partnership a legal agreement in which physicians share in the business operation of a medical practice and become responsible for the actions of the other partners.

Per diem daily rate.

Preferred provider organization (PPO) a managed care concept in which the patient must use a medical provider who is under contract with the insurer for an agreed-upon fee in order to receive co-payment from the insurer.

Primary care physician (PCP) HMO-designated physician to manage and control an enrolled patient's medical care.

Sole proprietorship a type of medical practice in which one physician may employ other physicians.

Solo practice a medical practice in which the physician works alone.

Third-party payers a party other than the patient who assumes responsibility for paying the patient's bills (for example, an insurance company).

2. Describe today's healthcare environment.

The environment has gone through major changes during the past fifteen years: an increased number of older adults, an increase in technological advances and discoveries, the addition of managed care plans, and an increased impact from government legislation.

3. Discuss the similarities and differences among HMOs, PPOs, and EPOs.

All three are types of managed care plans. A health maintenance organization (HMO) offers a wide range of services to plan members for a predetermined fee (capitation fee) per member by a limited group of providers.

A preferred provider organization (PPO) is a plan that restricts the use of providers to those who are under contract with the insurer for an agreed-upon fee. The PPO is not based on a prepayment or capitation fee, as is an HMO. The PPO reimburses the provider for each medical service. A PPO offers a greater choice of physician and/or hospital.

An exclusive provider organization (EPO) is a combination of the HMO and PPO concepts. The selection of providers is limited to a certain group of defined providers, such as in an HMO. However, the providers are paid on a modified fee-for-service basis, as in a PPO.

4. Describe five types of medical practice.

Solo practice is one in which the physician practices alone.

A partnership is one in which there is a legal agreement to share in the business operation of a medical practice. Under this arrangement, each partner becomes responsible for the actions of all the other partners.

An associate practice is a legal agreement in which physicians agree to share a facility and staff but not the profits and losses.

A group practice consists of three or more physicians who share the same facility and practice medicine together. They all share expenses, income, personnel, equipment, and records.

The professional corporation is managed by a board of directors. There are legal and financial benefits to incorporating the practice.

5. Discuss the term *diplomat* as it relates to medical specialty boards.

A diplomat is a physician who has successfully passed a specialty board examination and is certified by the American Board of Medical Specialists.

6. Identify three categories of licensed nurses and describe their educational requirements.

A registered nurse (RN) is a licensed professional who has received education and training in either a two-year associate degree program or a four-year baccalaureate program and has passed a licensing examination.

A nurse practitioner (NP) is a registered nurse who has received additional training in a nursing specialty area such as obstetrics or community health.

A licensed practical nurse (LPN) is a technically trained professional who can perform basic to moderately complex nursing tasks.

7. Describe five categories of certified healthcare professionals.

Some of the certified healthcare professionals discussed in this chapter include the physician assistant, medical assistant, medical transcriptionist, laboratory technician, and laboratory technologist.

NOTE: The instructor and students may wish to include a discussion of other certified professionals not included in this chapter.

8. Describe the diagnostic related group (DRG) system of classification.

The DRG system is a method for hospital payment, implemented in 1983, that classifies each Medicare patient by illness. The DRG classification system has additional use in healthcare facilities such as medical offices to facilitate insurance reimbursement. The DRG system categorizes 467 illnesses. Each category has a preset sum that limits the reimbursable costs for the treatment of that condition. The plus side of DRGs is the ability to keep costs for treatment down by setting a limit. The negative side of DRGs is that care for the severely ill patient is often compromised, since they are often discharged too early from hospital care.

9. State the differences between Medicare and Medicaid.

Medicare is a federal program that provides health care coverage for the elderly as well as for some disabled patients. It is meant to provide for free choice of health care. However, as costs for health care have risen, so have the out-of-pocket costs that the Medicare patient must pay. Most patients try to have a supplemental insurance policy to cover those expenses that Medicare won't cover.

Medicaid, also a federal program, is meant to provide health care coverage for the poor and indigent patient. However, it is implemented by the individual states; therefore, the coverage is not the same in each state.

Under Medicaid, health care service is sometimes rationed so that some procedures, such as liver transplants, are not covered in all states.

THE CASE OF MARION AND THE PACEMAKER

Marion is a 92-year-old patient who weighs 78 pounds. She has had poor eating habits for at least twenty years and refused all attempts by her two daughters to improve her nutrition. In addition, Marion had been a heavy smoker all her life and suffered frequent respiratory problems. During the past two years she has become quite forgetful, has suffered a broken hip as a result of a fall out of bed, and has been treated for pneumonia. Her daughters, who have their own family responsibilities and cannot bring their mother to live with them, have found an excellent nursing home near them. In spite of Marion's protests, she enters the nursing home. However, she quickly adjusts to her new home and the attention that she receives.

During her third week in the nursing home, Marion develops a cough, high temperature, and respiratory problems. She is hospitalized with a diagnosis of pneumonia. Marion immediately becomes disoriented and attempts to remove her intravenous and oxygen tubing. Since she tried to climb out of bed, her daughters must remain at her side. The attending physician tells the daughters that in addition to treatment for pneumonia, Marion will also need to have a pacemaker inserted to regulate her heartbeat. Marion would then be unable to return to the nursing home since the facility is not equipped to care for someone recovering from surgery.

One of Marion's daughters has been granted a medical power of attorney for her mother. Before Marion became confused, she clearly explained to her daughters her wishes not to receive extraordinary measures to prolong her life. She also signed a living will indicating her wishes. After thoughtful discussion with other family members, Marion's daughters tell the physician that they do not want to put their confused mother through the surgical procedure. They state that they want to spare her the pain of recovery from a surgical procedure since she is quite confused and elderly. Further, they are concerned that their mother will not survive an anesthetic and surgical procedure in her frail condition.

The physician seems to be understanding of this decision. He says that he will place their request in Marion's chart not to have the pacemaker inserted. However, the floor nurses take the daughters aside on several occasions to tell them that this is not a dangerous procedure and that they need to sign a permit for surgery. In fact, the nurses make the daughters feel that they are not acting in their mother's best interests by not signing the surgical permit. Marion returns to the nursing home without a pacemaker. She lives another four years without any cardiac problems.

Case Questions

1. Were the nurses carrying out their responsibility as licensed healthcare professionals or were they overstepping their role?

   The hospital nurses believed they were acting in the best interests of their patient by encouraging the daughters to sign a permit for the mother to have the pacemaker inserted. However, the nurses could not know all of the circumstances involved in the daughters' decision.

2. Were Marion's daughters acting in the best interests of their mother since they knew that if she had the surgery she could not return to the nursing home where she was receiving good care?

   Marion's daughters knew what their elderly and frail mother could tolerate. They were concerned that she might not even survive a surgical procedure involving a general anesthetic. If the daughters' based their decision only on the fact that they might have to care for Marion if she could not return to the nursing home, then their decision may have been suspect. However, the physician agreed with the daughters and wrote a medical chart note to that effect.

3. What should happen when a physician agrees with the family members and the nursing staff does not?

   Unless there is a question of improper, unethical, or illegal behavior on the part of the physician, the nurses must respect and obey a physician's orders. There would be chaos if this principle were not respected. Nurses, with the exception of nurse practitioners, cannot order treatments and prescribe medications.

[*Note:* This case is included to alert students to the need to listen to families. The students, as potential healthcare professionals, will most likely agree with the hospitals nurses who seemed to just be doing their job. However, they must also be able to understand the family's viewpoint and carry out the orders of the physician.]

POINTS TO PONDER (from textbook)

Teaching note: These questions are meant to provoke critical thinking. In many cases, there is no definitive answer to the question, such as with question 8. In other cases, the student should consider the question a review of material covered in the chapter. Student responses may vary.

1. What impact will managed care have upon your career as an allied health professional?

2. What type of practice does your physician/employer have? If it is not a solo practice, what are the other specialties involved in the practice?

3. What are the advantages of forming a corporation?

4. Why is it important to include the medical specialty and initials indicating a particular degree or license after one's name?

5. What should you say if a patient refers to you as "doctor" or "nurse" even though your degree is in another discipline?

6. How should healthcare plans balance the interests of all the enrolled patients with the interests of a patient who has special medical needs and extraordinary expenses?

7. In the interests of maintaining a successful practice, should a physician refuse to provide care for patients who are uninsured or minimally insured?

8. Consider the question of ethics that arises when we ask ourselves if we are reducing unnecessary tests, as the HMOs and others believe we should, or if we are limiting tests for patients who really need them.

REVIEW QUESTIONS (from textbook)
Discussion Questions

1. Discuss your role as a medical professional in relation to the physician and other healthcare providers.

   Answers will vary. Students should discuss their specialty areas as they relate to other healthcare professionals such as physicians, nurses, medical assistants, and technicians.

2. Discuss the impact that managed care is likely to have on your career in healthcare.

   Answers will vary. Students should include the current emphasis on cost containment, the growing aging population, and technological advances.

3. What can be done to ensure that MCOs provide ethical care for all patients?

   Answers may vary. Every effort should be made to provide all the necessary services for excellent patient care. Financial incentives to physicians who reduce the number of patient tests and treatments are inherently unethical and should be avoided.

Matching

Column A	Column B
1. HMO	c. health maintenance organization
2. EPO	f. exclusive provider organization
3. PPO	a. preferred provider organization
4. solo practice	i. physician practices alone
5. associate practice	b. physicians agree to share expenses of a facility
6. sole proprietorship	g. one physician may employ others
7. corporation	d. managed by a board of directors
8. third-party payer	j. insurance company
9. Medicaid	h. financial assistance for the indigent
10. Medicare	e. financial assistance for the elderly

Multiple Choice

1. Under this plan, a healthcare provider is paid a set amount based on the category of care provided to the patient.
   a. AMA
   b. DRG
   c. ANA
   d. HHS
   e. UNOS

   Answer: b

2. Medicare patients who are members of HMOs may now, by law
   a. not make any deductible payment
   b. select any physician they want
   c. appeal a denial of treatment
   d. have all their nursing home expenses paid
   e. none of the above

   Answer: c

3. A type of managed care in which the selection of providers is limited to a defined group who are all paid on a modified fee-for-service basis is
    a. exclusive provider organization
    b. group practice
    c. preferred provider organization
    d. health maintenance organization
    e. sole proprietorship

    Answer: a

4. A legal agreement in which physicians agree to share a facility and staff but not the profits and losses is
    a. solo practice
    b. sole proprietorship
    c. partnership
    d. associate practice
    e. none of the above

    Answer: d

5. The advantage of a corporation is that it
    a. offers protection from loss of individual assets
    b. may offer fringe benefits
    c. will remain in effect after the death of a member
    d. offers the opportunity for a large increase in income
    e. a, b, and c only

    Answer: e

6. A physician who is board certified may be addressed as
    a. diplomat
    b. fellow
    c. partner
    d. associate
    e. a and b only

    Answer: e

7. MCOs are able to manage costs by
    a. shifting some financial risk back to the physicians
    b. shifting some financial risk back to the hospitals
    c. using a fee-for-service payment method
    d. a and b only
    e. a, b, and c

    Answer: d

8. This federal legislation provides healthcare for indigent persons and is administered by individual states.
    a. Medicare
    b. Medicaid
    c. HMO
    d. PPO
    e. COBRA

    Answer: b

9. The managed care system
   a. has a gatekeeper to determine who will receive medical treatments
   b. provides a mechanism for approval for all nonemergency services
   c. provides care for a fixed monthly fee
   d. includes HMOs, PPOs, and EPOs
   e. all of the above

   Answer: e

10. The American College of Surgeons confers a fellowship upon its applicants
    a. whenever a surgeon places a request
    b. when they complete additional training
    c. when they have documentation of 50 surgical cases during the previous three years
    d. a, b, and c
    e. b and c only

    Answer: e

Fill in the Blanks

1. A <u>fixed-payment</u> plan form of insurance offers its members complete medical care in return for a fixed monthly fee.
2. A physician responsible for a patient's medical care and referrals to other physicians is the <u>primary care physician</u>.
3. A type of hospital payment system that classifies each Medicare patient by illness is the <u>Diagnostic Related Group (DRG)</u>.
4. A daily rate of payment for a patient's care is called <u>per diem</u>.
5. <u>Fee splitting</u> is the unethical practice of a physician's paying another physician for the referral of patients.
6. A medical specialty of the ear, nose, and throat is called <u>otorhinolaryngology</u>.
7. A <u>conscience clause</u> exists in some states to provide protection for medical personnel who do not wish to participate in a procedure that violates their moral or religious beliefs.
8. A predetermined fee charged to members of an insurance plan is called a <u>capitation</u> rate.
9. A fee charged that an insured patient must pay at the time of service is called a <u>co-payment</u>.
10. The federal program that assists the indigent with medical care is <u>Medicaid.</u>

PUT IT INTO PRACTICE

Interview a senior citizen and ask about his or her health insurance needs. Does he or she have difficulty with the paperwork required by the insurance company? Ask what could be done to make this a less difficult task.

WEB HUNT

1. Discuss the type of information that is available on the website for the American Medical Association (*www.ama-assn.org*).

2. Review the website for an organization such as the American Nurses Association (*www.nursinworld.org/readroom*), American Association of Medical Assistants (*www.aama-ntl.org*), or your own professional organization. What are the categories listed on this website?

CASE STUDY

Jerry McCall is Dr. Williams's office assistant. He has received professional training as both a medical assistant and an LPN. He is handling all the phone calls while the receptionist is at lunch. A patient calls and says he must have a prescription refill for Valium, an antidepressant medication, called in right away to his pharmacy, since he is leaving for the airport in 30 minutes. He says that Dr. Williams is a personal friend and always gives him a small supply of Valium when he has to fly. No one except Jerry is in the office at the time. What should he do?

Case Questions

1. Does Jerry's medical training qualify him to issue this refill order? Why or why not?

   No. Only the physician can issue a prescription refill order.

2. Would it make a difference if the medication requested were for control of high blood pressure that the patient critically needs on a daily basis? Why or why not?

   No. Jerry's professional credentials do not allow him to issue prescription orders. However, if the patient has a critical need for this medication, then Jerry must make every attempt to get the patient in touch with the physician for a refill order. Since he is just covering the telephone during the lunch hour, he can pass on the information as soon as the regular staff returns.

3. If Jerry does call in the refill and the patient has an adverse reaction to it while flying, is Jerry protected from a lawsuit under the doctrine of *respondeat superior*?

   Both Jerry and his employer may be liable for negligence (malpractice). The doctrine of *respondeat superior* means that if an employee commits an error, the employer is responsible for that employee's actions.

4. What is your advice to Jerry?

   The student should recognize that Jerry must use integrity. He should be honest and tell the patient that he is not qualified to call in the prescription.

SUPPLEMENTAL QUESTIONS

Chapter Review

Cover the terms in the left-hand column with a piece of paper. Read the statement and fill in the blank with the answer before uncovering the correct response.

Managed care	Healthcare has undergone several changes in the last fifteen years. _____ _____ organizations have become the most common form of health insurance. One such organization in which a range of healthcare services is made available to plan members for a predetermined

health maintenance	fee per member, by a limited group of providers, is called a(n) _____ _____ organization.
solo practice	In the early part of the twentieth century, the main form of medical practice was the _____ _____. Since then, several new forms have become popular.
group	Members of a(n) _____ practice share expenses, income, personnel, equipment, and records. The majority
associate	of physicians work in _____ practice fields such as anesthesiology, psychiatry, and specialized surgical areas. Boards covered by the American Board of Medical Specialists can certify these physicians. The board seeks to improve the quality of medical care and treatment by en-
education	couraging physicians to further their _____ and
training	_____. The physician who successfully passes the
diplomat	board review then becomes a certified _____. There
oncology	are several types of specialty areas, such as _____, the study of cancer and cancer-related tumors;
neurology	_____, the treatment of patients who have a disor-
pathology	der or disease of the nervous system; and _____, a specialization in abnormal changes in tissues that are removed during surgery or an autopsy.
	Depending on the physician's area of specialization, he or she will work with a variety of trained personnel. To be li-
registered nurse	censed as a _____ _____ requires successful completion of a national licensure examination known as the NCLEX. Other healthcare professionals include the
phlebotomist	_____, who draws blood from patients, and the
pharmacist	_____, who orders, maintains, prepares, and distributes prescription medications. Healthcare professionals who use inaudible sound waves to outline shapes of tissues
ultrasound	and organs are known as _____ technologists.

Multiple Choice

Select the one best response to the following questions.

1. An advantage of a sole proprietorship is
   a. it will remain after the death of a member
   b. physician retains all assets
   c. there is protection from loss of individual assets
   d. expenses and staff are shared
   e. all of the above

   Answer: b

2. Three or more physicians who share the same facility and practice medicine together are known as
   a. a group practice
   b. an associate practice
   c. a solo practice
   d. an exclusive provider organization
   e. a sole proprietorship

   Answer: a

3. A type of managed care that combines the concepts of an HMO and PPO is a(n)
   a. modified health maintenance organization
   b. managed care association
   c. health maintenance-provider organization
   d. preferred provider association
   e. exclusive provider organization

   Answer: e

4. A professional corporation is
   a. designated as an HMO or IPA
   b. managed by a board of directors
   c. owned by shareholders
   d. b and c only
   e. a, b, and c

   Answer: d

5. A medical specialty concerned with the prevention and correction of disorders of the musculoskeletal system is
   a. hematology
   b. neurology
   c. orthopedics
   d. pathology
   e. dermatology

   Answer: c

6. All of the following are licensed allied health professionals except
   a. nurse practitioner
   b. pharmacist
   c. nursing assistant
   d. registered nurse
   e. all of the above are licensed

   Answer: c

7. Managed care providers
   a. include HMOs and EPOs
   b. protect physicians against malpractice suits
   c. have a mechanism for a gatekeeper
   d. a and c only
   e. all of the above are correct

   Answer: d

8. Medical expense reimbursement, profit-sharing, pension plans, and disability insurance are examples of tax-deductible benefits that can be offered by a(n)
   a. professional corporation
   b. solo practice
   c. group practice
   d. associate practice
   e. sole proprietorship

   Answer: a

9. What specialist uses inaudible sound waves to outline shapes of tissues and organs?
   a. electrocardiograph technologist?
   b. x-ray technologist
   c. phlebotomist
   d. ultrasound technologist
   e. social worker

   Answer: d

10. The term *diplomat,* as it relates to a medical specialty board, means
    a. the physician is a governmental spokesperson for the board
    b. the physician successfully passed the board review
    c. the physician has successfully passed the board's examination
    d. b and c only
    e. all of the above

    Answer: d

True/False Questions

1. The gatekeeper function of the primary physician is meant to keep healthcare costs down. (true)

2. Medicaid is a federal assistance program for all persons over the age of 65. (false)

3. Diagnostic related groups classify illnesses into 467 categories. (true)

4. Rationing of medical care is not a concern with the Medicaid program. (false)

5. A bait-and-switch approach is never used in an MCO. (false)

6. In a sole proprietorship, the physician is alone in the practice. (false)

7. In an associate practice, the physicians do not usually share the profits and losses of the practice. (true)

8. Physicians have only been allowed by law to incorporate since the 1960s. (true)

9. Fee splitting is a legal method for a physician to receive referrals. (false)

10. A person who has a Ph.D. can be addressed as "Doctor." (true)

Short Answer Questions

1. What are three types of managed care organizations?
   a. health maintenance organization (HMO)
   b. preferred provider organization (PPO)
   c. exclusive provider organization (EPO)

2. List five types of medical practice.
   a. solo practice
   b. partnership
   c. associate practice
   d. group practice
   e. professional corporation

3. Define the following medical and surgical specialties.
   a. anesthesiology—administers both local and general drugs to induce a complete or partial loss of feeling (anesthesia) during a surgical procedure.
   b. immunology—treats abnormal responses and acquired hypersensitivity to substances with medical methods such as testing and desensitization.
   c. geriatric medicine—focuses on the care of diseases and disorders of the elderly.
   d. nephrology—specializes in pathology of the kidney, including diseases and disorders.
   e. neurology—treats the nonsurgical patient who has a disorder or disease of the nervous system.
   f. otorhinolaryngology—specializes in medical and surgical treatment of the ear (otology), nose (rhinology), and throat (laryngology).
   g. physical medicine—treats patients after they have suffered an injury or disability.
   h. thoracic—surgically treats disorders and diseases of the chest.

4. Discuss the functions of the following allied health professionals.
   a. physician assistant—assists the physician in the primary care of the patient.
   b. nurse practitioner—a registered nurse who has additional training in a specialty area such as obstetrics, gerontology, or community health.
   c. certified medical transcriptionist—types dictation from a tape recorded by a physician or surgeon.
   d. certified medical assistant—works in a variety of healthcare settings, including physicians' offices and clinics. Duties of the medical assistant are grouped into two categories: administrative and clinical.
   e. laboratory technologist—performs laboratory analysis, directs the work of laboratory personnel, and maintains quality assurance standards for all equipment.

5. What advantages does a corporation offer?
   a. protection from loss of individual assets
   b. many fringe benefits
   c. corporation will remain after death of a member

6. What are the disadvantages of a solo practice?
   a. difficulty raising capital
   b. sole responsibility for liability and management functions
   c. inadequate coverage of patients' needs
   d. practice may die with owner

7. In what capacity is a primary physician acting when he or she is responsible for the patient's medical care and all referrals to other physicians?

   The physician is in a gatekeeper role.

8. What are some of the areas that MCOs try to control?
   a. choice of physician
   b. treatments a physician can order
   c. number and type of diagnostic tests that can be ordered

d. number of days a patient can stay in the hospital with a particular diagnosis
e. choice of hospitals
f. drugs a physician can prescribe
g. referrals to specialists
h. choice of specialists
i. ordering a second opinion for diagnosis and treatment

9. What are the two federal programs that provide healthcare for the elderly and the indigent?
   a. Medicare
   b. Medicaid

10. What is the difference between a solo practice and a sole proprietorship?

   In solo practice, a physician practices alone without the assistance of other physicians. This is a common practice for dentists.

   In a sole proprietorship, one physician may own the practice but hires other physicians to work in it. He or she pays all the expenses, including the salaries of the staff physicians, and retains all the assets. An example is a dialysis center owned by one urologist.

TEACHING STRATEGIES

1. Invite a physician and surgeon into the classroom. Ask the guest speakers to discuss their work and what they believe to be the role of the allied healthcare professionals who work with them.
2. Invite allied professionals into the classroom to speak about their functions as members of the healthcare team.
3. Invite an office manager from a managed care organization into class to discuss that role in the organization.
4. Have the students write to a professional association for information on one of the allied health fields discussed in this chapter.
5. Have students share with the class the healthcare specialty they have selected and compare and contrast their choice with others in the class. If all the students are entering the same profession, such as nursing, medical assisting, or physician assistant, then have the students discuss the particular areas in that discipline that they are attracted to.
6. Have the students prepare flash cards for the key words (glossary) terms in the chapter.

5

The Physician–Patient Relationship

CHAPTER SYNOPSIS

A relationship must be established between a patient and his or her physician in order for a contract for medical services to be provided. Patients can expect that physicians will care for them as long as is necessary. However, both ethical and legal dilemmas can occur when the relationship is broken. This chapter discusses the rights and responsibilities of the physician; the patient's rights and responsibilities, including those of minors; and the role of the healthcare consumer. There is a special focus on advance directives and the issue of consent.

Chapter Lecture Outline	Instructor's Notes

I. The Physician–Patient Relationship
  A. Both physician and patient must agree to form a relationship for there to be a contract for services.
  B. In order to receive proper treatment, the patient must confide truthfully in the physician.
II. Physician's Rights and Responsibilities
  A. Physicians have many ethical and professional rights.
  B. Physicians have the right to select the patients they wish to treat.
  C. From an ethical standpoint, most physicians treat patients who need their skills. This is particularly true in cases of emergency.
  D. Physicians may state the types of services they will provide.
  E. The physician has the right to expect payment for all treatment provided.
  F. A physician can withdraw from a relationship if the patient is noncooperative or refuses to pay bills when able to do so.
  G. Physicians have the right to take vacations and time off from their practice and to be unavailable to care for their patients during those times.
  H. The physician has many other responsibilities, including ethical ones.
III. Professional Practice Responsibilities
  A. Duties During a Medical Emergency
  B. Duty to Treat Indigent Patients
  C. Duty Not to Abandon a Patient
  D. Duty to Treat Patients with AIDS
  E. Duty to Properly Identify Patients
  F. Duty to Tell the Truth	

Chapter Lecture Outline	Instructor's Notes

IV. Patient's Rights
  A. Standard of care—The patient can expect that the physician will use the same skill that other physicians use in treating patients with the same ailments.
  B. The patient has multiple rights.
    1. The patient has the right to approve or give consent—permission—for all treatment.
    2. In giving consent for treatment, patients may reasonably expect that their physician will use the appropriate standard of care in providing care and treatment.
    3. The patient's right to privacy prohibits the presence of unauthorized persons during physical examinations or treatments.
    4. Patients have the right to be informed of the advantages and potential risks of treatment—including the risk of not having the treatment.
    5. Patients have the right to refuse treatment.
  C. Confidentiality
    1. Patients have the right to expect all information and records about their treatment will be kept confidential by all medical personnel.
    2. Privileged communication refers to confidential information that has been told to a physician or attorney by the patient.
  D. A Patient's Bill of Rights—A published statement called "A Patient's Bill of Rights," which describes the physician–patient relationship, was developed by the American Hospital Association.
  E. Patient Self-Determination Acts
    1. Living will—A legal document in which a person states that life-sustaining treatments and artificial nutrition either be used or not be used to prolong life.
      a. DNR—A Do Not Resuscitate order is put in the patient's chart if the patient has requested that no extraordinary medical treatment, such as being placed on a respirator, be given.
      b. The living will document must be signed by the patient and witnessed by another person.
    2. Durable power of attorney—When signed by the patient, the durable power of attorney allows an agent or representative to act on behalf of the patient.
      a. An agent is a person authorized to act on behalf of a patient.
      b. Because the power of attorney is "durable," the agent's authority continues even if the patient is physically or mentally incapacitated.
    3. The Uniform Anatomical Gift Act allows persons 18 years or older and of sound mind to make a gift of any or all body parts for purposes of organ transplantation or medical research.
      a. A donor can revoke documents containing his or her wishes by destroying them and asking anyone holding them to do the same.
      b. If a person has not indicated a desire to be a donor, the family may consent on the patient's behalf. Generally, if a member of the family opposes the donation of organs, then the

physician and hospital do not insist on it, even if the patient signed for the donation to take place.

V. Rights of Minors

    A. A minor is a person who has not reached the age of maturity, which in most states in 18.

    B. In most states, minors are unable to give consent for treatment, except in special cases.

VI. Patient's Responsibilities

    A. Consent

        1. Informed or expressed consent means that the patient agrees to the proposed course of treatment after having been told about the possible consequences of having or not having certain procedures or treatments.

            a. The physician must be honest with the patient and explain the diagnosis, the purpose of the proposed treatment, and the probability that the treatment will be successful.

            b. The doctrine of informed consent requires the physician to explain certain things in understandable language.

            c. The physician must explain the advantages and the disadvantages of the treatment.

            d. The physician must explain alternative treatments available to the patient.

            e. The physician must explain the potential outcomes of the proposed treatment.

        2. The patient's signature on the consent form indicates that the patient understands the limits or risks involved in the pending treatment or surgery as explained by the physician.

            a. Except in emergency situations, the process of obtaining consent cannot be delegated by the physician to someone else.

            b. Except in cases of emergency, all patients must sign a consent form before undergoing a surgical procedure.

    B. A patient's informed consent is limited to those procedures to which the patient has consented.

    C. Implied consent occurs when patients indicate by their behavior that they are accepting the procedure. The patient's nonverbal communication may indicate an implied consent for treatment or examination.

    D. A patient has the right to refuse to grant consent.

VII. Role of the Healthcare Consumer

LEARNING OBJECTIVES

(Student answers may vary.)

    1. Define the glossary terms.

        Abandonment   withdrawing medical care from a patient without providing sufficient notice to the patient.

        Acquired immunodeficiency syndrome (AIDS)   a disease resulting in infections that occur as a result of exposure to the human immunodeficiency virus (HIV), which causes the immune system to break down.

        Advance directive   the various methods by which a patient has the right to self-determination prior to a medical necessity; includes living wills, durable power of attorney, and organ donation.

Against medical advice (AMA) when a noncompliant patient leaves a hospital without the physician's permission.

Agent person authorized to act on behalf of a patient.

Consent the voluntary agreement that a patient gives to allow a medically trained person the permission to touch, examine, and perform a treatment.

Do not resuscitate (DNR) a designation placed on a patient's medical record indicating that in the case of cessation of circulation and breathing, artificial respiration (CPR) is not to be done.

Durable power of attorney a legal agreement that allows an agent or representative of the patient to act on behalf of the patient.

Human immunodeficiency virus (HIV) the virus that causes the immune system to break down and can eventually result in the disease AIDS.

Implied consent consent inferred by signs, inaction, or silence of a patient.

Informed (or expressed) consent consent granted by a patient after the patient has received knowledge and understanding of potential risks and benefits.

In loco parentis a person assigned by a court to stand in place of the parents and possess their legal rights and responsibilities toward the child.

Living will a legal document in which a person states that life-sustaining treatments and artificial nutritional support should not be used to prolong life; a type of advance directive.

Minor a person who has not reached the age of maturity, which in most states is 18.

Parens patriae authority occurs when the state takes responsibility from the parents for the care and custody of minors under the age of 18.

Privileged communication confidential information that has been told to a physician (or attorney) by the patient.

Proxy a person who acts on behalf of another person.

Uniform Anatomical Gift Act a state statute allowing persons 18 years of age or older and of sound mind to make a gift of any or all body parts for purposes of organ transplantation or medical research.

2. Describe the rights a physician has when practicing medicine and when accepting a patient.

   The physician has the right to select patients needing treatment and the right to refuse service to patients. Physicians can also determine the type of services they will provide, the hours their offices will be open, and where they will be located. The physician has the right to expect payment for services and can withdraw from treating the patient if the patient is uncooperative or refuses to pay.

3. Discuss the nine principles of medical ethics as designated by the American Medical Association (AMA).

   a. Human dignity: A physician shall be dedicated to providing competent medical service with compassion and respect for human dignity.
   b. Honesty: A physician shall deal honestly with patients and colleagues, and strive to expose those physicians deficient in character or competence, or who engage in fraud or deception.

   c. Responsibility to society: A physician shall respect the law and recognize a responsibility to seek changes in those requirements that are contrary to the best interests of the patient.

   d. Confidentiality: A physician shall respect the rights of patients, of colleagues, and of other health professionals, and shall safeguard patient confidence within the constraints of the law.

   e. Continued study: A physician shall continue to study, apply, and advance scientific knowledge; make relevant information available to patients, colleagues, and the public; obtain consultation; and use the talents of other health professionals as needed.

   f. Freedom of choice: A physician shall, in the provision of appropriate healthcare, except in emergencies, be free to choose whom to serve, with whom to associate, and the environment in which to provide service.

   g. Responsibility to improved community: A physician shall recognize a responsibility to participate in activities contributing to an improved community.

   h. Responsibility to the patient: This is of paramount importance.

   i. Support access to medical care for all people.

4. Summarize "A Patient's Bill of Rights."

Under "A Patient's Bill of Rights," patients have the right to

   a. considerate and respectful care.

   b. current information concerning diagnosis, treatment, and prognosis.

   c. make their own decisions about the care prior to and during the course of treatment.

   d. have an advance directive.

   e. every consideration of privacy.

   f. expect that all records pertaining to their care are kept confidential.

   g. review the records pertaining to their medical care.

   h. expect a hospital to make a reasonable response to a request for appropriate medical care and service.

   i. ask and be informed of business relationships that might influence their care and treatment.

   j. consent or decline to participate in medical research studies.

   k. expect reasonable continuity of care.

   l. be informed of hospital policies and practices that relate to patient care and treatment.

5. Understand *standard of care* and how it is applied to the practice of medicine.

Standard of care refers to a physician or other healthcare professional using the same skill that other physicians or healthcare professionals use in treating patients with the same ailments.

6. Discuss three patient self-determination acts.

   a. A living will is a document that allows patients to set forth their intentions as to their treatment. For example, the patient may request that no extraordinary medical treatment, such as resuscitation, be given.

   b. A durable power of attorney, when signed by a patient, allows an agent or representative to act on behalf of the patient.

   c. The Uniform Anatomical Gift Act allows a person 18 years or older and of sound mind to make a gift of any or all body parts for purposes of organ transplantation or medical research.

7. Describe the difference between implied consent and informed consent.

Implied consent is consent for treatment that is given by a patient through signs, inaction, or silence.

Informed consent is consent granted by the patient after the patient has received knowledge and understanding of potential risks and benefits.

THE CASE OF DAVID Z. AND AMYOTROPHIC LATERAL SCLEROSIS (ALS)

David, who has suffered from ALS for twenty years, is now hospitalized in a private religious hospital on a respirator. He spoke with his physician before he became incapacitated and asked that he be allowed to die if the suffering became too much for him. The physician agreed that, while he would not give David any drugs to assist a suicide, he would discontinue David's respirator if asked to do so. David has now indicated through a prearranged code of blinking eye movements that he wants the respirator discontinued. David had signed his living will before he became ill, indicating that he did not want extraordinary means keeping him alive.

The nursing staff has alerted the hospital administrator about the impending discontinuation of the respirator. The administrator tells the physician that this is against the hospital's policy. She states that once a patient is placed on a respirator, the family must seek a court order to have him or her removed from this type of life support. In addition, it is against their policy to have staff members present during such a procedure. After consulting with the family, the physician orders an ambulance to transport the patient back to his home, where the physician discontinues the life support.

Case Questions

1. What were the primary concerns of the hospital?

This case presents a delicate situation since the patient's needs were not the primary concern for the hospital. The hospital was concerned about its policy against removal of life support and the potential negative effect this could have on its reputation.

2. What was the physician's primary concern?

The physician was concerned about keeping his promise to his patient. Physicians will often avoid making promises to patients, but this physician believed that it was his duty to support his patient's wishes.

3. When should the discussion about the patient's future plans have taken place with the hospital administrator?

This should have taken place as soon as the patient was admitted. Ideally, a discussion regarding taking a patient off a respirator should take place before the patient is placed on the respirator, but this is not always possible due to emergency situations.

NOTE: When students discuss this case, they may wish to take a devil's advocate approach and examine it from the perspective of the patient, the physician, and the hospital.

POINTS TO PONDER (FROM TEXTBOOK)

Teaching note: These questions are meant to promote critical thinking and classroom discussion. The student responses will vary.

1. Does it surprise you to find out that physicians have the right to select the patients they wish to treat?

2. Can a physician receive a payment from a hospital for referring patients to that particular institution? Why or why not?

3. If a deceased relative signed a statement (Uniform Anatomical Gift Act) requesting that any or all body parts be used for organ transplantation or medical research, can a family member overturn that statement?

4. Do you believe that it is appropriate for a physician to report the unethical conduct of a fellow physician?

5. Do you think that physicians should treat their own family members? Why or why not?

6. Can a nurse obtain consent from a patient for a surgical procedure if the physician is extremely busy handling an emergency case?

7. What can you say to your patient's employer who calls to find out if the employee's medical condition has improved?

REVIEW QUESTIONS (FROM TEXTBOOK)

Discussion Questions

1. Explain what it means when one physician "covers" for another.

   This means that one physician will take care of the patients of a physician who is away from the office.

2. Describe the three advance directives that a patient can use. When are they appropriate?

   A living will is appropriate when patients wish to let relatives know how they want to be medically treated if they are in an emergency situation or as they approach death.

   A durable power of attorney is appropriate if there is a concern that patients may become incapable of making decisions on their own behalf.

   The Uniform Anatomical Gift Act can be used by all persons over the age of 18; it allows them to donate their organs after death.

3. Jack Black is being treated by Dr. Williams after having fallen off a ladder at work. His employer calls to find out how Jack is doing. Can Dr. Williams discuss Jack's progress with his employer? Why or why not?

   Dr. Williams cannot say anything to the employer. She cannot even state if Jack Black is a patient. This is a violation of the patient's confidentiality.

4. Dr. Williams is treating a popular performer who has attempted suicide. What statement can Dr. Williams or her staff give to reporters when they call Dr. Williams's office?

   There is no statement that can be made. It is a violation of the patient's confidentiality to make any statement.

Matching

Column A	Column B
1. agent	e. representative acts on patient's behalf
2. minor	g. person under 18 years of age
3. standard of care	d. same skill that is used by other physicians
4. implied consent	b. consent granted by inference
5. privileged communication	j. confidential information
6. informed consent	i. knowledgeable consent
7. exception to consent	a. commonly known risks
8. right to be informed	h. "A Patient's Bill of Rights"
9. durable power of attorney	c. document that allows an agent to represent a patient
10. abandonment	f. withdrawing medical care without notice

Multiple Choice

1. A patient rolling up a sleeve to have a blood sample taken is an example of
   a. standard of care
   b. informed consent
   c. implied consent
   d. advance directive
   e. agent

   Answer: c

2. A condition in which a patient understands the risks involved by not having a surgical procedure or treatment performed is known as
   a. standard of care
   b. informed consent
   c. implied consent
   d. advance directive
   e. agent

   Answer: b

3. The Uniform Anatomical Gift Act is applicable for
   a. persons up to the age of 18
   b. persons 18 years of age and older
   c. persons who are mentally handicapped
   d. very few people
   e. the purpose of selling organs

   Answer: b

4. Which of these refers to a physician's using the same skill that is used by other physicians in treating patients with the same ailment?
   a. privileged communication
   b. informed consent
   c. implied consent
   d. standard of care
   e. none of the above

   Answer: d

5. The physician's rights include
   a. the right to decline to treat a new patient
   b. the ability to receive payment from hospitals for referring patients
   c. the right to protect fellow physicians who are guilty of deception
   d. the right to publish confidential information about a patient if it is in the physician's best interests
   e. all of the above

   Answer: a

6. In what document are patients able to request the type and amount of artificial nutritional and life-sustaining treatments that should or should not be used to prolong their life?
   a. Uniform Anatomical Gift Act
   b. Medical Patients Rights Act
   c. living will
   d. standard of care
   e. euthanasia

   Answer: c

7. The patient's obligations include
   a. honesty about past medical history
   b. payment for medical services
   c. following treatment recommendations
   d. a and c only
   e. a, b, and c

   Answer: e

8. Exceptions to informed consent include
   a. telling the patient about the risk involved in not having the procedure
   b. the discussion of sensitive sexual matters
   c. not having to explain risks that are commonly known
   d. all of the above
   e. none of the above

   Answer: c

9. The doctrine of informed consent
   a. can be delegated by the physician to a trusted assistant
   b. may have to be waived in the event of an emergency situation
   c. does not have to be signed by every patient
   d. could result in a lawsuit for assault and battery if not performed
   e. b and d only

   Answer: e

10. A newspaper reporter seeks information from a receptionist about a prominent personality who has been hospitalized. What information can be given to the reporter?
    a. none
    b. the basic fact that the person is a patient
    c. the name and phone number of the attending physician
    d. a very brief statement about the person's medical condition
    e. there are no restrictions

    Answer: a

Fill in the Blanks

1. A person who acts on behalf of another person is said to be a <u>proxy.</u>
2. A <u>minor</u> is a person who has not yet reached the age of maturity, which is 18 in most states.
3. A legal agreement that allows a representative of the patient to act on behalf of the patient is called a <u>durable power of attorney</u>.
4. *In loco parentis* is a person assigned by the court to stand in place of the parents.
5. A <u>living will</u> is a legal document in which a person states that life-sustaining treatment and artificial nutritional support should or should not be used to prolong life.
6. A form of consent for treatment that is inferred by signs, inaction, or silence of the patient is called implied consent.
7. The <u>Uniform Anatomical Gift</u> Act allows persons over the age of 18 and of sound mind to make a gift of their body parts after their death for organ transplantation.
8. A <u>Do Not Resuscitate</u> order indicates that a person does not want to be resuscitated if his or her breathing stops.
9. Aspirin and vitamins are examples of <u>over-the-counter</u> medications.
10. Except in the case of an emergency, all patients must sign a <u>consent</u> form before undergoing a surgical procedure.

PUT IT INTO PRACTICE

Interview someone you know who has recently been a patient. Ask that person to tell you what he or she believes are the patient's responsibilities and the physician's responsibilities. Do these statements agree with those in the textbook. How do they differ?

WEB HUNT

1. Search the website of the U.S. Department of Health and Human Services (*www.hhs.gov*) and examine "The Patient's Bill of Rights in Medicare and Medicaid." What does the document have to say about the confidentiality of health information?
2. On the website *www.findlaw.com*, click on Medical Malpractice. Search for an article on "Understanding Informed Consent." According to this article, what are the situations discussed in which informed consent may not be necessary or may be implied?

CASE STUDY

Dr. Williams has just telephoned Carl, her office nurse, explaining that she is behind schedule doing rounds at one of the hospitals. She has asked Carl to do her a favor and interpret Mrs. Harris's EKG, sign her name, and fax the report to Mrs. Harris's internist, who is expecting the results. Carl learned to take and read EKGs while he was in nursing school. Dr. Williams' EKG machine includes new technology that interprets EKGs. Carl will not have any difficulty carrying out Dr. Williams' request.

Case Questions

1. Given the scope of Carl's education and training, would this "favor" fall within his scope of practice?

Carl may have received training in reading EKGs, but it is beyond his scope of practice as a nurse to interpret the EKG and to sign the physician's name.

2. Would any portion of Dr. Williams's request fall within the scope of practice for Carl?

   Carl can take the EKG and fax the printed report that comes off the machine to another physician if so requested by his employer.

3. Does Dr. Williams's request violate the physician-patient relationship? Why or why not?

   Yes. The patient expects her physician to interpret and report on the EKG results.

4. What, if anything, should Carl say to Dr. Williams?

   Carl should calmly explain to Dr. Williams that what she is asking him to do is outside the scope of his practice.

SUPPLEMENTAL QUESTIONS

Chapter Review

Cover the terms in the left-hand column with a piece of paper. Read the statement and fill in the blank with the answer before uncovering the correct response.

American Medical human	The _____ _____ Association formed its first code of ethics in 1847. This code covers _____ dignity, in which a physician shall be dedicated to providing competent medical service with compassion and respect;
responsibility	and _____ to society, in which a physician shall respect the law and recognize a responsibility to seek to change those requirements that are contrary to the best interests of the patient. Patients reasonably expect that
standard of care skill	their physician will use the appropriate _____ _____ _____; that is, that the physician will use the same _____ that other physicians use in treating patients with the same ailment in the same
geographic	_____ area.
Privileged	_____ communication is confidential information that has been confided to a physician. "A Patient's Bill of Rights" describes the physician-patient relationship. This
advance directive	gives the patient the right to an _____ _____ such as a living will or durable power of attorney. The patient also has the right to be informed of hospital policies
care treatment/power/ attorney/agent	and practices that relate to the patient's _____ and _____. The durable _____ of _____ allows an _____ or representative to act on behalf of the patient.
Informed	_____ consent means that a patient agrees to the proposed course of treatment after having been told the consequences of having or not having treatment. The doc-

advantages	trine requires that the physician explain the _____
alternatives	and risks of the treatment, the _____ available, the
	potential outcomes of treatment, and what might occur if
refused	the treatment is _____. The patient's nonverbal
implied consent	communication may indicate an _____ _____
	for treatment or examination. Therefore, with this con-
	sent, any touching required for the physical examination
battery	would not be considered the crime of _____.

Multiple Choice

Select the one best response to the following questions.

1. According to the American Medical Association, the physician's responsibilities include
   a. respecting the rights of patients, colleagues, and other health professionals
   b. continuing to study, apply, and advance scientific knowledge
   c. dealing honestly with patients and colleagues
   d. respecting the law
   e. all of the above

   Answer: e

2. The document that allows patients to set forth their intentions as to treatment is known as a(n)
   a. uniform Anatomical Gift Act
   b. living will
   c. durable power of attorney
   d. implied consent
   e. privileged communication

   Answer: b

3. In most states, a minor can give consent in the case of
   a. pregnancy
   b. minor surgical procedures
   c. abortion
   d. a and c only
   e. all of the above

   Answer: d

4. The Doctrine of Informed Consent requires the physician to explain all of the following except
   a. what might occur if treatment is refused
   b. potential outcomes of treatment
   c. specific details of how the treatment is administered
   d. alternative treatments that are available
   e. the advantages and risks of the treatment

   Answer: c

5. A patient must sign a consent form before undergoing a surgical procedure
   a. except in the case of an emergency
   b. only if the AMA has deemed the procedure risky
   c. in all cases
   d. only in the case of an emergency
   e. at the patient's request

   Answer: a

6. Patients' rights include
   a. an expectation that their physician will use the appropriate standard of care
   b. the right to privacy
   c. the right to refuse medical treatment
   d. being informed of the advantages and potential risks of treatment
   e. all of the above

   Answer: e

7. A representative acting on behalf of the patient after durable power of attorney is granted is a(n)
   a. physician
   b. HMO
   c. minor
   d. agent
   e. phlebotomist

   Answer: d

8. The safeguards included in the Uniform Anatomical Gift Act are
   a. it requires a durable power of attorney agreement
   b. the time of death is determined by a physician who is not involved with the transplant
   c. no money is allowed to change hands
   d. b and c
   e. all of the above

   Answer: d

9. "A Patient's Bill of Rights"
   a. must be followed by all healthcare professionals
   b. was developed by the United States Congress
   c. only applies to informed consent situations
   d. is the sole responsibility of the physician
   e. is the sole responsibility of the patients

   Answer: a

10. The Medical Patients Rights Act provides confidentiality for which of the following?
    a. the fact that the patient is a patient
    b. test results
    c. privileged communication
    d. patient histories
    e. all of the above

    Answer: e

True/False Questions

1. A minor is a person who has not yet reached the age of maturity, which in most states is twenty. (false)

2. A physician is bound ethically and legally to treat a patient in an emergency situation. (true)

3. COBRA contains an amendment against "dumping" patients. (true)

4. There is currently a cure for AIDS. (false)

5. There have been major changes among physicians in the area of truth-telling during the past two decades. (true)

6. In the *Tarasoff v. Regents of the University of California* case, the court stated that a psychiatrist must protect the patient's privacy (confidentiality) at all costs. (false)

7. The patient's rights include being informed about the risk of not having a treatment. (true)

8. An advance directive does not have to be in writing. (false)

9. A durable power of attorney for healthcare allows the designated family member to make financial decisions on behalf of the patient. (false)

10. People who have a living will that states their opposition to nutritional support are generally referring to artificial nutritional support such as tube feedings and IVs. (true)

Short Answer Questions

1. State five rights of the physician.
   a. to select the patients they wish to treat
   b. to refuse service to patients
   c. to state the type of service they will provide
   d. to expect payment for all treatment provided
   e. to take vacations and time off from the practice

2. Describe the AMA's nine Principles of Medical Ethics.
   a. Human dignity: A physician shall be dedicated to providing competent medical service with compassion and respect for human dignity.
   b. Honesty: A physician shall deal honestly with patients and colleagues, and strive to expose those physicians deficient in character or competence, or who engage in fraud or deception.
   c. Responsibility to society: A physician shall respect the law and recognize a responsibility to seek changes in those requirements that are contrary to the best interests of the patient.
   d. Confidentiality: A physician shall respect the rights of patients, of colleagues, and of other health professionals, and shall safeguard patient confidence within the constraints of the law.
   e. Continued study: A physician shall continue to study, apply, and advance scientific knowledge; make relevant information available to patients, colleagues, and the public; obtain consultation; and use the talents of other health professionals as needed.
   f. Freedom of choice: A physician shall, in the provision of appropriate healthcare, except in emergencies, be free to choose whom to serve, with whom to associate, and the environment in which to provide service.
   g. Responsibility to improved community: A physician shall recognize a responsibility to participate in activities contributing to an improved community.
   h. Responsibility to the patient is of paramount importance.
   i. Support access to medical care for all people.

3. Describe at least six rights as stated in "A Patient's Bill of Rights."

   Answers will vary but might include patients' rights to:
   a. considerate and respectful care
   b. current information concerning diagnosis, treatment, and prognosis
   c. make their own decisions about the care prior to and during the course of treatment
   d. have an advance directive
   e. every consideration of privacy
   f. expect that all records pertaining to care are kept confidential

g. review the records pertaining to their medical care
h. expect a hospital to make a reasonable response to a request for appropriate medical care and service
i. ask and be informed of business relationships that might influence their care and treatment
j. consent or decline to participate in medical research studies
k. expect reasonable continuity of care
l. be informed of hospital policies and practices that relate to patient care and treatment

4. List and discuss three types of patient self-determination acts.
   a. A living will is a document that allows patients to set forth their intentions as to their treatment. For example, the patient may request that no extraordinary medical treatment, such as resuscitation, be given.
   b. A durable power of attorney, when signed by a patient, allows an agent or representative to act on behalf of the patient.
   c. The Uniform Anatomical Gift Act allows a person 18 years or older and of sound mind to make a gift of any or all body parts for purposes of organ transplantation or medical research.

5. According to the doctrine of informed consent, what information must be relayed to the patient?
   a. the advantages and risks of the treatment
   b. the alternative treatments available to the patient
   c. potential outcomes of the treatment
   d. what might occur if treatment is refused

6. What are three exceptions to the informed consent doctrine?
   a. a physician need not inform a patient if the risks are commonly known
   b. if the physician believes the disclosure of risks may be detrimental to the patient
   c. if the patient asks the physician not to disclose the risks

7. What are some frequently asked questions about advance directives?

   (Student responses may vary.)
   a. To whom should the advance directive be given?
   b. Where should they be stored?
   c. How can the advance directive be changed or amended?
   d. Can the advance directive be revoked?
   e. What does the law say about advance directives?

8. What are classifications of minors mentioned in this chapter?
   a. minor—a person under the age of 18 (termed *infant* under the law). The signature of a parent or legal guardian is needed for consent to perform a medical treatment in nonemergency situations.
   b. mature minor—a person judged to be mature enough to understand the physician's instructions. Such a minor may seek medical care for treatment of drug or alcohol abuse, contraception, venereal disease, and pregnancy.
   c. emancipated minor—a person between the ages of 15 and 18 who is either married, in the military, or self-supporting and no longer lives under the care of a parent. Parental consent for medical care is not required. Proof of emancipation (for example, marriage certificate) should be included in the medical record.

9. What are the duties of a physician as discussed in the text?
   a. duty to care for a person during a medical emergency
   b. duty to treat indigent patients

    c. duty not to abandon a patient
    d. duty to treat patients with AIDS
    e. duty to properly identify patients
    f. duty to tell the truth

10. What does the term *durable* mean in durable power of attorney?

    It means that even if the patient becomes physically or mentally incapacitated, the power of the patient's agent to act on his or her behalf will be in effect (durable).

TEACHING STRATEGIES

1. Invite a physician into the classroom to discuss the AMA's Principles of Medical Ethics.
2. Pair off the students and have them take turns role-playing as the patient/parent/employer and the healthcare professional. Suggested role-playing topics include:

    a. an angry patient who believes his or her privacy has been violated
    b. the parent of a critically ill child who is asking about the child's condition
    c. an employer calling to find out the condition of an employee
    d. a patient who asks the healthcare professional to perform a service that is beyond the person's scope of practice

3. Have the students design a poster that summarizes the twelve points of "A Patient's Bill of Rights."
4. Have the students Interview someone they know who has recently been a patient. Have them ask that person to tell them what he or she believes are the patient's responsibilities and what are the physician's responsibilities.
5. Have the students prepare flash cards for the key terms (glossary).

6

Professional Liability and Medical Malpractice

CHAPTER SYNOPSIS

Healthcare professionals need to be on constant alert for practices that could result in injury to the patient. Even though the employer/physician is responsible for the actions of his or her employees through the doctrine of *respondeat superior,* healthcare professionals have been held responsible for negligence. This chapter discusses the tort of negligence, defenses to malpractice suits, professional liability of both physicians and other healthcare workers, and guidelines for malpractice prevention.

Chapter Lecture Outline	Instructor's Notes

I. Professional Negligence and Medical Malpractice
  A. Malpractice is professional misconduct or demonstration of unreasonable lack of skill resulting in injury, loss, or damage to the patient.
  B. A tort is a civil wrong.
  C. The tort of negligence, which is an unintentional action, occurs when a person either performs or fails to perform an action that a reasonable person would or would not have committed in a similar situation.
    1. Feasance refers to doing an act or performing a duty.
    2. Malfeasance refers to performing a wrong or illegal act.
    3. Misfeasance is the improper performance of an otherwise proper or lawful act.
    4. Nonfeasance is the failure to perform a necessary action.
  D. The "four Ds" of negligence—in order to obtain a judgment of negligence against a physician, the patient must be able to show what are called the "four Ds"
    1. *Duty* is the responsibility established by the physician–patient relationship.
    2. *Dereliction of duty* is a physician's failure to act as an ordinary and prudent physician (a peer) within the same community would act in a similar circumstance.
    3. *Direct cause* is the continuous sequence of events, unbroken by any intervening cause, that produces an injury and without which the injury would not have occurred.
    4. *Damages* refers to any injuries caused by the physician for which compensation (financial or otherwise) is due.
      a. Compensatory damages are payment for the actual loss of income, emotional pain and suffering, or injury suffered by the patient.	

Chapter Lecture Outline	**Instructor's Notes**

    b. Punitive damages, also called exemplary damages, are a monetary award by a court to a person who has been harmed in an especially malicious or willful way.
    c. Nominal damages refer to a slight or token payment to a patient to demonstrate that, while there might not have been any physical harm done, the patient's legal rights were violated.
  E. Preponderance of evidence—One side of a case must demonstrate a greater weight of evidence than the other side.
  F. The doctrine of *res ipsa loquitur*, meaning "the thing speaks for itself," applies to the law of negligence. This doctrine tells us that the breach of duty is so obvious that it doesn't need further explanation.
  G. If a patient's death has been caused by the physician's negligence, the deceased person's dependents and heirs may sue for wrongful death. Many states have placed a cap on the amount of money that can be awarded in wrongful death cases.
  H. Fraud—The deliberate concealment of the facts from another person for unlawful or unfair gain. This is contrary to negligence, which is an unintentional action.
    1. Fraud in healthcare is one of the fastest growing criminal areas.
    2. Office of Inspector General—one of the major players in war against healthcare fraud.
II. Defense to Malpractice Suits
  A. Denial defense—Most common defense in a malpractice lawsuit is denial on the part of the physician.
  B. Assumption of risk—Legal defense that prevents a plaintiff from recovering damages if the plaintiff voluntarily accepted a risk associated with the activity.
  C. Contributory negligence—Refers to conduct on the part of the plaintiff that is a contributing cause of an injury; a complete bar to recovery of damages.
  D. Comparative negligence—A defense similar to contributory negligence in that the plaintiff's own negligence helped cause the injury; not a complete bar to recovery of damages but only damages based on the amount of the plaintiff's fault.
  E. Borrowed servant—Doctrine is a special application of *respondeat superior.* This occurs when an employer lends an employee to someone else.
  F. Ignorance of facts and unintentional wrongs—ignorance of the law or arguing that the act was unintentional is not a defense.
  G. Statute of limitations—All states have statutes of limitations, which set a time limit for the injured party to file a lawsuit. This time period varies by state and is usually between one and three years.
  H. *Res judicata*—Means "the thing has been decided" or "matter decided by judgment." Thus, if a court decides a case, then the case is firmly decided between two parties, and the plaintiff cannot bring a new lawsuit on the same subject against the same defendant.
III. Professional Liability—Liable means having legal responsibility for one's own actions.
  A. Civil liability cases—Physicians and other medical professionals may be sued under a variety of legal theories. 1. Unfortunately, a fear of lawsuits has influenced the practice of medicine.

Chapter Lecture Outline	**Instructor's Notes**

   B. Physical conditions of the premises—An institution may be liable when regulatory standards have been violated, such as when an accident occurs in a clinic that has not followed regulations for maintaining a safe environment.

   C. Promise to cure—A promise to cure a patient with a certain procedure or form of treatment is considered under contract law rather than civil law.

   D. Law of agency—The law of agency governs the legal relationship formed between two persons when one person agrees to perform work for another person.

   E. Who is liable?—Under the doctrine of *respondeat superior,* or "let the master answer," the employer is liable for the consequences of the employee's actions committed in the scope of employment.

   F. Liability insurance—A contract by which one person promises to compensate or reimburse another if he or she suffers a loss from a specific cause or negligent act.

   G. Malpractice insurance—Physicians carry malpractice insurance to cover any damages they must pay if they are sued for malpractice and lose.

      1. Since physicians treat the human body, not all medical outcomes are predictable or desirable—sometimes through no fault of the physicians.

      2. Malpractice insurance is expensive. Depending on the type of medical practice, it can cost more than $100,000 a year.

      3. Most physicians carry a rider to these policies that covers malpractice suits based on injuries caused by employees and assistants during the course of carrying out their duties.

IV. Arbitration—Submitting a civil dispute to a person other than a judge to resolve.

V. Liability of Other Health Professionals

   A. Dental assistant

   B. Laboratory technician

   C. Medical assistant

   D. Nurse

   E. Nursing assistant

   F. Paramedic

   G. Pharmacist

   H. Physical therapist

   I. Physician assistant

   J. Respiratory therapist

VI. Role of the Supervisor

VII. Working in High Risk Areas

VIII. Malpractice Prevention

   A. General guidelines

   B. Safety

   C. Communication

   D. Documentation

LEARNING OBJECTIVES

(Student answers may vary.)

1. Define the glossary terms.

   Affirmative defenses   allow the defendant (usually physician or hospital) to present evidence that the patient's condition was the result of factors other than the defendant's negligence.

   Alternative dispute resolution (ADR)   methods for resolving a civil dispute that do not involve going to court.

   Arbitration   submitting a dispute for resolution to a person other than a judge.

   Arbitrator   a person chosen to decide a disagreement between two parties.

   Assumption of risk   a legal defense that prevents a plaintiff from recovering damages if the plaintiff voluntarily accepts a risk associated with the activity.

   Borrowed servant doctrine   a special application of *respondeat superior* in which an employer lends an employee to someone else.

   Cap   limit.

   Claims-made insurance   liability insurance that will cover the insured party for only the claims made during the time period the policy was in effect (or policy year).

   Comparative negligence   a defense, similar to contributory negligence, that the plaintiff's own negligence helped cause the injury; not a complete bar to recovery of damages but only damages based on the amount of the plaintiff's fault.

   Compensatory damages   court-awarded payment to make up for the loss of income or emotional pain and suffering.

   Contributory negligence   conduct on the part of the plaintiff that is a contributing cause of the injuries; a complete bar to recovery of damages.

   Damages   any injuries caused by the defendant; usually a monetary award is given as compensation.

   Defensive medicine   ordering more tests and procedures than are necessary in order to protect oneself from a lawsuit.

   Dereliction   neglect, as in neglect of duties.

   Direct cause   the continuous sequence of events, unbroken by any intervening cause, that produces an injury and without which the injury would not have occurred.

   Duty   obligation or responsibility.

   Feasance   doing an act or performing a duty.

   Federal Rules of Evidence   rules that govern the admissibility of evidence into federal court.

   Fraud   the deliberate concealment of the facts from another person for unlawful or unfair gain.

   Law of agency   the legal relationship formed between two people when one person agrees to perform work for another person.

   Liable   legal responsibility for one's own actions.

Malfeasance   performing an illegal act.

Malpractice   professional misconduct or demonstration of an unreasonable lack of skill with the result of injury, loss, or damage to the patient.

Mediation   using the opinion of a third party to resolve a civil dispute in a non-binding decision.

Misfeasance   the improper performance of an otherwise proper or lawful act.

Negligence   an unintentional action that occurs when a person either performs or fails to perform an action that a "reasonable person" would or would not have committed in a similar situation.

Nominal damages   a slight or token payment awarded by the court.

Nonfeasance   the failure to perform an action when it is necessary.

Occurrence insurance   also called claims-incurred insurance, liability insurance that covers the insured party for all injuries and incidents that occurred while the policy was in effect (policy year), regardless of when they are reported to the insurer or the claim was made.

Proximate   means that the injury was proximately or closely related to the defendant's negligence.

Punitive damages   also called exemplary damages, a monetary award by a court to a person who has been harmed in an especially malicious and willful way; meant to punish the offender.

Res ipsa loquitur   Latin phrase meaning "the thing speaks for itself."

Res judicata   Latin phrase meaning "the thing has been decided."

Rider   additional component to an insurance policy.

Settlement   the act of determining the outcome of a case outside a courtroom; settling a case is not an indication of legal wrongdoing.

2. Define the four Ds of negligence for the physician.

   a. Duty refers to the responsibility established by the physician–patient relationship.
   b. Dereliction, or neglect, of duty refers to the physician's failure to act as any ordinary and prudent physician (a peer) within the same community would act in a similar circumstance.
   c. Direct or proximate cause refers to the continuous sequence of events, unbroken by any intervening cause, that produces an injury and without which the injury would not have occurred.
   d. Damages refer to any injuries caused by the defendant.

3. Discuss the meaning of *respondeat superior* for the physician and the employee.

   This Latin phrase means "let the master answer." It is an application of the borrowed servant doctrine, which means that the employee is the "servant" of the employer, and thus the employer is legally responsible for the employee's actions.

4. Discuss the meaning of *res ipsa loquitur*.

   This Latin phrase means "the thing speaks for itself" and tells us that the breach or neglect of duty is so obvious that it needs no further explanation. An example is a piece of surgical equipment or a surgical sponge left inside a patient during surgery that ultimately causes an injury. This injury would not have occurred without the negligence of someone.

5. Explain the term *liable* and what it means for the physician and other healthcare professionals.

   Liable means legal responsibility for one's own actions. If medical professionals cause an injury to a patient and are found to be negligent by a court of law, they may be required to make payment in the form of compensatory, punitive, or nominal damages.

6. List ten ways to prevent malpractice.

   Responses will vary but should include information from the following topics: general guidelines, safety, communication, and documentation.

7. State two advantages to arbitration.

   It can save time and money by not having to go to court to solve a dispute.

8. Discuss three types of damage awards.

   a. Compensatory damages are payment for the actual loss or injury suffered by the patient.
   b. Punitive damages are monetary awards by a court to a person who has been harmed in an especially malicious or willful way.
   c. Nominal damages are a slight payment to a patient to demonstrate that, while there may not have been any physical harm done, the patient's legal rights were violated.

9. Describe two types of malpractice insurance.

   a. Claims-made insurance policies cover only those claims that were made during the policy year, regardless of when they occurred.
   b. Occurrence insurance covers all incidents that arise during a policy year, regardless of when they are reported to the insurer.

10. Explain the law of agency.

    The law of agency governs the legal relationship formed between two people when one person agrees to perform work for another person.

THE CASE OF JOHN F. AND THE HMO

John, a 34-year-old father of two children, is a member of an HMO in Texas. John has made several trips to an area clinic that was recommended by his HMO to seek medical attention since finding blood in his bowel movements. He has been taking large amounts of aspirin for persistent headaches but did not realize that this could cause internal bleeding. John was always seen at the clinic by a physician assistant, Robert M., but never by a physician. Robert didn't ask John about taking any nonprescription medications. John didn't realize that he should mention the over-the-counter medication (aspirin) consumption. Robert tells John to take an antacid preparation to control the bleeding, but does not order any tests.

He tells John to return if he is not any better. Two days later, John is rushed to an area emergency room with a bowel hemorrhage.

Case Questions

1. What responsibility, if any, does Robert have for John's emergency condition?

   A physician assistant (PA) assists the physician in the primary care of the patient. The job description includes evaluation, monitoring, diagnostics, therapeutics, counseling, and referral skills. In most states a PA can prescribe medications. A PA has the equivalent of a master's degree and, in most cases, will have completed an internship or work experience before taking an accreditation exam.

In the John's case the PA should have asked more questions to evaluate his medication use, ordered tests to determine if his blood loss was significant, monitored his aftercare, and consulted with the primary care physician if he had any doubt about John's prognosis and treatment. A qualified and trained PA should be familiar with the side effects of medications such as aspirin. Robert did have to assume some responsibility for John's emergency condition.

2. Does the clinic have a responsibility to provide its HMO members with the services of a physician?

A clinic can, and does, use physician assistants whenever possible since their training and skills allow them to provide excellent assistance to the primary care physician. However, while a physician does not have to physically present while the PA is working, nevertheless, a PA must work under the supervision of a physician. Therefore, a clinic, by hiring the services of a PA, does provide the services of a physician for oversight.

3. What responsibility, as a healthcare consumer, does John have for his own medical condition?

Today's consumer must become a well-informed consumer familiar with his or her own healthcare needs, since there is an increasing number of over-the-counter medications available that can be dangerous when used too frequently or in combination with other medications. In this case, John's problem was further compounded because he never saw a physician.

NOTE: This case is included because many students will be employed in the managed care field. There are everyday instances of the situation discussed in this case.

POINTS TO PONDER (FROM TEXTBOOK)

Teaching note: These questions are meant to promote critical thinking and classroom discussion. The student responses will vary.

1. Is it true that if a patient is injured through no fault of yours, you could still be sued for negligence?

2. If you are trained in CPR and fail to use it on a patient in your facility, could you be sued for malpractice (nonfeasance)?

3. Do all four Ds of negligence need to be present in order to obtain a judgment of negligence against a physician?

4. Does the doctrine of *res ipsa loquitur* apply to all healthcare professionals or only to physicians?

5. Can an employee be sued even if the employer (physician) is liable under the doctrine of *respondeat superior*?

6. What are some of the issues that cause the most problems in high-risk medical areas?

REVIEW QUESTIONS (FROM TEXTBOOK)

Discussion Questions

1. List five ways to prevent malpractice based on good communication.

   Responses might include:

   - maintain confidentiality
   - return phone calls promptly
   - refrain from criticizing other medical professionals
   - discuss all fees before beginning treatment
   - provide emergency telephone numbers to patients
   - take all patient complaints seriously
   - never discuss patient information within hearing distance of other patients
   - use a coding system, rather than the patient's name, on the registration log
   - place all special instructions in writing
   - listen carefully to all patient remarks
   - fully inform the patient of a physician's withdrawal of care
   - call patients to check on their progress after surgery or treatments
   - follow up on all missed and canceled appointments
   - inform patients of all risks associated with treatments

2. Give examples of malpractice cases involving healthcare workers, other than physicians, as discussed in this chapter.

   Answers will vary. Note that it is not necessary for student to memorize the case citations. They should be able to discuss the main issues in the cases.

3. Name and discuss the four Ds of negligence.
   a. Duty refers to the responsibility established by the physician–patient relationship.
   b. Dereliction, or neglect, of duty refers to the physician's failure to act as any ordinary and prudent physician (a peer) within the same community would act in a similar circumstance.
   c. Direct or proximate cause refers to the continuous sequence, unbroken by any intervening cause, that produces an injury and without which the injury would not have occurred.
   d. Damages refer to any injuries caused by the defendant.

4. Discuss the law of agency and why it is an important concept for the healthcare worker to understand.

   The law of agency refers to the legal relationship formed between two people when one person authorizes another person to act on his or her behalf. Healthcare professionals, with the exception of pharmacists, work for and are paid by their physician employer. Therefore, they are the agents of the physician, and as such, the physician is liable for their actions.

5. Explain the difference between malfeasance, misfeasance, and nonfeasance.

   Malfeasance is the performance of an illegal act.
   Misfeasance is the improper performance of an otherwise proper or lawful act.
   Nonfeasance is the failure to perform an action when it is necessary.

6. What is an exception to the statute of limitations?

   The discovery rule.

7. Why do you need a thorough understanding of the law as it impacts your employer's practice?

Answers will vary but should include the fact that the employee's negligent behavior can cause the employer to be liable for the negligence.

8. State ten steps that may protect a physician and staff from liability.

Responses will vary but should include information from the following topics: general guidelines, safety, communication, and documentation.

Matching

Column A	Column B
1. liable	c. legally responsible for one's actions
2. rider	f. add-on to an insurance policy
3. tort	i. a civil wrong
4. proximate	j. direct cause of injury
5. misfeasance	b. improper doing of a lawful act
6. nonfeasance	g. failure to perform a necessary action
7. *res ipsa loquitur*	d. "the thing speaks for itself"
8. *res judicata*	a. "the thing has been decided"
9. cap	h. limit
10. dereliction	e. neglect

Multiple Choice

1. Carl Simon, a pharmacy technician, fills a prescription for Coumadin, a blood-thinning agent, for Beth White. He hands Beth the prescription without giving her any instructions. Beth has been taking large doses of aspirin for arthritis. The aspirin and Coumadin cause excessive bleeding when Beth takes them together. What is the legal term to describe a potential liability that Carl may have committed?
   a. malfeasance
   b. misfeasance
   c. nonfeasance
   d. arbitration
   e. standard of proof

   Answer: c

2. Emily King mistakenly administers syrup of ipecac, which causes vomiting, instead of syrup of cola, which soothes the stomach lining, to Jacob Freeman. Jacob immediately begins to vomit. Which term could be used to describe Emily's action?
   a. *res judicata*
   b. *res ipsa loquitur*
   c. nonfeasance
   d. misfeasance
   e. rider

   Answer: b

3. Which of the four Ds is violated when a physician fails to inform the patient about the risks of not receiving treatment?
   a. duty
   b. dereliction
   c. direct cause
   d. damages
   e. none of the above is correct

   Answer: b

4. A phlebotomist draws blood from Sam Ford's right arm. Sam experiences pain and numbness in that arm immediately after the blood is drawn. This is an example of what legal doctrine?

   a. duty

   b. feasance

   c. *res judicata*

   d. proximate cause

   e. rider

   Answer: d

5. Allan Walker continues to smoke after his physician warns him that smoking carries the risk of lung cancer. His physician documents this admonition in Allan's medical record. When Allan develops lung cancer, he sues his doctor for malpractice. Allan states that he did not know about the risk of continued smoking. What malpractice defense might apply in this case?

   a. denial

   b. assumption of risk

   c. contributory negligence

   d. borrowed servant

   e. b and c both apply

   Answer: e

6. Once the court has decided a case and the appeals process is over, there can be no new lawsuit on the same subject between the same two parties. This is referred to as

   a. statute of limitations

   b. *res ipsa loquitur*

   c. *res judicata*

   d. contributory negligence

   e. comparative negligence

   Answer: c

7. To cover their employees, some physicians carry additional insurance that is added onto the physician's liability insurance. This is called a

   a. liability

   b. rider

   c. tort

   d. cap

   e. standard of proof

   Answer: b

8. In a medical office, the list of agents for the physician includes the

   a. nurse, medical assistant, and LPN

   b. technicians

   c. cleaning staff

   d. a and b only

   e. a, b, and c

   Answer: e

9. The doctrine of *respondeat superior* does not apply between the physician and the

   a. nurse

   b. medical assistant

   c. phlebotomist

   d. pharmacist

   e. physical therapist

   Answer: d

10. Using a third person to help settle a dispute in a nonbinding decision is called
    a. mediation
    b. arbitration
    c. malpractice lawsuit
    d. civil lawsuit
    e. none of the above

    Answer: a

Fill in the Blanks

1. A special application of *respondeat superior* in which an employer lends an employee to someone else is known as the <u>borrowed servant</u> doctrine.
2. <u>Compensatory</u> damages are an amount of money awarded by the court to make up for loss of income or emotional pain and suffering.
3. When the outcome of a case is mutually agreed upon outside a courtroom, it is called a <u>settlement.</u>
4. A defense that the plaintiff's own negligence helped cause the injury is called <u>comparative</u> negligence.
5. <u>Assumption</u> of risk is a legal defense that prevents a plaintiff from recovering damages if the plaintiff voluntarily accepts a risk associated with the activity.
6. Conduct on the part of the plaintiff that causes, in part, the injuries is called <u>contributory</u> negligence.
7. Claims-incurred insurance is also called <u>occurrence</u> insurance.
8. Performing an illegal act is known as <u>malfeasance.</u>
9. Submitting a dispute for resolution to a person other than a judge is called <u>arbitration.</u>
10. Slight or token payments ordered by the court are called <u>nominal</u> damages.

PUT IT INTO PRACTICE

Call an insurance company that handles malpractice insurance. Inquire about the cost and coverage for someone in your profession. Request an informational brochure. Write a summary of the information and report it back to your class or your instructor.

WEB HUNT

1. Using the website for the National Association for Healthcare Quality (NAHQ), *www.nahq.org*, discuss the six values (transformational leadership, customer-driven continuous improvement, team work, diversity, integrity, and professional development) listed as they relate to your chosen profession.
2. Use the website for Healthcare Providers Service Organization (HPSO), *www. hpso.com*, to get information regarding healthcare professionals' insurance services information. Click on More Sites About Medical Malpractice Insurance. Look under Allied Healthcare Professionals Insurance Center to determine if your field of study is included in their coverage. Look under Nurses Service Organization to find out what the yearly malpractice insurance premium would be for $1,000,000 coverage for a registered nurse with more than one year of experience, and who works full-time.
3. Using the website *www.findlaw.com*, click on Medical Malpractice and summarize the article on *res ipsa loquitur*.

CASE STUDY

Jessica Mass, a phlebotomist, drew a blood sample from Glenn Ross, a 30-year-old patient of Dr. Williams, to test for AIDS. As Glenn was leaving the office, his friend Harry came in, and they greeted each other. Jessica took Harry into an exam room, and in the course of making conversation, he told her that he was a good friend of Glenn's. He asked Jessica why Glenn was seeing the doctor. Jessica responded that it was just a routine test for AIDS.

When Harry arrived back home, he called Glenn and told him what the phlebotomist had said. Glenn called Dr. Williams and complained about Jessica's action and said that he planned to sue Dr. Williams. Dr. Williams dismissed Jessica. Dr. Williams told Jessica that if Glenn did bring a lawsuit against her and she lost, then she would sue Jessica.

Case Questions

1. What should Jessica have done or said when Harry asked about Glenn's reason for being in the office?

   Jessica should have said that she was unable to discuss any patient information with a third party. She might also have explained to Harry that she would practice the same level of confidentiality about Harry's examination by the physician.

2. Did Dr. Williams have a legal right to sue Jessica if she was sued and lost?

   Dr. Williams's reputation is affected by what Jessica said to Harry. This might be considered defamation of character. Dr. Williams, as Jessica's employer, is being sued (under the doctrine of *respondeat superior*) simply because of Jessica's action.

3. What important right did Jessica violate?

   Jessica violated the important right the patient has to expect confidentiality.

SUPPLEMENTAL QUESTIONS

Chapter Review

Cover the terms in the left-hand column with a piece of paper. Read the statement and fill in the blank with the answer before uncovering the correct response.

	Both actions and inactions (omissions) can be considered
negligence	_____. Performing an illegal act is called
malfeasance	_____. The improper performance of an otherwise
misfeasance	lawful act is _____. The failure to perform a neces-
nonfeasance	sary action is _____.
	In order to obtain a judgment for negligence against a
four	physician, the patient must show the _____
Ds	_____. The responsibility established by the physi-
	cian–patient relationship—the first D—is called
duty/dereliction	_____. The second D, _____, or neglect, is the
	physician's failure to act as any prudent physician would.
proximate	Also, the plaintiff must prove direct or _____ cause
	(the third D), which means that the injury was closely re-
	lated to the physician's negligence. The fourth D is
damages	_____.

Preponderance	_____ of evidence, which means the evidence more likely to support one side, is the standard of proof gener-
civil	ally used in _____ cases.
Compensatory	_____ damages are payments for the actual loss or injury suffered by the patient. The court will consider the
physical disability	amount of _____ _____, loss of earnings to date, and any future loss of earnings. Monetary awards by a court to a person who is harmed in an especially mali-
punitive	cious or willful way are called _____ damages.
burden	The _____ of proof to prove the defendant per-
plaintiff	formed the wrongful act is upon the _____. The ex-
assumption of	ception to this is _____ _____ risk. The most
denial	common defense is _____. Another possible defense that prevents the plaintiff from recovering damages occurs when the plaintiff voluntarily accepts the risk. In order for assumption of risk to be valid, the plaintiff must know and
understand/ voluntary	_____ the risk, and the choice must be _____.
rider	Most physicians carry a _____, or addition, to a mal- practice insurance policy, which covers malpractice suits based on injuries caused by employees. Such coverage is important because the employer is liable under the doc-
respondeat superior	trine of _____ _____.

Multiple Choice

Select the one best response to the following questions.

1. The improper performance of an otherwise proper or lawful act is
   a. malfeasance
   b. misfeasance
   c. nonfeasance
   d. arbitration
   e. standard of care

   Answer: b

2. In order to obtain a judgment for negligence, the patient must show
   a. direct or proximate cause
   b. duty
   c. damages
   d. dereliction, or neglect, of duty
   e. all of the above

   Answer: e

3. The standard of proof generally used in a civil case is
   a. evidence beyond a reasonable doubt
   b. *res ipsa loquitur*
   c. preponderance of evidence
   d. probable cause
   e. none of the above

   Answer: c

4. A patient is given specific instructions, does not follow those instructions, and later injures himself. If the patient sues for malpractice, what defense might apply?
   a. contributory negligence
   b. standard of proof
   c. borrowed servant doctrine
   d. denial
   e. a and d could both apply

   Answer: e

5. A physician's failure to act as any ordinary and prudent physician within the same community would act is
   a. neglect of duty
   b. *res ipsa loquitur*
   c. dereliction
   d. a and c only
   e. a, b, and c

   Answer: d

6. Under the doctrine of *res ispa loquitur,* the burden of proof falls to the
   a. patient
   b. defendant
   c. prosecutor
   d. American Medical Association
   e. *res ipsa loquitur* does not require burden of proof

   Answer: b

7. Monetary awards by a court to a person who has been harmed in an especially malicious or willful way are known as what type of damages?
   a. nominal
   b. liable
   c. punitive
   d. compensatory
   e. arbitration

   Answer: c

8. Under the borrowed servant doctrine
   a. the employer is liable for any negligence caused by the servant while in service of a temporary employer
   b. the employer is liable for 50 percent of any negligence caused by the servant
   c. the employer is not liable for negligence by the servant while in service of a temporary employer
   d. the employee is no longer associated with the employer after the servant contract is signed
   e. the employee is liable for all negligence

   Answer: c

9. General guidelines to avoid malpractice include all of the following except
   a. treat all patients with courtesy and respect
   b. do not make promises of a cure or recovery
   c. make sure the staff is aware of what is lawful
   d. give care beyond the scope of one's training or experience only if it is necessary
   e. all of the above

   Answer: d

10. Mike Smith is trained in CPR and yet does not administer this lifesaving technique when a patient collapses and requires CPR. What is the legal term to describe a potential liability that Mike may have committed?
    a. malfeasance
    b. misfeasance
    c. nonfeasance
    d. arbitration
    e. standard of care

    Answer: c

True/False Questions

1. The courts now find that everyone associated with negligent actions is liable for damages. (true)
2. For many people, the terms *negligence* and *malpractice* are synonymous. (true)
3. The term *damages,* in medical malpractice, refers to property damages. (false)
4. The four Ds of negligence include diagnosis. (false)
5. Malfeasance refers to performing a wrong and illegal action. (false)
6. Proximate cause means that the injury to the patient was closely related to the defendant's negligent actions. (true)
7. In *res ipsa loquitur,* the burden of proof, as always, falls onto the plaintiff. (false)
8. Exemplary damages are also called compensatory damages. (false)
9. Patients can seek damages for pain and suffering. (true)
10. Affirmative defenses allow the defendant to present evidence that the patient's condition is the result of factors other than those caused by the defendant's negligence. (true)

Short Answer Questions

1. What are the four Ds of negligence?
   a. duty
   b. dereliction, or neglect, of duty
   c. direct or proximate cause
   d. damages

2. What are the three types of compensatory damages?
   a. special compensatory
   b. punitive
   c. nominal

3. For *res ipsa loquitur* to be used, what three conditions must be met?
   a. The injury could not have occurred without negligence.
   b. The defendant had total and direct control over the cause of injury, and the duty had to be within the scope of duty owed to the patient or injured party.
   c. The patient did not, and could not, contribute to the cause of the injury.

4. Who bears the burden of proof in a malpractice suit?

   The burden of proof is on the plaintiff.

5. Other than going to court, what three methods are used to solve civil disputes?
   a. arbitration
   b. mediation
   c. med-arb

6. What are examples of affirmative defenses?
   a. assumption of risk
   b. contributory negligence
   c. comparative negligence
   d. borrowed servant
   e. ignorance of the facts
   f. unintentional wrongs
   g. statute of limitations
   h. Good Samaritan laws

7. What is the borrowed servant doctrine?

   It is a special application of *respondeat superior* that occurs when an employer (physician) lends an employee, such as a surgical nurse or technician, to someone else.

8. What is fraud?

   The deliberate concealment of the facts, such as when an error is concealed from a patient.

9. What are two types of liability insurance?
   a. claims-made insurance, which covers the insured party only for claims made during the time period the policy is in effect (or policy year).
   b. occurrence insurance (also called claims-incurred insurance) in which the insured party is covered for all injuries and incidents that occurred while the policy was in effect (policy year), regardless of when the insured reported to the insurer or the claim was made.

10. What does the term *nurse* signify?

    That the person is a registered nurse who has passed an examination to become licensed to practice nursing.

TEACHING STRATEGIES

1. Show the movie *Verdict* to the class, then lead a discussion on how the legal system operated in the movie in regard to medical malpractice.
2. Invite an attorney who specializes in medical malpractice law to discuss with the class some favorite cases, preferably ones that involve the medical specialty of your students. Students should prepare questions before the presentation.
3. Divide the class into groups of three. Ask them to review the four Ds of negligence. Their task should be to write a fifth D of negligence, then read it and defend it to the class.
4. Brainstorm with students about situations in which an employee is "borrowed." remind students that the one who does the borrowing is liable.
5. Have small groups of students present to the class ways to avoid malpractice in their profession.
6. Have the students prepare flash cards for key terms (glossary).

Public Duties of the Physician

CHAPTER SYNOPSIS

All of the states have passed public health statutes that protect their citizens from a variety of dangers, including communicable diseases, medical waste products, drug abuse, child abuse, and elder abuse. In order to enforce these statutes, physicians, with the help of their assistants, are required to report certain information to public officials. This chapter discusses many of these reports, including birth and death certificates, immunization records, communicable disease statistics, abuse information, and the distribution of addictive drugs (narcotics).

Chapter Lecture Outline	Instructor's Notes

I. Public Health Records and Vital Statistics
   A. Births
   B. Deaths
   C. Communicable diseases—Childhood vaccines and toxoids
      1. Diphtheria, tetanus toxoid, pertussis (DPT)
      2. Measles, mumps, rubella (MMR)
      3. Poliovirus vaccine, live
      4. Poliovirus vaccine, inactivated
      5. Hepatitis B vaccine
      6. Tuberculosis test
      7. *H. influenza* type b vaccine (HiB)
      8. Hepatitis A vaccine
      9. Varicella (chickenpox) vaccine
     10. Pneumococcal (pneumonia) vaccine (PCV7)
   D. Child abuse
   E. Elder abuse
   F. Spousal abuse
   G. Signs of abuse
      1. Repeated injuries
      2. Bruises such as blackened eyes
      3. Unexplained fractures
      4. Bite marks
      5. Swelling, bruising, and pain in the genital area
      6. Signs of inadequate nutrition
      7. Venereal disease	

Chapter Lecture Outline	Instructor's Notes

H. Substance abuse
 I. Gathering evidence in cases of abuse
   1. Photo of bruises and other signs of abuse
   2. Female child's urine specimen (containing sperm)
   3. Clothing (soiled)
   4. Body fluids, such as semen, vomitus, or gastric contents
   5. Various samples such as blood, semen, vaginal or rectal smears
   6. Chain of custody of evidence
 J. Other reportable conditions
II. Controlled Substances Act and Regulations
  A. Food and Drug Administration (FDA)
  B. Drug Enforcement Administration (DEA)
  C. Controlled Substances Act of 1970
  D. The Bureau of Narcotics and Dangerous Drugs (BNDD)
  E. Controlled substances
    1. Schedule I drugs
    2. Schedule II drugs
    3. Schedule III drugs
    4. Schedule IV drugs
    5. Schedule V drugs
  F. Prescriptions of controlled drugs
III. Protection of the Employee and the Environment
  A. Employee Assistance Programs (EAPs)
  B. Medical waste	

LEARNING OBJECTIVES

(Student answers may vary.)

1. Define the glossary terms.

   Addiction   an acquired physical or psychological dependence on a drug.

   Autopsy   a postmortem examination of organs and tissues to determine the cause of death.

   Bureau of Narcotics and Dangerous Drugs (BNDD)   an agency of the federal government responsible for enforcing laws covering statutes of addictive drugs.

   Controlled Substances Act of 1970   a federal statute that regulates the manufacture and distribution of the drugs that are capable of causing dependency.

   Coroner   a public health officer who holds an investigation (inquest) if a person's death is from an unknown or violent cause.

   Data   statistics, figures, or information.

   Drug Enforcement Administration (DEA)   a division of the Department of Justice that enforces the Controlled Substances Act of 1970.

   Employee Assistance Program (EAP)   a management-financed, confidential counseling and referral service designed to help employees and/or their family members assess a problem such as alcoholism.

Food and Drug Administration (FDA)   an agency within the Department of Health and Human Services that ultimately enforces drug sales and distribution.

Habituation   the development of an emotional dependence on a drug due to repeated use.

Inquest   an investigation held by a public official, such as a coroner, to determine the cause of death.

Morbidity rate   the rate of sick people or cases of disease in relationship to a specific population.

Mortality rate   death rate.

Postmortem   after death.

Public duties   responsibilities the physician owes to the public.

Restraining or protective order   court order that prohibits an abuser from coming Into contact with the victim.

Vital statistics   major events or facts from a person's life, such as live births, deaths, induced termination of pregnancy, and marriages.

2. Describe the public duties of a physician.

   Public duties of the physician include collecting patients' vital statistics such as birth, death, illness, and abuse cases.

3. Discuss the guidelines that should be used when completing a legal record or certificate.

   a. Request information from the state registrar for specific requirements on completing certificates.
   b. Type all documents when possible. If the record is completed manually, then print using black ink.
   c. Make sure that all blank spaces are completed.
   d. Verify correct spelling of all names.
   e. Use full original signature, not a rubber stamp.
   f. File original certificates or reports with the appropriate registrar.
   g. Avoid abbreviations.
   h. Do not alter the certificate or make erasures.
   i. Keep a copy in the patient's file.

4. List the information that must be included in a death certificate.

   a. The date and time of death.
   b. The cause of death.
   c. How long the deceased person was treated for the disease or injury before dying.
   d. The presence or absence of pregnancy (for female decedent).
   e. If an autopsy took place.

5. Describe the cases in which a coroner or health official would have to sign a death certificate.

   a. No physician present at the time of death.
   b. A violent death, including homicidal, suicidal, or accidental.
   c. Death as a result of a criminal action.
   d. An unlawful death, such as assisted suicide.
   e. Death from an undetermined cause.
   f. Death resulting from chemical, electrical, thermal, or radiation injury.

    g. Death caused by criminal abortion, including self-induced.

    h. Death occurring less than twenty-four hours after hospital admission.

    i. No physician attending the patient within thirty-six hours preceding death.

    j. Death occurring outside a hospital or licensed care facility.

    k. Suspicious death.

    l. Death of a person whose body is not claimed by friends or relatives.

    m. Death of a person whose identity is unknown.

    n. Death of a child under the age of 2 years if the death is from an unknown cause or if it appears the death is from Sudden Infant Death Syndrome (SIDS).

    o. Death of a person in jail or prison.

6. List the ten reportable communicable diseases.

    a. Tuberculosis

    b. Rubeola

    c. Rubella

    d. Tetanus

    e. Diphtheria

    f. Cholera

    g. Poliomyelitis

    h. AIDS

    i. Meningococcal meningitis

    j. Rheumatic fever

7. Discuss the Child Abuse Prevention and Treatment Act of 1974.

This act requires reporting of all child abuse cases. All states have statutes that define child abuse and require that all abuse must be reported.

8. Describe eight signs that indicate a child, spouse, or elderly person may be abused.

    a. Repeated injuries

    b. Bruises such as blackened eyes and unexplained swelling

    c. Unexplained fractures

    d. Bite marks

    e. Unusual marks such as those occurring from a cigarette burn

    f. Bruising, swelling, or pain in the genital area

    g. Signs of inadequate nutrition such as sunken eyes and weight loss

    h. Venereal disease

9. Discuss the federal legislation of controlled substances.

The Food and Drug Administration (FDA), an agency within the Department of Health and Human Services, ultimately enforces drug (prescription and over-the-counter) sales and distribution. Drugs that have a potential for addiction, habituation, or abuse are regulated and controlled by the Drug Enforcement Administration (DEA) of the Department of Justice.

10. List and explain the five schedules of drugs.

    a. Schedule I: Has the highest potential for addiction and abuse. These drugs cannot be prescribed and are not accepted for medical use. They may be used for research purposes. Examples are marijuana, heroin, and LSD.

    b. Schedule II: Has a high potential for addiction and abuse. They are accepted for medical use in the United States and can be prescribed by a DEA-licensed physician. Examples are codeine, cocaine, morphine, opium, and secobarbital.

    c. Schedule III: Has a moderate-to-low potential for addiction and abuse. A DEA number is not required to prescribe these drugs, but the physician must handwrite the order. Examples are butabarbital, anabolic steroids, and APC with codeine.

 d. Schedule IV: Has a lower potential for addiction and abuse than Schedule III drugs. The physician must sign the prescription. Examples include chloral hydrate, phenobarbital, and diazepam.

 e. Schedule V: Has a low potential for addiction and abuse.

11. Explain how an Employee Assistance Program (EAP) can help troubled employees.

This management-financed, confidential counseling and referral service is designed to help employees and/or their family members assess a problem such as alcoholism. The EAP is aimed at helping employees to maintain their job performance and keep their job while finding assistance with an emotional or abuse problem.

THE CASE OF BRIAN B. AND THE AIDS TEST

Brian B. is taken into an exam room in the office of Dr. K. by the medical assistant, Amy. Amy gets into an animated discussion with Brian about their mutually favorite baseball team. As Amy leaves the exam room, she accidentally places Brian's medical file on the counter. While Brian waits for Dr. K., he reads through his file folder. He is shocked to discover that his recent test for AIDS came back positive. Brian panics and runs out of the office before seeing Dr. K. The doctor tries to reach Brian by phone but there is no answer. Dr. K. then sends a letter marked "Confidential" to Brian and explains that he must be treated for his disease and also needs to inform his sexual partners about his disease. Brian does not respond to the letter.

Case Questions

1. What else can Doctor K. do to meet his obligation to report a communicable disease?

Dr. K. must still report the AIDS case to the public health department. Depending on the role that the local health department takes, Dr. K. may eventually have to reveal the patient's name in order to allow the health department to track any of Brian's sexual partners. There are statutes in some states that impose criminal liability on a person who is an HIV or AIDS carrier and knowingly engages in activities that could have spread the virus to others. Physicians have been named in lawsuits when a person was not warned that his or her partner tested positive for AIDS.

2. What responsibility does the medical assistant, Amy, have relating to this problem?

If Amy had not carelessly left the chart in plain sight for Brian to read, this situation may not have happened the way it did. Physicians are often able to convince their patients to come in for treatment when they can talk to them face to face. However, letters do not have the same capacity to bring a patient in for treatment. Amy did not do anything illegal, but she clearly was not performing her job correctly. She could lose her job over this error.

3. How might Brian be encouraged to report his condition to his sexual partners?

It may be necessary for Dr. K to make a personal visit to Brian's home. Physicians are often reluctant to do this. However, in small towns it is often more common for physicians to personally know all their patients and to make every attempt to followup with their care. [NOTE: We do not know if Dr. K. practiced in a small town or in a large city medical center.]

POINTS TO PONDER (FROM TEXTBOOK)

Teaching note: These questions are meant to promote critical thinking and classroom discussion.

1. Is it only the responsibility of the physician to report child abuse cases? To whom, in your community, should such a report be made?

2. How soon after death does a death certificate have to be signed?

3. Does a woman have to report a stillbirth if it happens at home?

4. Who signs a death certificate in a death resulting from a fall from a window?

5. Does the physician have to report a case of genital warts or can this information be kept confidential?

6. Is the "battered child syndrome" a legitimate medical diagnosis?

7. Can a physician who reports a suspected case of child abuse be sued by parents?

8. Can a "wasted" controlled substance be poured down a sink?

9. Wouldn't it be better for a person who has personal problems to be counseled by a supervisor or employer who knows him or her than to be counseled by a stranger in EAP?

10. Should healthcare workers be tested to see if they are HIV-positive?

REVIEW QUESTIONS (FROM TEXTBOOK)
Discussion Questions

1. What drugs fall under each of the five categories of controlled substances?
   a. Schedule I: Has the highest potential for addiction and abuse. These drugs cannot be prescribed and are not accepted for medical use. They may be used for research purposes. Examples are marijuana, heroin, and LSD.
   b. Schedule II: Has a high potential for addiction and abuse. They are accepted for medical use in the United States and can be prescribed by a DEA-licensed physician. Examples are codeine, cocaine, morphine, opium, and secobarbital.
   c. Schedule III: Has a moderate-to-low potential for addiction and abuse. A DEA number is not required to prescribe these drugs, but the physician must handwrite the order. Examples are butabarbital, anabolic steroids, and APC with codeine.
   d. Schedule IV: Has a lower potential for addiction and abuse than Schedule III drugs. The physician must sign the prescription. Examples include chloral hydrate, phenobarbital, and diazepam.
   e. Schedule V: Has a low potential for addiction and abuse.

2. To what does the term *public duties* refer?

   Public duties are responsibilities that a physician owes to the public.

3. What are the physician's public duties?

   Public duties of the physician include collecting patients' vital statistics, such as birth, death, illness, and abuse cases.

4. What records must physicians keep if they dispense or administer controlled substances?

   Schedule I drugs require approval from the FDA as well as the DEA for use in research.

Schedule II drugs require a special DEA order form that is completed in triplicate. Inventory records, or logs, must be maintained for all five drug schedules.

5. What are the four categories of medical waste?
   a. solid
   b. chemical
   c. radioactive
   d. infectious

6. What is the healthcare worker's responsibility with medical waste?

   The healthcare worker must protect the public and other healthcare workers from the dangers of medical waste. Protective actions include using correctly labeled containers for medical waste and using correct decontamination onsite or having it removed by a licensed removal facility.

7. What are some conditions surrounding death that require an autopsy?

   Many of the same situations that require a coroner to sign a death certificate also require an autopsy. See the answer to question 5 in Learning Objectives.

Matching

Column A	Column B
1. data	b. statistics
2. coroner	e. public health official who investigates cause of death
3. Schedule II drug	h. codeine
4. postmortem	a. after death
5. Schedule I drug	g. LSD
6. addiction	c. physical dependence
7. inquest	j. investigation to determine cause of death
8. DPT	d. diphtheria, tetanus toxoid, pertussis vaccine
9. STDs	i. sexually transmitted diseases
10. public duty	f. report child abuse

Multiple Choice

1. Vital statistics from a person's life include all of the following except
   a. pregnancies
   b. marriages and divorces
   c. animal bites
   d. sensitive information such as rape and abuse
   e. all of the above are considered to be vital statistics

   Answer: e

2. A coroner does not have to sign a death certificate in the case of
   a. suicide
   b. death of an elderly person over the age of 90
   c. death occurring less than 24 hours after hospital admission
   d. death from electrocution
   e. death of a prison inmate

   Answer: b

3. All of the following vaccines and toxoids are required for children by law except
   a. measles
   b. polio
   c. hepatitis
   d. a and b only
   e. a, b, and c are all required

   Answer: e

4. The Controlled Substances Act is also known as the
   a. drug Enforcement Administration Act
   b. food and Drug Administration Act
   c. comprehensive Drug Abuse Prevention and Control Act
   d. bureau of Narcotics and Dangerous Drugs Act
   e. none of the above

   Answer: c

5. Schedule III drugs
   a. can be refilled by an order over the phone from the office assistant
   b. are allowed only five refills during a six-month period
   c. require the DEA number of the physician on the prescription
   d. require the order to be typed on the prescription form
   e. all of the above

   Answer: b

6. An EAP program may help an employee cope with
   a. marital problems
   b. alcoholism and drug abuse
   c. criminal charges
   d. a and b only
   e. a, b, and c

   Answer: d

7. Infectious waste
   a. should be separated from chemical waste at the site of the origin
   b. can be safely removed by a licensed removal facility
   c. consists of blood and blood products
   d. may contain the HIV and hepatitis A and B viruses
   e. all of the above

   Answer: e

8. Phenobarbital is an example of a
   a. schedule I drug
   b. schedule II drug
   c. schedule III drug
   d. schedule IV drug
   e. schedule V drug

   Answer: d

9. The best method to "waste," or destroy, a narcotic is to
   a. place it in a medical waste container that is clearly marked
   b. return it to the pharmaceutical company
   c. flush it down the toilet
   d. do it without any witnesses
   e. none of the above

   Answer: c

10. Elder abuse is clearly defined in the
    a. Food and Drug Administration Act
    b. Controlled Substances Act of 1970
    c. Amendment to the Older Americans Act of 1987
    d. Amendment to the Older Americans Act of 1974
    e. none of the above

    Answer: c

Fill in the Blanks

1. A physician's duty to report vital events is called <u>public duties</u>.
2. A coroner or health official must sign a death certificate for any death occurring less than <u>twenty-four</u> hours after hospital admission.
3. An <u>inquest</u> is an investigation if a death is from an unknown or violent cause.
4. Employees, in daycare, healthcare, and food services are more carefully monitored by public health departments for <u>contagious</u> diseases.
5. Some statutes impose <u>criminal</u> liability on a person who is an HIV carrier and knowingly engages in activities that could spread the virus to others.
6. <u>Probable cause</u> is a reasonable belief that something improper has happened.
7. A protective court order that prohibits an abuser from coming into contact with a victim is called a <u>restraining</u> order.
8. A violation of controlled substances laws is a <u>criminal</u> offense.
9. Evidence that is gathered in an abuse case must have a clear chain of <u>custody</u>.
10. Schedule V drugs have a <u>low</u> potential for abuse.

PUT IT INTO PRACTICE

Find a newspaper or magazine article that discusses an abusive situation (spousal, child, elder, or drugs). Write your thoughts on what could have been done to prevent this from happening. Discuss the role of the healthcare team in reporting abuse cases.

WEB HUNT

1. Search the website of the Centers for Disease Control (*www.cdc.gov*). Provide a definition for the morbidity tables and mortality tables using the CDC's definition as stated on its website.
2. Search the website *www.findlaw.com* to find information on your state's child abuse laws. Summarize them.

CASE STUDY

A pharmaceutical salesperson has just brought in a supply of nonprescription vitamin samples for the physicians in your practice to dispense to their patients. These vitamins are a new, expensive variety that is being given away to patients who are on a limited income and cannot afford to buy them. The other staff members take the samples home for their families' personal use. They tell you to do the same since the samples will become outdated before the physicians can use all of them. It would save you money.

Case Questions

1. What do you do?

   You cannot use them for yourself or your family, since they have been given with the expectation that they will be dispensed by a licensed physician to patients as free samples.

2. Is your action legal? Why or why not?

   If you take the samples and give them to your family members, it can be considered stealing.

3. Is your action ethical? Why or why not?

   Illegal actions are always unethical.

4. Does your physician/employer have any responsibility for the dispensing of these free nonprescription vitamins? Explain your answer.

   Yes. He or she has the ultimate responsibility, since only the physician can dispense medication. He or she is aware of other medications the patient may be taking that could interact with the vitamins.

SUPPLEMENTAL QUESTIONS

Chapter Review

Cover the terms in the left-hand column with a piece of paper. Read the statement and fill in the blank with the answer before uncovering the correct response.

vital statistics	Vital events or _____ _____ from a life, such
government	as birth and death, are used by the _____, public
	health agencies, and other institutions to determine popu-
trends	lation _____ and needs.
coroner	A _____ or medical examiner completes the death
certificate	_____ if the deceased has not been under the care
	of a physician. This public health officer holds an investi-
inquest	gation or _____ if the death is from an unknown or
violent/autopsy	a _____ cause. An _____, which is a
postmortem	_____ examination of the organs and tissues of the
	body, may have to be performed to determine the cause of
	death.
	Physicians must report all diseases that are considered a
general threat	_____ _____ to the public. All states require
rubeola/rubella	reports of _____, _____, tuberculosis, tetanus,
poliomyelitis	diphtheria, cholera, AIDS, _____, meningococcal
rheumatic	meningitis, and _____ fever.
Food/Drug	The _____ and _____ Administration, an
	agency within the Department of Health and Human
	Services, enforces drug (prescription and over-the-
sales/distribution	counter) _____ and _____.

I	A Schedule _____ drug has the highest potential for addiction and abuse and cannot be prescribed. In con-
III	trast, a Schedule _____ drug can be prescribed, but only five refills are allowed over a six-month period of time.
Good Samaritan	_____ _____ laws are state laws that help protect physicians from claims of negligence while giving emergency treatment. Persons responding to an emergency situation are only required to act within the
limits/training	_____ of their skill and _____.

Multiple Choice

Select the one best response to the following statements.

1. A physician must include all of the following information on a death certificate except
   a. the presence or absence of pregnancy
   b. if an autopsy took place
   c. the cause of death
   d. the date and time of death
   e. all of the above must be included

   Answer: e

2. A person who reports child abuse is protected by law
   a. if the accused is found guilty
   b. if the person reports the crime in good faith
   c. only if the person has evidence beyond a reasonable doubt
   d. under the Good Samaritan laws
   e. only if the person is a trained healthcare professional

   Answer: b

3. Physicians who administer controlled substances to patients must renew their registration with the DEA every
   a. six months
   b. year
   c. two years
   d. three years
   e. the registration does not have to be renewed

   Answer: d

4. The agency of the federal government authorized to enforce drug control is known as the
   a. Food and Drug Administration
   b. Drug Enforcement Administration
   c. Controlled Substances Agency
   d. Bureau of Narcotics and Dangerous Drugs
   e. none of the above

   Answer: d

5. Anabolic steroids are an example of a
   a. Schedule I drug
   b. Schedule II drug
   c. Schedule III drug
   d. Schedule IV drug
   e. Schedule V drug

   Answer: c

6. The Good Samaritan laws
   a. try to encourage physicians to offer aid to accident victims
   b. only require people to act within the limits of their skill and training
   c. apply when aid is given in which a physician–patient relationship has been established
   d. a and b only
   e. a, b, and c

   Answer: d

7. Signs of abuse include.
   a. poor growth
   b. lack of hygiene
   c. malnutrition
   d. bite marks
   e. all of the above

   Answer: e

8. Diphtheria is an example of
   a. a reportable disease
   b. a Schedule I drug
   c. a narcotic
   d. a Schedule V drug
   e. a sign of abuse

   Answer: a

9. A Schedule I controlled substance
   a. has a low potential for addiction and abuse
   b. is acceptable for medical use within the United States
   c. includes cocaine and opium
   d. cannot be prescribed
   e. c and d

   Answer: d

10. A coroner or health official will have to sign a death certificate in the case of
    a. a death as a result of a criminal action
    b. an unlawful death such as assisted suicide
    c. unexplained or unexpected death
    d. a and b only
    e. a, b, and c

    Answer: e

True/False Questions

1. There are very few physical indications on a child who may have suffered abuse. (false)

2. If an elderly person dies from natural causes, an autopsy may not be required. (true)

3. If a baby is born at home and dies immediately upon birth, the only documentation that is needed is a death certificate. (false)

4. A person's marriages are considered to be a personal matter and thus are not considered to be a vital statistic. (false)

5. An Employee Assistance Program can help a troubled employee who is abusing drugs or alcohol to keep his or her job. (true)

6. For purposes of the death certificate, it is unimportant how long the deceased person had the disease before he or she died. (false)

7. A case of genital warts must be reported to public health authorities. (true)

8. The license of a psychiatrist or psychologist who fails to report sexual abuse in a child can be revoked. (true)

9. When there is not enough evidence to prove a suspected case of child abuse, the person reporting the suspected abuse will always lose a case of defamation of character. (false)

10. The Older Americans Act protects the elderly from financial exploitation. (true)

Short Answer Questions

1. What childhood vaccines and toxoids does the law require?
   a. diphtheria, tetanus toxoid, pertussis vaccine
   b. pertussis vaccine
   c. measles, mumps, rubella
   d. poliovirus vaccine, live
   e. poliovirus, inactivated
   f. hepatitis B vaccine
   g. tuberculosis test

2. What sort of report(s) do most states require if abuse is suspected?
   a. an oral report immediately
   b. written report

3. How can medical office personnel assist the physician in maintaining compliance with controlled substance laws?
   a. alerting the physician to the license renewal date
   b. maintaining accurate inventory records
   c. keeping all controlled substances in a secure cabinet
   d. keeping prescription blanks and pads locked in a secure cabinet, office, or physician's bag

4. What information should a communicable disease report include?
   a. name, address, age, and occupation of the patient
   b. the name of the disease or suspected disease
   c. date of onset of the disease
   d. name of the person issuing the report

5. What is the responsibility of the Food and Drug Administration?

   The Food and Drug Administration enforces prescription and over-the-counter drug sales distribution.

6. What is an investigation to determine the cause of death called?

   An inquest.

7. What are some of the uses for a valid birth certificate?
   a. to obtain a social security card
   b. to obtain a passport
   c. to obtain a driver's license
   d. to obtain a voter's registration card

8. What happens to a death certificate once it is signed by a physician?

   It is given to the mortician, who files it with the state or county clerk's office.

9. What documentation must be completed in the case of a baby who is born alive but dies shortly after birth?
   a. a certificate of birth
   b. a certificate of death

10. What does the National Childhood Vaccine Injury Act of 1986 require of the physician?
    a. to file a report of all vaccinations
    b. to file a report of all adverse reactions to vaccines and toxoids

TEACHING STRATEGIES

1. Invite someone from the local coroner's office to class to discuss the types of deaths that require an autopsy and the importance of notifying the coroner about unusual deaths.
2. Have students work in small groups to role-play the following scenarios:

   a. Discuss with a parent the bruises that you notice on a small child.
   b. Explain to a new employee the recommendations for completing a birth certificate.
   c. Describe to a new employee when a Good Samaritan law is in effect.
   d. Prepare a short lecture for grade-school teachers on the signs of abuse.

3. Invite a medical office manager into class to discuss methods used to maintain compliance with the law regarding controlled substances.
4. Ask the students to bring into class examples of data or vital statistics to share.
5. Have each student partner with another student. Ask each pair to share the experience of death in their families. Have them discuss whether those around them were helpful, and why or why not.
6. Have small groups of students discuss what to do if abuse is suspected. Ask them to consider the difficulties involved in these situations. Have them report back to the class about their conclusions.
7. Have the students prepare flash cards for the key terms (glossary).

8

Workplace Law and Ethics

CHAPTER SYNOPSIS

Both the employer (physician) and the employee (staff) work under federal and state regulations. Therefore, it is important that everyone working in the healthcare field be knowledgeable about regulations affecting employment practices, such as health, safety, workers' compensation, unions, and discrimination in the workplace. This chapter addresses these regulations and provides examples of lawsuits relating to them. Cultural differences and religious practices that have an influence on the practice of medicine are also discussed.

Chapter Lecture Outline	Instructor's Notes

I. Professionalism in the Workplace
  A. Discrimination in the workplace
  B. Privacy and the workplace
  C. Cultural considerations
  D. Religious considerations
II. Effective Hiring Practices—Legal and Illegal Interview Questions
III. Federal Regulations Affecting the Medical Professional
  A. Equal employment opportunity and employment discrimination
    1. Employment-at-will concept—means that employment takes place at the will of either the employer or the employee.
    2. Title VII of the Civil Rights Act of 1964—This law prohibits discrimination, or unfair treatment, in employment based on race, color, religion, gender, or national origin.
      a. Title VII includes several exceptions.
      b. Discrimination in all aspects of patient care in institutions that receive federal financial assistance is forbidden.
      c. Title VII also makes sexual harassment a form of unlawful sex discrimination.
    3. Equal Employment Opportunity Act (EEOA) of 1972—This law authorizes the Equal Employment Opportunity Commission (EEOC) to sue employers in federal court on behalf of a class of people or an individual whose Title VII rights have been violated.
    4. Pregnancy Discrimination Act of 1978—Under this law, employers must treat pregnant women as they would any other employee, providing they can still do the job.	

Chapter Lecture Outline	Instructor's Notes

     5. Civil Rights Act of 1991—This law permits the court to award both compensatory damages and punitive damages to mistreated employees.

       a. Compensatory damages are paid for loss of income or emotional pain and suffering.

       b. Punitive damages are paid to punish the defendant and to deter others from committing this action.

     6. Age Discrimination in Employment Act of 1967—This act prohibits employment discrimination because of age against persons 40 years or older. This law applies to employers who have twenty or more persons working for them.

     7. Rehabilitation Act of 1973

       a. This act prohibits discrimination based on disability in any institution that receives federal financial assistance.

       b. A hospital or agency that receives Medicare or Medicaid must comply with this law.

     8. Americans with Disabilities Act (ADA) of 1990

       a. ADA prohibits employers who have more than fifteen employees from discriminating against disabled persons.

       b. An exception occurs if necessary accommodations would be an undue hardship for the employer, such as the significant difficulty of installing an elevator in an old building.

       c. The ADA protects employees with disabilities, including those with AIDS.

       d. Patients are also protected under this statute.

  B. Employee health and safety

     1. Occupational Safety and Health Act (OSHA) of 1970

       a. Many jobs are dangerous by their very nature. OSHA regulations seek to protect workers in these jobs.

       b. These standards apply to employees who have occupational exposure, which is defined as reasonable anticipation that employees' duties will result in skin, mucous membrane, eye, or parenteral contact with bloodborne pathogens or other potential infectious material.

       c. The OSHA standards mandate that each employee with occupational exposure must be offered the hepatitis B vaccination at the employer's expense.

     2. Clinical Laboratory Improvement Act (CLIA)—This law requires that all clinical laboratories that test human specimens must be controlled. CLIA divides laboratories into three categories:

       a. Simple testing

       b. Intermediate-level testing

       c. Complex testing

     3. Health Maintenance Organization (HMO) Act of 1973

       a. The HMO Act requires any company with twentyfive employees to provide an HMO alternative to regular group insurance for their employees if an HMO is available in the area.

       b. Preventive care—An HMO must pay for procedures such as mammograms and well-baby physicals since these tests and examinations may prevent major illness.

Chapter Lecture Outline	Instructor's Notes

4. Consolidated Omnibus Budget Reconciliation Act (COBRA) of 1985
    a. COBRA has helped to decrease the number of Americans without health insurance.
    b. This insurance may be costly, but some people would not be able to obtain insurance any other way.
5. Drug-Free Workplace Act of 1988
    a. Under the Drug-Free Workplace Act, employers contracting to provide goods and services to the federal government must certify that they maintain a drug-free workplace.
    b. The employer must inform the employee of the intent to maintain a drug-free workplace and of any penalties that the employee would incur for violation of the policy.
C. Compensation and benefits regulations—These laws influence the compensation (salary) and benefits provided to employees.
    1. Social Security Act of 1935—This federal law laid the groundwork for unemployment compensation In the United States.
        a. Social Security is paid by the employer and the employee in equal payroll taxes and Medicare participant premiums.
        b. It is composed of several different but related programs including retirement, disability, dependent and survivor's benefits.
        c. Amount paid to the retiree or disabled or dependent widow is based on the worker's average wages during his or her working life.
    2. Fair Labor Standards Act (FLSA) of 1938—This is the main statute regulating employee benefits.
        a. FLSA establishes minimum wage, requires payment for overtime work, and sets the maximum hours employees covered by the act may work.
        b. One exception allows hospitals to negotiate an agreement with their employees to establish a work period of fourteen days.
        c. This law affects only full-time hourly employees.
    3. Unemployment Compensation—The Social Security Act of 1935 was the origin of the current unemployment insurance program.
    4. Equal Pay Act of 1963
        a. This act is an amendment to the FLSA.
        b. This act makes it illegal for an employer to discriminate on the basis of gender in the payment of men and women who are performing the same job.
    5. Federal Insurance Contribution Act (FICA) of 1935
        a. The Federal Insurance Contribution Act (FICA) of 1935 is the oldest act relating to compensation.
        b. Under FICA, employers are required to contribute to Social Security plans for their employees.
    6. Workers' Compensation Act
        a. Workers' compensation statutes protect workers and their families from financial problems resulting from employment-related injury, disease, and even death.
        b. The goal of workers' compensation is to get the employee back to work as soon as possible.

Chapter Lecture Outline	Instructor's Notes

      c. Even if an employee is covered by workers' compensation, the employee may still sue and recover for injuries caused by nonemployees.

    7. Employee Retirement Income Security Act (ERISA) of 1974

      a. ERISA regulates employee benefits and pension plans. Employers are required to put aside money that can be used only to pay future benefits.

      b. Vesting refers to a time, such as after ten years of employment, when an employee has the right to receive benefits from a retirement plan.

    8. Family and Medical Leave Act (FMLA) of 1994

      a. FMLA allows both the mother and the father to take a leave of absence of up to twelve weeks, in any twelve-month period, when a baby is born.

      b. Employees may also request leave for their own or a family member's medical or family-related situation, such as birth, death, or adoption, and may receive unpaid leave of up to twelve weeks.

      c. The company must maintain the employee's health coverage while the employee is on a medical leave.

      d. The employee must be returned to the original or equivalent position he or she held before going on the leave.

      e. There cannot be any loss of employment benefits that accumulated prior to the start of the leave.

  D. Consumer protection and collection practices

    1. Emergency Medical Treatment and Active Labor Acts (EMTALA)—This act is a section of the Consolidated Omnibus Budget Reconciliation Act (COBRA) that deals with patient "dumping."

    2. Fair Credit Reporting Act of 1971—This act establishes guidelines for use of an individual's credit information.

    3. Equal Credit Opportunity Act of 1975—This act prohibits businesses, including hospitals and medical offices, from with holding credit based on the applicant's race or gender.

    4. Truth in Lending Act (Regulation Z) of 1969

      a. This act requires a full written disclosure about interest rates or finance charges concerning the payment of any fee that will be collected in more than four installments.

      b. This is also called Regulation Z of the Consumer Protection Act.

    5. Fair Debt Collection Practices Act of 1978—This act prohibits unfair collection practices by creditors (institutions or persons who are owed money).

      a. Using a collection agency

        i. Professional collection agencies are available when all other attempts to collect unpaid bills fail.

        ii. Once the patient is told the account is going to a collection agency, it must, by law, go.

      b. Bankruptcy is a legal method for providing protection to debtors and establishing a fair distribution of the debtor's assets to all creditors.

Chapter Lecture Outline	Instructor's Notes

6. Federal Wage Garnishment Law of 1970
   a. Garnishment refers to a court order that requires an employer to pay a portion of an employee's paycheck directly to one of the employee's creditors.
   b. Claims against estates—When a patient dies, a bill should be sent to the estate of the deceased.
   c. Statute of limitations—This statute defines how long a medical practice has to file suit to collect on a past-due account.

E. Antitrust laws—The Sherman Antitrust Act. This law, and others like it, seek to preserve the private competitive market system by prohibiting activities that are anti-competitive. The Sherman Antitrust Act seeks to eliminate restraints of trade and to prevent the formation of monopolies.

F. Federal labor law—The National Labor Relations Act (NLRA) of 1935
   1. The NLRA, also called the Wagner Act, gives employees the right to form and join unions, to bargain collectively, and to strike for better benefits and working conditions.
   2. The NLRA determines the procedures employees use when selecting a union as the collective bargaining unit to negotiate with a healthcare employer or facility (elections).

LEARNING OBJECTIVES

(Student answers may vary.)

1. Define the glossary terms.

   Autonomy   independence.

   Bias   unfair dislike or preference for something.

   Bloodborne pathogens   disease-producing microorganisms transmitted by means of blood and body fluids containing blood.

   Creditor   person or institution to whom a debt is owed.

   Debtor   person who owes money to another person.

   Discrimination   unfair or unequal treatment.

   Employment-at-will   employment that takes place at either the will of the employer or the employee.

   Equal Employment Opportunity Commission (EEOC)   monitors Title VII of the Civil Rights Act.

   Ethnocentric   a belief that one's cultural background is better than any other.

   Garnishment   court order that requires an employer to pay a portion of an employee's paycheck directly to one of the employee's creditors until the debt is resolved.

   Just cause   legal reason.

   Parenteral   medication route other than the alimentary canal (oral and rectal), including subcutaneous, intravenous, and intramuscular routes.

Patient dumping   a slang term for transferring patients from one hospital to another if the patient is unable to pay for services.

Preempt   overrule.

Principle of double effect   when an action can have two effects: one that is morally good or desirable and one that is not.

Stereotyping   negative generalities concerning specific characteristics about a group are applied to an entire population.

Vesting   a point in time, such as after ten years of employment, when an employee has the right to receive benefits from a retirement plan.

Wrongful discharge   lawsuit in which the employee believes the employer does not have a just cause, or legal reason, for the firing.

2. Discuss cultural differences that might affect a patient's medical care and treatment.

   Various cultural issues might include practices relating to personal hygiene, concern for privacy, sexual preferences, communication and language skills.

3. Discuss the regulations concerning equal employment opportunity and employment discrimination.

   Title VII of the Civil Rights Act of 1964: This act prohibits discrimination in employment based on race, color, religion, sex, or national origin. It also prohibits discrimination in all aspects of patient care in institutions that receive federal financial assistance such as Medicare and Medicaid.

   Equal Employment Opportunity Act of 1972: This act authorizes the Equal Employment Opportunity Commission (EEOC) to sue employers in federal court on behalf of a class of people or an individual whose rights under Title VII have been violated.

   Pregnancy Discrimination Act of 1978: Under this law, employers must treat pregnant women as they would any other employee, providing they can still do the job.

   Civil Rights Act of 1991: All wrongful discharge suits fall under this law, which is an amendment to Title VII. This law permits the court to award both compensatory and punitive damages to mistreated employees.

   Age Discrimination in Employment Act of 1967: This law protects persons 40 years or older against employment discrimination because of age.

   Rehabilitation Act of 1973: This act prohibits discrimination based on disability in any institution that receives federal financial assistance.

   Americans with Disabilities Act (ADA) of 1990: This act prohibits employers who have more than fifteen employees from discriminating against disabled persons. Persons with AIDS are also covered under this act.

4. Describe the regulations affecting employee health and safety.

   Occupational Safety and Health Act (OSHA) of 1970: Under OSHA, an employer is required by law to provide a safe and healthy work environment. The employer must protect the worker against hazards.

   Clinical Laboratory and Improvement Act (CLIA) of 1992: The federal government now requires that all clinical laboratories that test human specimens must be controlled. These standards mandate written policies and procedures for a comprehensive quality assurance program to evaluate the overall quality of the laboratory testing process.

   Health Maintenance Organization (HMO) Act of 1973: This act requires any company with at least twenty-five employees to provide an HMO alternative to regular group insurance for their employees if an HMO is available in the area.

Consolidated Omnibus Budget Reconciliation Act (COBRA) of 1985: Under COBRA, a company with twenty or more employees must provide extended healthcare insurance to terminated employees for as long as eighteen months—usually, but not always, at the employee's expense.

Drug-Free Workplace Act of 1988: Under this act, employers contracting to provide goods or services to the federal government must certify that they maintain a drug-free workplace.

5. Discuss the regulations affecting employee compensation and benefits.

Social Security Act of 1935: This federal law covers all private and most public sector employees. It laid the groundwork for unemployment compensation in the United States. Social Security is paid by the employer and the employee in equal payroll taxes and Medicare participant premiums.

Fair Labor Standards Act (FLSA) of 1938: This is the main statute regulating benefits. It establishes the minimum wage, requires payment for overtime work, and sets the maximum hours employees covered by the act may work.

Equal Pay Act of 1963: This act makes it illegal for an employer to discriminate on the basis of sex in the payment to men and women who are performing the same job.

Unemployment Compensation: The unemployment compensation laws provide for temporary weekly payments for the unemployed worker.

Federal Insurance Contribution Act (FICA) of 1935: Under this law, employers are required to contribute to Social Security plans for their employees.

Workers' Compensation Act: This statute protects workers and their families from financial problems resulting from employment-related injury, disease, and even death.

Employee Retirement Income Security Act (ERISA) of 1974: ERISA regulates employee benefits and pension plans.

Family and Medical Leave Act (FMLA) of 1994: This law allows both parents to take a leave of absence of up to twelve weeks in any twelve-month period when a baby is born. The employees' jobs, or equivalent ones, must be available when both return to work. The FMLA also requires employers to provide unpaid leave for up to twelve weeks to employees who request leave for their own or a family member's medical or family-related situation, such as birth, death, or adoption.

6. Give examples of regulations affecting consumer protection and collection practices.

Emergency Medical Treatment and Active Labor Act (EMTALA): EMTALA Is a section of the Consolidated Omnibus Reconciliation Act (COBRA) dealing with patient dumping, a slang term for transferring emergency patients from one hospital to another if the patient Is unable to pay for services.

Fair Credit Reporting Act of 1971: This act establishes guidelines for use of an individual's credit information.

Equal Credit Opportunity Act of 1975: This act prohibits businesses, including hospitals and medical offices, from denying credit based on the applicant's race or sex—an unfair treatment referred to as discrimination.

Truth in Lending Act (Regulation Z) of 1969: This act requires a full written disclosure about interest rates or finance charges concerning the payment of any fee that will be collected in more than four installments.

Fair Debt Collection Practices Act of 1978: This act prohibits unfair collection practices by creditors.

Federal Wage Garnishment Law: This law restricts the amount of the employee's paycheck that can be used to pay off a debt (garnishment).

7. Define and explain the federal labor act discussed in this chapter.

The National Labor Relations Act of 1935: This act, also called the Wagner Act, gives employees the right to form and join unions, to bargain collectively, and to strike for better benefits and working conditions. The purpose of the law is to protect employees.

8. Describe accommodations that can be made in the workplace for persons with disabilities.
   - Parking spaces, marked for the handicapped, near an accessible doorway
   - Inclined ramps into buildings and over curbs in parking lots
   - Elevator floor numbers accessible to wheelchair-bound persons
   - Handicapped accessible bathrooms with handrails
   - Hallways with 36 inches of clearance for a wheelchair
   - Desks and counters that accommodate a wheelchair
   - Telephone adapters for the hearing impaired

9. List several questions that may be legally asked during an employment interview. List several questions that are illegal to ask during the interview.

   Legal questions

   a. Age—Only legal to ask if the person is between 17 and 70; if the person's age falls outside this boundary, then it is legal to ask only the birth date.
   b. Birthplace—Legal, but inadvisable to ask where the applicants, their parents, spouse, or children were born. It is illegal to ask about their national heritage or nationality or that of their spouse.
   c. Address—Legal to ask, along with how long applicant has lived there.
   d. Married—Legal, but inadvisable.
   e. Citizenship—Legal to ask, "Are you a citizen of the United States?"
   f. Organizations person belongs to—Legal to ask if applicant belongs to any organizations.
   g. Languages—Legal to ask what languages a person can speak and write, but can be discriminatory if used as a method to determine a person's national origin.
   h. Military experience—Legal to ask if person was a member of the armed forces and when how the was discharged. Cannot ask what type of discharge was received.
   i. If ever convicted of a crime—legal.

   Illegal questions

   a. Age—Cannot ask for the applicant's specific age if it falls between 17 and 70.
   b. National heritage or that of applicant's spouse.
   c. If applicant rents or owns home.
   d. If applicant has children.
   e. Height and weight.
   f. Race or color.
   g. Religion or creed.
   h. If applicant has ever been arrested.
   i. Any handicaps.
   j. Memberships in any specific organizations.
   k. What type of military discharge.

10. Discuss guidelines for good hiring practices.

   Responses will vary but could include:

   a. Develop clear policies and procedures on hiring, discipline, and termination of employees.
   b. Effectively screen backgrounds.
   c. State in writing that the employee handbook is not a contract.
   d. Use a two-tier interview screening process.
   e. Carefully assess the applicant's skill level.
   f. Develop an application form that provides accurate information about the applicant's qualifications.
   g. Provide a job description for every position.
   h. Develop a progressive disciplinary procedure and make this policy known to all employees and supervisors.
   i. Provide in-service training to supervisors on how to conduct job interviews and how to motivate and discipline employees.
   j. Become familiar with the legal and illegal employment interview questions.

11. Describe several religious practices that have an influence upon the practice of medicine.

[NOTE: These are generalities about religious beliefs in order to alert the student to be aware of how believers of other faiths approach medical care. It is by no means meant to provide definitive or judgmental statements about particular religions.]

   Members of the Christian Scientist religion and Jehovah Witnesses may refuse to receive blood transfusions for themselves and their children. Christian Scientists may wish to use a healer rather than a physician to attempt to heal a person with the use of prayer. Members of the Jewish faith often prefer that a rabbi perform a circumcision. The Jewish religion has a set of laws that govern circumcision, abortion, autopsy, and food practices. Members of the Church of the Latter-Day Saints, known as Mormons, believe in promoting health by avoiding alcohol and caffeine-based beverages. Muslims, members of the Islamic faith, fast during the month of Ramadan, forbid the drinking of alcohol, have certain clothing restrictions, have strict regulations log gender, and say prayers five times a day. Muslim women may have to have another member of their family present during certain procedures and examinations. Members of the Roman Catholic Church are opposed to abortion and stem cell research. Members of the Protestant religions generally support the individual person to make moral decisions about each person's own life.

THE CASE OF JANET K. AND EPILEPSY

Janet K. had suffered from epilepsy since she was an infant. Her condition was well controlled as she entered adulthood, and she was able to complete a nursing program in good health. She particularly enjoyed working as a scrub nurse in the operating room. Upon graduation she applied at the large university teaching hospital where she had performed her clinical work during her nursing program. The hospital knew of her epilepsy history and offered her a job in their medical records department. Janet petitioned to be able to work in surgery, but the hospital administrators felt that it was too dangerous for Janet and the surgical patients if she should have a seizure there.

   While working in medical records, Janet's seizures began to return. She would have a seizure at least every month, even though her medications had been changed. Janet noticed that some of her fellow medical technicians would stay away from her for fear of having to help her during a seizure. One afternoon a physician was dictating his case records in a cubicle next to Janet's when she had a seizure. He helped her and then went to the hospital administrator and told her that Janet should not be allowed to work in a hospital since it gave the hospital, with its image of healing, a bad reputation.

Janet was terminated at the age of 27 due to health issues. She died of a brain tumor five years later.

[NOTE: This is a good case to use for a general discussion since there are many "gray" areas relating to hiring practices in a healthcare setting, as well as individual health issues.]

Case Questions

1. Are there some medical or mental conditions that should prevent a person from working in a hospital or other medical setting? If so, what are they?

   Students should understand that, with few exceptions, everyone has the same right to employment. Women, especially those who are over 40, are protected by laws from discrimination in the workplace. Persons with disabilities, including AIDS, are also protected from discrimination in hiring by law. However, there are some areas in which patients have to be protected from injury or receiving a contagious disease such as AIDS.

2. What should have been done when Janet's co-workers shunned her?

   Their supervisor should have immediately put a stop to this discriminatory behavior.

3. Was the physician who helped Janet when she had a seizure correct in asking the hospital administrator to dismiss (fire) her?

   Janet's work, as far as we are able to determine from this case, was satisfactory. It was inappropriate for a physician to ask to have her fired to protect the hospital's image. Many workplaces, including hospitals, are hiring mentally challenged individuals who perform their work with perseverance and dedication.

4. Should Janet have been given the opportunity to work in surgery? Why or why not?

   There are several positions on a surgical unit that do not require the employee to provide hands-on care to the surgical patient, such as admitting personnel. In addition, the circulating nurse, a non-sterile nurse who assists the surgical team by getting needed materials, does not have direct contact with the patient. However, the fact is that this type of environment could be dangerous for Janet if she did have a seizure.

POINTS TO PONDER (FROM TEXTBOOK)

Teaching note: These questions are meant to promote critical thinking and classroom discussion. The student answers will vary.

1. Why did the federal government enact laws such as Title VII, the ADA, and COBRA?

2. How do you respond to an illegal interview question?

3. Isn't it important for an employer to know if a potential employee has a disability? Why or why not?

4. Should all healthcare employees be tested for HIV? Why or why not?

5. Should healthcare employees be unionized? Why or why not?

6. In your opinion, does the Family and Medical Leave Act of 1994 discriminate against working persons who do not have children or elderly parents?

7. Are you entitled to take off a couple of days to re-energize yourself if you do not use up all of your sick days during the year?

REVIEW QUESTIONS (FROM TEXTBOOK)
Discussion Questions

1. Identify the principal kinds of illegal discrimination that result in unequal employment opportunities.

   Discrimination based on race, color, religion, sex, or national origin.

2. What amendments to Title VII are discussed within this chapter?

   Title VII of the Civil Rights Act of 1964: This act prohibits discrimination in employment based on race, color, religion, sex, or national origin. It also prohibits discrimination in all aspects of patient care in institutions that receive federal financial assistance such as Medicare and Medicaid.

   Equal Employment Opportunity Act of 1972: This act authorizes the Equal Employment Opportunity Commission (EEOC) to sue employers in federal court on behalf of a class of people or an individual whose rights under Title VII have been violated.

   Pregnancy Discrimination Act of 1978: Under this law, employers must treat pregnant women as they would any other employee, providing they can still do the job.

   Civil Rights Act of 1991: All wrongful discharge suits fall under this law, which is an amendment to Title VII. This law permits the court to award both compensatory and punitive damages to mistreated employees.

   Age Discrimination in Employment Act of 1967: This law protects persons 40 years or older against employment discrimination because of age.

   Rehabilitation Act of 1973: This act prohibits discrimination based on disability in any institution that receives federal financial assistance.

   Americans with Disabilities Act (ADA) of 1990: This act prohibits employers who have more than fifteen employees from discriminating against disabled persons. Persons with AIDS are also covered under this act.

3. What are considered potential infectious materials under OSHA guidelines?
   a. body fluid contaminated with blood
   b. saliva in dental procedures
   c. amniotic fluid
   d. cerebrospinal fluid
   e. tissues, cells, or fluids known to be HIV-infected
   f. microbiological waste
   g. pathological waste (human tissue)
   h. any unidentified body fluid

4. What regulation assists terminated employees in obtaining extended health-care coverage?

   Consolidated Omnibus Budget Reconciliation Act (COBRA) of 1985.

5. What does the Fair Labor Standards Act of 1938 control?

   This is the main statute regulating benefits. It establishes the minimum wage, requires payment for overtime work, and sets the maximum hours employees covered by the act may work. The act covers all nonmanagement employees in profit and not-for-profit institutions.

6. What purpose does the Sherman Antitrust Act serve?

This act seeks to eliminate restraints of trade and to prevent the formation of monopolies.

7. Who is eligible to receive a leave of absence under the Family and Medical Leave Act of 1994?

This law allows both the mother and father to take a leave of absence of up to twelve weeks, in any twelve-month period, when a baby is born. The act also requires employers to provide unpaid leave for up to twelve weeks to employees who request leave for their own or a family member's medical or family-related situation, such as birth, death, or adoption.

8. What does ERISA control?

The Employee Retirement Income Security Act of 1974 regulates employee benefits and pension plans.

9. Discuss the National Labor Relations Act.

The National Labor Relations Act of 1935, also called the Wagner Act, gives employees the right to form and join unions, to bargain collectively, and to strike for better benefits and working conditions. The purpose of the law is to protect employees.

Matching

Column A	Column B
1. creditor	f. to whom a debt is owed
2. preempt	d. overrule
3. vesting	h. employee gains the rights to receive benefits
4. discrimination	g. unfair treatment
5. just cause	c. having a legal reason
6. employment-at-will	j. employment can be terminated
7. OSHA	b. Occupational Safety and Health Act
8. ADA	i. Americans with Disabilities Act of 1990
9. Title VII	a. Civil Rights Act of 1964
10. debtor	e. one who owes money to another

Multiple Choice

1. In most cases, federal laws
   a. are better than state laws
   b. are not followed as closely as state laws
   c. preempt state laws
   d. are used when state laws are not effective
   e. none of the above

   Answer: c

2. Title VII of the Civil Rights Act of 1964 prohibits discrimination based on
    a. color, race, and national origin
    b. religion
    c. sex
    d. income level and education
    e. a, b, and c only

    Answer: e

3. The following acts are covered as amendments under Title VII with the exception of the
    a. Pregnancy Discrimination Act of 1978
    b. Drug-Free Workplace Act of 1988
    c. Equal Employment Opportunity Act of 1972
    d. Civil Rights Act of 1991
    e. Age Discrimination in Employment Act of 1967

    Answer: b

4. The Occupational Safety and Health Act (OSHA) developed standards in 1991 stating that infectious materials include all of the following except
    a. any unidentified body fluid
    b. amniotic fluid
    c. saliva in dental procedures
    d. cerebrospinal fluid
    e. all of the above are included under OSHA

    Answer: e

5. The most important act covered under compensation and benefits regulations is said to be the
    a. Workers' Compensation Act
    b. Social Security Act of 1935
    c. Federal Insurance Contribution Act of 1935
    d. Fair Labor Standards Act
    e. Family and Medical Leave Act of 1994

    Answer: d

6. Regulation Z of the Consumer Protection Act is also referred to as
    a. Equal Credit Opportunity Act of 1975
    b. Fair Credit Reporting Act of 1971
    c. Truth in Lending Act of 1969
    d. Employee Retirement Income Security Act of 1974
    e. Workers' Compensation Act

    Answer: c

7. When making a claim for payment after a patient has died, the claim (or bill) must be
    a. sent in the name of the deceased person to his or her last known address
    b. sent to the administrator of the estate of the deceased person
    c. sent to a collection agency with specific instructions to collect payment from the next of kin
    d. waived
    e. none of the above

    Answer: b

8. When using a collection agency to collect outstanding debts (unpaid bills) from a patient,
   a. allow the collection agency to take a tough, aggressive attitude with patients who owe money
   b. stay closely involved in the process and make frequent follow-up phone calls to the delinquent patient
   c. it is wise to first threaten the patient that you will send the unpaid account to a collection agency and then give the patient a second chance
   d. review the delinquent account with the physician or office manager before turning over the account to the agency
   e. all of the above

   Answer: d

9. ERISA
   a. controls employee benefit plans
   b. controls employee pension plans
   c. determines eligibility
   d. determines vesting
   e. all of the above

   Answer: e

10. Under the Workers' Compensation Act
    a. employers must pay into a fund to help cover costs when an employee is hurt
    b. every state, without exception, has enacted mandatory laws regarding schedules of payment for injured workers
    c. a worker who accepts a workers' compensation payment may still sue the employer for the injury
    d. employees may not sue nonemployees
    e. there is a guarantee of receiving a full salary while on workers' compensation

    Answer: a

Fill in the Blanks

1. The Equal Employment Opportunity Commission monitors Title VII of the Civil Rights Act.
2. A lawsuit in which an employee believes that an employer does not have a legal reason for firing him or her is called wrongful discharge.
3. Stereotyping is making negative generalities concerning specific characteristics about a group and then applying these generalities to an entire population.
4. A legal reason for terminating an employee is considered to be just cause.
5. A patient's sense of independence is called autonomy.
6. An unfair dislike or preference for someone is called having a bias against that person.
7. Employment-at-will occurs when employment takes place at the will of the employer or employee.
8. Title VII of the Civil Rights Act of 1964 prohibits discrimination, or unfair treatment of employees.
9. The Americans with Disabilities Act protects persons with AIDS.
10. A mandatory pregnancy leave violates Title VII of the Civil Rights Act.

PUT IT INTO PRACTICE

Write a letter of application for a position you may wish to seek upon graduation from your program of study. Submit this letter, along with an updated resume, to your instructor for comments. Using Table 8-2 as a guide, review the personal information you provided in your cover letter and resume. Have you given any information that is not required? Are there any gaps in your employment record? If so, why? How will you answer any of the questions in Table 8-2 if you are asked them during an interview?

WEB HUNT

1. Searching the website of the Occupational Safety and Health Act (*www.osha.org*), find an article that relates to OSHA or workers' compensation. Summarize the article.
2. Search the website *www.findlaw.com*. Under the title of "U.S. State Laws, Cases, Codes, Statutes, and Regulations," find information on unemployment compensation in your state.

CASE STUDY

Nancy Moore, a registered nurse, is assisting Dr. Brown while he performs a minor surgical procedure. Dr. Brown is known to have a quick temper, and he becomes very angry if a surgical procedure is delayed for any reason. As Nancy is handing a needle with suture thread to Dr. Brown, she feels a slight prick in her sterile gloves. She tells Dr. Brown about this and explains that she will have to be excused from the procedure for a few minutes while she changes gloves. He becomes angry and tells her to "forget about it and help me finish."

Case Questions

1. Will it be harmful to anyone if Nancy wears the gloves during the rest of the procedure, since it was just a slight prick and the patient's wound does not appear to be infected?

   Nancy has no way of knowing if either she or the patient is harboring an infection. The prick in Nancy's gloves leaves open an avenue for infection to either Nancy or the patient.

2. Who is at fault if the patient does develop an infection?

   Both Dr. Brown, who is the employing physician, and Nancy are at fault.

3. What recourse does Nancy have if she develops a bloodborne pathogen infection, such as hepatitis, from the small hole in her gloves?

   She can file a complaint against her employer under OSHA.

4. Is this an ethical or a legal issue, or both?

   It is both an ethical and a legal issue. The physician was unethical in his refusal to allow Nancy to change gloves. Nancy is at fault, since she did not insist on making the glove change. The patient's health and safety were jeopardized. OSHA is a federal regulation, and since Dr. Brown refused to allow Nancy to change her gloves, he is at fault if she develops an infection.

5. Are there any federal regulations that might help Nancy in the event of an injury or infection?

   Occupational Safety and Health Act (OSHA).

SUPPLEMENTAL QUESTIONS

Chapter Review

Cover the terms in the left-hand column with a piece of paper. Read the statement and fill in the blank with the answer before uncovering the correct response.

Employment-at-will	_____ _____ _____ means that employment takes place at the will of either the employer or the employee.
terminated at will	Thus, the employment may be _____ _____ _____ at any time for no reason.
Title VII	_____ _____ of the Civil Rights Act of 1964 prohibits discrimination in employment based on race,
gender/national public	color, religion, _____, or _____ origin. However, this act does not apply to _____ officials and their staffs.
Pregnancy medical	The _____ Discrimination Act of 1978 states that a woman cannot be refused a job because she has had an abortion. Also, the employer's _____ plan must cover the pregnancy in the same way it would cover other medical conditions.
Civil Rights compensatory/ punitive compensatory	In 1991, Congress amended Title VII, passing the _____ _____ Act of 1991. This law permits the court to award _____ and _____ damages. Prior to this amendment, only _____ damages were awarded.
OSHA occupational reasonable parenteral pathogens	In 1991, _____ developed rules to protect health-care workers from bloodborne diseases. These standards apply to any employee who has _____ exposure. This exposure is defined as a _____ anticipation that the employee's duties will result in skin, mucous membrane, eye, or _____ contact with bloodborne _____ or other potential infectious material.
Fair Equal Pay	In 1963, Congress amended the _____ Labor Standards Act, passing the _____ _____ Act. This act makes it illegal for an employer to discriminate on the basis of sex in the wages of men and women.
collection agencies harassment	Professional _____ _____ are available when all other attempts to collect bills fail. Once the account has been turned over, no further collection attempts can be made by the physician, or else this could be considered _____.
Antitrust	_____ laws seek to preserve the competitive market by prohibiting anticompetitive activities.

Multiple Choice

Select the one best response to the following questions.

1. Physician and staff relationships are regulated by
   a. state law
   b. local law
   c. federal law
   d. federal labor acts
   e. all of the above

   Answer: e

2. The Age Discrimination in Employment Act of 1967
   a. protects persons 40 or older from age discrimination
   b. establishes a mandatory retirement age of 65
   c. protects persons between the ages of 16 and 20 from age discrimination
   d. established Social Security benefits
   e. a and c

   Answer: a

3. A company with twenty or more employees must provide extended healthcare insurance to terminated employees for as long as eighteen months under
   a. the Health Maintenance Organization Act of 1973
   b. FLSA
   c. COBRA
   d. the Fair Labor Standards Act of 1938
   e. OSHA

   Answer: c

4. The Drug-Free Workplace Act of 1988 requires
   a. the employer to inform the employee of the intent to maintain a drug-free workplace
   b. employees contracting to the federal government to certify that they maintain a drug-free workplace
   c. the employee be informed of penalties for violation of the drug policy
   d. a and c only
   e. a, b, and c

   Answer: e

5. The Civil Rights Act of 1991 permits the court to award
   a. compensatory damages
   b. regulatory agencies the power to enforce civil rights laws
   c. punitive damages
   d. a and c only
   e. a, b, and c

   Answer: d

6. This act establishes guidelines for the use of an individual's credit information:
   a. Truth in Lending Act of 1969
   b. Fair Credit Reporting Act of 1971
   c. Fair Debt Collection Practices Act
   d. Fair Labor Standards Act
   e. Equal Credit Opportunity Act of 1975

   Answer: b

7. The National Labor Relations Act includes each of the following except
   a. employers may not threaten employees who become active in union activity
   b. employers cannot refuse to bargain in good faith
   c. employers cannot attempt to control union activity
   d. employers cannot discriminate because of union activity
   e. all of the above are included in this act

   Answer: e

8. In an interview, it is illegal, in all circumstances, to ask a question relating to
   a. place of birth
   b. age
   c. race or color
   d. marital status
   e. the person's address

   Answer: c

9. Wrongful discharge suits fall under the
   a. Equal Employment Opportunity Act of 1972
   b. Americans with Disabilities Act of 1990
   c. Civil Rights Act of 1991
   d. Rehabilitation Act of 1973
   e. Equal Pay Act of 1963

   Answer: c

10. OSHA
    a. protects healthcare workers from bloodborne disease
    b. regulations preempt all other state and local regulations
    c. requires employers to provide a safe and healthy work environment
    d. requires employers to provide detailed instructions that identify chemicals and the appropriate safety precautions
    e. all of the above

    Answer: e

True/False Questions

1. A debtor is a person to whom a debt is owed. (false)

2. Vesting within a company or organization usually occurs after ten years of employment. (true)

3. Bloodborne pathogens are considered to be any disease-producing microorganisms. (false)

4. State laws always preempt federal laws. (false)

5. Employment-at-will is a guarantee that if a person is doing a good job, he or she will remain employed. (false)

6. Title VII restrictions, in general, only apply to employers who have more than ten employees. (true)

7. Women are protected from discrimination by both Title VII and the Age Discrimination Act of 1967. (true)

8. Persons with AIDS are not covered under the Americans with Disabilities Act. (false)

9. OSHA guidelines are available through the U.S. Department of Labor. (true)

10. Hospitals are able to require drug testing as a condition of employment. (true)

Short Answer Questions

1. What are compensatory damages?

   Compensatory damages are amounts of money awarded by the court to make up for loss of income or emotional pain and suffering.

2. Title VII of the Civil Rights Act of 1964 prohibits discrimination in employment based on what criterion?
   a. race
   b. color
   c. religion
   d. sex
   e. national origin

3. What type(s) of damages could the court award after the Civil Rights Act of 1991?
   a. compensatory damages
   b. punitive damages

4. The workers' compensation statutes protect workers and their families from financial problems resulting from what?
   a. injury
   b. disease
   c. death as a result of the worker's employment

5. Who is an employer under Title VII?

   An employer under Title VII is a person who employs the services of another and provides a payment for those services.

6. What is an employer required by law to do under OSHA?
   a. provide a safe and healthy work environment
   b. protect the worker against hazards

7. What is OSHA's definition of *occupational exposure* to bloodborne pathogens?

   Occupational exposure is defined as a reasonable anticipation that the employee's duties will result in skin, mucous membrane, eye, or parenteral contact with bloodborne pathogens (disease-producing microorganisms) or other potentially infectious material.

8. To what groups of people do OSHA's Occupational Exposure to Bloodborne Pathogens Standards apply?

   To any employee who has occupational exposure to bloodborne pathogens or other potentially infectious materials. Such employees include physicians, nurses, medical assistants, laboratory workers, and housekeeping personnel.

TEACHING STRATEGIES

1. Invite a medical office manager into the classroom to describe how to hire, fire, and discipline employees.
2. Invite a lawyer into the class to discuss the potential legal pitfalls involved with interviewing potential employees, checking references, and hiring a new employee.
3. Videotape two students doing a mock interview and then have the class offer suggestions.
4. Divide the students into groups of three and have them draft an OSHA Exposure Plan for a medical office. The plan should include a description or list of the materials that are considered to be infectious. The students should include OSHA

guidelines, which can be obtained from the U.S. Department of Labor, Washington, DC, or from the website listed under Web Hunt at the end of Chapter 8 in the textbook.

5. Ask each student to research on the Internet one of the major categories of federal laws regulating the employer–employee relationships for a report to the class.

6. Have the students prepare flash cards for all the key terms (glossary).

9

The Medical Record

CHAPTER SYNOPSIS

The medical record is a legal document that contains all the written documentation pertaining to the patient. Various laws cover the reporting, disclosure, and confidentiality of medical records. This chapter contains information relating to the contents of the medical record and the types of documentation. Also included are ownership, retention, storage, reporting, and disclosure requirements pertaining to medical records.

Chapter Lecture Outline	Instructor's Notes

I. The Medical Record
  A. Each patient's medical record contains essentially the same categories of material.
  B. A patient's medical record should contain information unique to that patient. For example, not every patient has a consultation report from another physician or a surgical report.
  C. The format for the medical record varies, reflecting the physician's specialty.
II. Purpose of the Medical Record
  A. Medical records provide a medical picture and record of the patient from birth to death.
  B. The record is an important document for the continuous management of a patient's healthcare.
  C. Medical records provide data and statistics on health matters such as births, deaths, and communicable diseases.
  D. A physician can track the ongoing patterns of the patient's health through the medical record.
  E. Since the record documents a patient's medical condition and treatment, either the patient or the physician in a malpractice suit can use this information.
  F. The medical record is a legal document.
III. Contents of the Medical Record—Under the requirements of the Joint Commission on Accreditation of Healthcare Organizations (JCAHO), the medical record must include the following components:
  A. Admitting diagnosis.
  B. Evidence of a physician examination, including a health history, not more than seven days before admission or forty-eight hours after admission to a hospital.	

Chapter Lecture Outline	Instructor's Notes

C. Documentation of any complications such as hospital-acquired infections or unfavorable medication reactions.

D. Signed consent forms for all treatments and procedures.

E. Consultation reports from any other physician brought in on the case.

F. All physicians' notes, nurses' notes, treatment reports, medication records, radiology and laboratory reports, and any other information used to monitor the patient.

G. Discharge summary, with follow-up care noted.

IV. Guidelines for Charting

    A. General instructions that relate to all medical charting include:

        1. Double-check to make sure you have the correct patient medical record.

        2. Use dark ink, preferably black, and write legibly. Printing is preferred if your handwriting is difficult to read. The record must be legible.

        3. The patient's name should appear on each page of the medical record.

        4. Every entry must be dated and signed or initialed by the person writing the entry.

        5. Entries should be brief, but complete.

        6. Used only accepted medical abbreviations known by the general staff, and correctly spell all medical terms.

        7. Never erase or in any way remove information from a medical record.

        8. Document all telephone calls and other correspondence relating to the patient.

        9. Document any action(s) taken as a result of telephone conversations.

      10. Document all missed appointments.

      11. Charting notations should not be derogatory or offensive.

    B. Corrections and alterations

        1. Falsification of medical records is grounds for criminal indictment.

        2. Do not erase or use correction fluid.

        3. To make corrections, draw one line through the error, write the correction above the error, date the change, and then initial it.

    C. Timeliness of documentation

        1. Federal reimbursement guidelines mandate that all medical records be completed within thirty days of the patient's discharge from hospital.

        2. Late entries in the medical chart mean that, even for a brief period of time, the medical record is incomplete.

    D. Completeness of entries

        1. The medical record may be the most important document in a malpractice suit because it documents the type and amount of patient care that was given.

        2. A physician's inability to provide the patient's medical record may create an implication? of guilt.

    E. Credibility of medical record

Chapter Lecture Outline	**Instructor's Notes**

V. Confidentiality—Medical records should not be released to a third party without the patient's written consent.
VI. Ownership—State statutes may establish who owns the medical record. In most states, the general rule is that the physician or owners of a healthcare facility own the medical record.
  A. Release of information
    1. An original copy of a medical record should never be sent to a patient.
    2. Records should not be released to the patient without the physician's permission.
  B. Privacy Act of 1974—This law provides private citizens some control over information that the federal government collects about them by limiting the use of information for unnecessary purposes.
  C. State open-record laws—Some states have freedom of information laws (open-record laws) that grant public access to records maintained by state agencies.
  D. Alcohol and drug abuse patient records—The Public Health Services Act protects patients who are receiving treatment for drug or alcohol abuse.
VII. Retention and Storage of Medical Records
  A. Each state varies on the length of time that medical records and documents must be kept.
  B. Medical records may be destroyed after a period of time specified by law.
  C. Storage
    1. Records of current patients are usually kept within the physician's office for easy access.
    2. Older records are often kept in a storage space rented by the physician.
    3. Some physicians hire a service to convert their records to other physical or digital forms of storage.
  D. Computerized medical records
  E. Loss of medical record—Juries tend to be unsympathetic in a court case that revolves around a lost medical document or record.
VIII. Reporting and Disclosure Requirements
IX. Use of the Medical Record in Court
  A. Improper disclosure
  B. *Subpoena duces tecum*	

LEARNING OBJECTIVES

(Student answers may vary.)

1. Define the glossary terms.

Credible   believable or worthy of belief.

Credibility gap   an apparent disparity between what is said or written and the actual facts.

Disclosed   made known

Doctrine of professional discretion   a physician may determine, based on his or her best judgment, if a patient with mental or emotional problems should view the medical record.

Joint Commission on Accreditation of Healthcare Organizations (JCAHO) agency that oversees hospital accreditation standards.

Microfiche   miniaturized photographs of records.

Open-record laws   state freedom-of-information laws that grant public access to records maintained by state agencies.

Problem-oriented medical record (POMR)   method of documentation that focuses on the patient's problems and not just on the diagnosis.

SOAP   medical charting that includes subjective (S), objective (O), assessment (A), and a plan (P) of treatment for the patient.

Subpoenaed   ordered by the court.

2. List five purposes of the medical record.

   a. Provides a medical picture and record from birth to death.
   b. Is an important document for the continual management of a patient's healthcare.
   c. Provides data on births, deaths, and communicable diseases.
   d. Documents a patient's medical condition and treatment (information that may be used in a malpractice suit).
   e. Is a legal document.

3. List seven requirements for maintaining medical records as recommended by the Joint Commission on Accreditation of Healthcare Organizations (JCAHO).

   The JCAHO recommends that, at a minimum, the medical record should include:

   a. Admitting diagnosis.
   b. Evidence of a physician examination, including a health history, not more than seven days before admission or forty-eight hours after admission to a hospital.
   c. Documentation of any complications such as hospital-acquired infections or unfavorable medication reactions.
   d. Signed consent forms for all treatments and procedures.
   e. Consultation reports from any other physicians brought in on the case.
   f. All physicians' notes, nurses' notes, treatment reports, medication reports, radiology and laboratory reports, and any other information used to monitor the patient.
   g. Discharge summary, with follow-up care noted.

4. Discuss eleven guidelines for effective charting.

   a. Double-check to make sure you have the correct medical record.
   b. Use dark ink and write legibly.
   c. Place the patient's name on each page of the medical record.
   d. Every entry must be dated and signed or initialed by the person writing the entry.
   e. Entries should be brief but complete.
   f. Use only accepted medical abbreviations.
   g. Never erase or in any way remove information from the medical chart.
   h. Document all telephone calls relating to the patient.
   i. Document any action(s) taken as a result of a telephone conversation.
   j. Document all missed appointments.
   k. Do not chart any derogatory or defensive notations.

5. Discuss what is meant by timeliness of charting and why it is important in a legal context.

   All entries in the medical record should be made as soon as possible after they occur. This will prevent errors due to a lapse of memory. In addition, federal reimbursement guidelines mandate that all medical records should be completed within thirty days following the patient's discharge from a hospital.

6. Define the Privacy Act of 1974.

   This act provides private citizens some control over information that the federal government collects about them by limiting the use of information for unnecessary purposes. Under this law, an agency may maintain only the information that is relevant to its authorized purpose.

7. Describe twelve ways to protect patient confidentiality that relate to the use of fax, copiers, email, and computers.

   a. Make sure the intended receiver is there before sending confidential records via fax.
   b. Shred confidential fax papers that are no longer needed.
   c. Use a fax cover sheet that states "confidential."
   d. Send patient information via fax only when absolutely necessary.
   e. Only fax the specific document requested, not the entire medical record.
   f. Do not leave confidential material unattended on a fax machine
   g. Locate the fax machine in a restricted access area.
   h. Never leave medical records unattended on a copy machine where others may read them.
   i. Shred all discarded copies.
   j. Be diligent about removing all papers caught in a paper jam.
   k. Avoid using email to send confidential information.
   l. Do not allow other patients or unauthorized staff members to view a computer screen that displays confidential patient information.

8. Discuss the time periods for retaining adults' and minors' medical records, fetal heart monitor records, and records of birth, death, and surgical procedures.

   Each state varies on the length of time that medical records and documents must be kept. Legally, all medical records should be stored for seven years from the time of the last entry. Some of the time periods for retaining medical records as adopted by the American Health Information Management Association are as follows:

   a. Adult patient records—ten years after the most recent encounter.
   b. Minor's health records—age of maturity plus statute of limitations.
   c. Fetal heart monitor records—ten years after infant reaches maturity.
   d. Medicare and Medicaid records—five years.
   e. Register of birth—permanently.
   f. Register of death—permanently.
   g. Immunizations records—permanently.
   h. Chemotherapy—permanently.
   i. Surgical procedures—permanently.

9. Explain thirteen guidelines to follow when *subpoena duces tecum* is in effect.

   a. Notify the physician that a subpoena has been received.
   b. Notify the patient that his or her record has been subpoenaed.
   c. Notify the physician's attorney that a subpoena has been received.
   d. Verify that all the information on the subpoena is correct.

e. Make sure that the requesting attorney's name and phone number as well as the court docket number are listed on the subpoena.
f. Review the records to make sure that all the records requested are available.
g. Photocopy the original record and number all the pages.
h. Turn over only the specific materials that have been requested.
i. After the medical record materials relating to the subpoena have been compiled, lock the file in a secure place.
j. Turn the records directly over to the judge on the due date.
k. The healthcare professional who takes the records to court should be prepared to be sworn in to make the records admissible as evidence.
l. Check with the court to make sure that the trial date is the same as the date listed on the subpoena.

THE CASE OF ANESHA AND THE LOST MEDICAL RECORD

Anesha's 15-year-old daughter, Robin, is experiencing abdominal pain when exercising during her gym class. After reviewing the results of several tests, Robin's pediatrician still cannot determine the cause of Robin's abdominal pain. He asks Anesha if she had any obstetrical problems when she was pregnant with Robin. Anesha had just read a report in a national newspaper discussing the use of a hormonal treatment to control bleeding that was used on expectant mothers about the time that Anesha was pregnant with Robin. The report stated that female children could develop serious uterine problems, including cancer, during their adolescence if their mothers were given a particular hormone that was in use fifteen to twenty years ago during their pregnancy. The report went on to state that male children were unaffected. Anesha recalled that her obstetrician, Dr. C., had given her that particular hormone medication to control bleeding during her pregnancy and also when she was expecting Robin's brother, Sam. Anesha wrote Dr. C. to request her medical record and ask if the doctor had prescribed the hormone treatment during her pregnancy. She received a letter stating that Dr. C. could not recall what he prescribed fifteen or sixteen years previously. The letter also stated that all his records were destroyed in a fire five years ago.

Case Questions

1. What should Anesha tell Robin's pediatrician?

   She should give the pediatrician a copy of the Dr. C.'s letter. If he has concerns about Robin's condition, then he can contact Dr. C. personally. Physicians often communicate more information with other physicians than they might with a patient.

2. What does Robin need to know about her potential for a serious uterine diagnosis?

   Robin should be told by her mother about the possibility that she was given this potentially damaging hormonal treatment during her pregnancy with Robin. Robin can then pass this information on to her physician as she grows older.

3. How could this situation have been prevented?

   Most medical records are now placed on microfiche with a back-up copy kept at another location. In addition, the microfiche can be stored in fireproof containers to make it even more secure. When paper files are stored in cardboard boxes in overcrowded, overheated storage areas, there is a potential for fire or water damage.

Note: The main role of the healthcare worker in the above case is to make sure that medical records are safely preserved. If there is a concern for the storage of these records, then this should be discussed with the physician/owner. The counseling of Anesha and her daughter can only be done by the physician.

POINTS TO PONDER (FROM TEXTBOOK)

Teaching note: These questions are meant to promote critical thinking and classroom discussion. The student responses will vary.

1. How do you respond when a patient says, "Please give me my medical record, since I own it"?

2. Do you agree with the statement, "If it's not documented, it wasn't done"? Why or why not?

3. In order to protect your physician/employer, should you "hide" to avoid receiving a *subpoena duces tecum?* Why or why not?

4. As a healthcare professional, are you able to read the medical record of a person you know? Why or why not?

5. Would it be helpful to other healthcare professionals who will be using the same patient's medical record to document that patient's poor attitude by including a statement such as "bad attitude"? Why or why not?

6. Can you be liable if you or your staff lose a patient's medical record?

7. A patient requests her physician's office to change her diagnosis in her medical record from R/O (rule out) bladder infection to "bladder infection," since her insurance will not pay for a R/O diagnosis. Should the record be charged?

REVIEW QUESTIONS (FROM TEXTBOOK)
Discussion Questions

1. What is the significance of the medical record for the physician? For the healthcare professional? For the patient?

   Responses will vary but should include the following:
   a. Provides a medical picture and record of the patient from birth to death.
   b. Is an important document for the continual management of a patient's healthcare.
   c. Provides data and statistics on health matters such as births, deaths, and communicable diseases.
   d. Ongoing patterns of the patient's health can be tracked.
   e. May be used in a malpractice suit by the physician or patient.
   f. Is a legal document.

2. Describe the steps to follow when preparing a *subpoena duces tecum.*
   a. Notify the physician that a subpoena has been received.
   b. Notify the patient that his or her record has been subpoenaed.
   c. Notify the physician's attorney that a subpoena has been received.
   d. Verify that all the information on the subpoena is correct.
   e. Make sure that the requesting attorney's name and phone number as well as the court docket number are listed on the subpoena.
   f. Review the records to make sure they are complete and only turn over the records that have been requested.

g. Photocopy the original record and number all the pages.

h. Turn over only the specific materials that have been requested.

i. After the medical record materials relating to the subpoena have been completed, lock the file in a secure place.

j. Turn the records directly over to the judge on the due date.

k. The healthcare professional who takes the records to court should be prepared to be sworn in to make the records admissible as evidence.

3. What laws affect patient privacy issues?

The Privacy Act of 1974 and state open-record laws.

4. Who owns the medical chart?

In most states, the general rule is that the physician owns the medical records but patients have the legal right of "privileged communication" and access to their records.

Matching

Column A

1. subpoenaed
2. POMR
3. disclosed
4. chronological order
5. falsification of records
6. *subpoena duces tecum*
7. SOAP
8. timeliness
9. Privacy Act of 1974
10. JCAHO

Column B

d. when something has been requested by the court

g. problem-oriented medical record

a. made known

e. in the order of occurrence

h. grounds for criminal indictment

j. written order to bring materials to court

c. subjective, objective, assessment, plan

i. no late entries on medical chart

b. provides control over release of information

f. Joint Commission on Accreditation of Healthcare Organizations

Multiple Choice

1. Medicare and Medicaid records should be retained for
   a. one year.
   b. five years.
   c. ten years.
   d. for the lifetime of the patient.
   e. for an ingdefinite period of time.

   Answer: b

2. The contents of the medical record include all of the following except
   a. past medical problems.
   b. informed consent documentation.
   c. patient's income level.
   d. family medical history.
   e. a and b only.

   Answer: c

3. Medical record entries should be made
    a. within sixty days of the patient's discharge.
    b. at the physician's discretion.
    c. after the patient gives consent.
    d. as soon as possible.
    e. ten days after the procedure.

    Answer: d

4. The patient
    a. has the legal right of "privileged communication."
    b. owns the medical record.
    c. cannot have any portion of the medical record.
    d. a and c.
    e. a, b, and c.

    Answer: a

5. When correcting a medical record, one should
    a. use a professional brand of error correction fluid to make the correction.
    b. erase the error and make the correction.
    c. draw a line through the error, write the correction above the error, and initial the change.
    d. never make any corrections on the medical record.
    e. none of the above.

    Answer: c

6. The medical record is legally owned by the
    a. patient.
    b. physician.
    c. state.
    d. lawyer.
    e. no one.

    Answer: b

7. Medical records
    a. provide a record from birth to death.
    b. provide statistics on health matters.
    c. are legal documents.
    d. a and c only.
    e. a, b, and c.

    Answer: e

8. All of the following are guidelines to use when sending medical records by fax except
    a. make sure there is a receiver waiting for the fax.
    b. use a cover sheet marked "confidential."
    c. send the entire medical record via fax.
    d. do not place the original fax in a trash container.
    e. all of the above are correct.

    Answer: c

9. An exception to the open-records laws in some states is/are
    a. psychiatric history.
    b. confidential medical record information such as HIV test results.
    c. safety and criminal records of persons involved in the education of children.
    d. all of the above.
    e. none of the above.

    Answer: c

10. The records of all adult patients should be kept a minimum of
    a. two years.
    b. five years.
    c. ten years.
    d. twenty years.
    e. permanently.

    Answer: c

Fill in the Blanks

1. A type of medical documentation that focuses on the patient's problems, and not just on the diagnosis, is called the <u>problem-oriented medical</u> record.
2. A difference between what is written and the actual fact is called a <u>credibility</u> gap.
3. Saving medical documents in a miniaturized format onto film is called <u>microfiche.</u>
4. The doctrine of <u>professional discretion</u> occurs when a physician determines, based on his or her best judgment, that a patient with mental or emotional problems is capable of viewing his or her medical record.
5. To make a situation known to others is to <u>disclose</u> it.
6. A court order to supply certain documents is called a <u>*subpoena duces tecum.*</u>
7. Children's immunization records should be retained <u>permanently</u>.
8. The <u>physician</u> owns the medical record.
9. Some states have freedom of information laws that are called <u>open-record</u> laws, which grant public access to records maintained by state agencies.
10. Medical records should be completed within <u>30</u> days following the patient's discharge.

PUT IT INTO PRACTICE

Request a copy of your medical record from your primary care physician (PCP). Examine the contents to determine how well they document your medical history.

WEB HUNT

1. Using the website of the American Health Information Management Association (www.ahima.org), provide a description of the organization. Go into the Patient Resource Center of this site and summarize the statement concerning who owns the medical record.
2. Using *www.findlaw.com,* look up your state statute regarding the statute of limitations for medical records in your state.

CASE STUDY

Mary Smith has been a patient of Dr. Williams from 1985 to the present time. During that time, she has had three children and been treated for a variety of conditions, including depression in 1986 and herpes in 1990. Mary and her husband, George, have filed for divorce. George wants custody of the children and is claiming that Mary has a medical condition that makes her an unfit mother. An attorney, acting on George's behalf in the divorce proceedings, has obtained a subpoena for Mary's medical records for the years 1995 to the present. Dr. Williams's assistant, who is a medical records technician, copies Mary's entire medical record from 1985 to the present and sends it to the attorney.

Case Questions

1. What negative effects for Mary might this error cause?

   Once the attorney for the husband has all of Mary's medical records, he can then use them to give a negative impression of Mary.

2. Is there a violation of confidentiality? Why or why not?

   This is a violation of confidentiality, since Mary has not given permission to copy and send records that were not subpoenaed.

3. Do you believe that this is a common or uncommon error?

   This is a very common error, especially in medical offices.

4. Was it appropriate for the assistant to make a copy of any part of Mary's medical record?

   Yes, if her physician/employer instructed her to do so. The physician must comply when a *subpoena duces tecum* is served. However, as a courtesy, the patient should be notified that the records have been subpoenaed.

SUPPLEMENTAL QUESTIONS

Chapter Review

Cover the terms in the left-hand column with a piece of paper. Read the statement and fill in the blank with the answer before uncovering the correct response.

problem-oriented	The _____ _____ medical record method of medical record documentation is focused on a patient's problems.
one dating initialing/Falsification	A correction to a medical record should be made by drawing _____ line through the error, writing the correction above the error, _____ the change, and then _____ it. _____ of medical records is grounds for criminal indictment.
accurate/timely	Medical records must be _____ and _____.
Accreditation Organizations	The Joint Commission on _____ of Healthcare _____, which oversees hospital accreditation standards, also has issued guidelines for timeliness in charting.
written consent	Medical records should not be released to third parties without the patient's _____ _____.
ten permanently two	Legally, all medical records should be stored for _____ years from the time of the last entry. However, most physicians store medical records _____ because malpractice suits can still be filed within _____ years from the date of the knowledge of the malpractice.

subpoena duces tecum	A _____ _____ _____ is a written order
testimony	requiring a person to appear in court, give _____,
subpoena	and bring the records described. A _____ is often
	served by a local sheriff or federal marshal. They may be
certified mail	served either via _____ _____ or in person,
	depending on the state requirement.

Multiple Choice

Select the one best response to the following questions.

1. Medical records
   a. provide a record from birth to death
   b. provide statistics on health matters
   c. are legal documents
   d. document the continual management of the patient's healthcare
   e. all of the above

   Answer: e

2. A patient's record can be released if
   a. a family member requests the record
   b. an insurance company requests an electronic transfer of the record
   c. the patient gives written permission
   d. a and b only
   e. all of the above

   Answer: c

3. A problem-oriented medical record (POMR)
   a. is a chronological approach to documentation
   b. focuses on the patient's medical problems
   c. focuses on the patient's diagnosis
   d. focuses on the patient's attitude
   e. all of the above

   Answer: b

4. Patients who receive treatment for drug and alcohol abuse
   a. can expect to have their medical records released when requested
   b. are protected by the Public Health Services Act
   c. may have their medical records released in the event of an emergency
   d. b and c
   e. a, b, and c

   Answer: d

5. If a medical record has been subpoenaed, all of the following guidelines should be followed except
   a. notify the patient that the record has been subpoenaed
   b. notify the physician
   c. notify the physician's attorney
   d. verify that all the information in the subpoena is correct
   e. all of the above are correct

   Answer: e

6. The patient
   a. has the legal right of "privileged communication."
   b. owns the medical records

    c. may have to pay a fee for a copy of his or her medical records

    d. a and c

    e. a, b, and c

Answer: d

7. The Privacy Act of 1974

    a. applies to the federal government

    b. provides private citizens some control over their information

    c. applies to government contractors

    d. does not protect the confidentiality of veterans' hospital records

    e. all of the above

Answer: e

8. Medical record entries should be made

    a. as soon as possible

    b. within sixty days of the patient's discharge

    c. at the physician's discretion

    d. after the patient gives consent

    e. ten days after the procedure

Answer: a

9. A healthcare provider who releases medical records without proper patient authorization may face

    a. civil liability

    b. criminal liability

    c. a lawsuit to recover damages

    d. a and b only

    e. a, b, and c

Answer: e

10. The inference of guilt in a California case resulted when the

    a. patient claimed the physician did not own the medical chart

    b. physician was unable to provide the patient's medical record

    c. POMR method of documentation was not used

    d. b and c

    e. none of the above

Answer: b

True/False Questions

1. Falsification of medical records is grounds for a criminal indictment. (false)

2. The JCAHO provides guidelines for timeliness in charting. (false)

3. The chronological medical record requires the use of POMR charting. (false)

4. The medical record documents the care and treatment the patient receives but does not document any treatment that he or she refuses to receive. (false)

5. A patient's medical record is confidential and cannot be used in a malpractice suit. (false)

6. A patient's medical record is standardized and therefore cannot be unique to each patient. (false)

7. The doctrine of professional discretion means that a physician may determine if a patient is mentally fit to view his or her own medical record. (false)

8. A patient has to sign a release for all information in his or her medical record, except for the use of photos contained in the medical record. (false)

9. Veteran's Administration hospitals are bound under the Privacy Act to make their records available for public disclosure. (false)

10. If a nurse releases a patient's medical records without his or her consent, the physician can be sued for malpractice. (false)

Short Answer Questions

1. What are the five purposes of the medical record?
   a. Provides a medical picture and record from birth to death.
   b. Is an important document for the continual management of a patient's healthcare.
   c. Provides data on births, deaths, and communicable diseases.
   d. Documents a patient's medical condition and treatment and information that may be used in a malpractice suit.
   e. Is a legal document.

2. What are the steps that should be followed when correcting an error in a medical record?
   a. Draw one line through the error.
   b. Write the correction above the error.
   c. Date the change.
   d. Initial it.

3. What does a *subpeona duces tecum* require a person to do?
   a. Appear in court.
   b. Give testimony.
   c. Bring the particular records, files, books, or other information that are described in the subpoena.

4. What are two common methods for tracking a patient's care?
   a. Chronological records
   b. Problem-oriented medical records (POMR)

5. What procedures can be used to protect a patient's confidentiality that relates to fax, copiers, computers, and email?
   a. Shred confidential papers that are no longer needed.
   b. Make sure that the intended receiver is there before sending confidential records via fax.
   c. Use a fax cover sheet that states "confidential."
   d. Avoid using email to send confidential material.
   e. Do not allow other patients and unauthorized staff members to view a computer screen that displays confidential patient information.
   f. Send patient information via fax only when absolutely necessary.
   g. Only fax the specific document requested, not the entire medical record.

6. What is documented when using the SOAP method?
   a. The subjective statements of the patient
   b. Objective data
   c. Assessment or diagnosis
   d. Plan of treatment

7. What category of patients does the Public Health Services Act protect?

   The Public Health Services Act protects patients receiving treatment for drug and alcohol abuse.

8. In what two ways can a subpoena be served?
   a. In person
   b. Certified mail

9. To whom does the Privacy Act of 1974 apply?
   a. Federal agencies
   b. Government contractors

10. Ideally, how long should medical records be stored?
   a. Adult patient records—ten years after the most recent encounter.
   b. Minor's health records—age of maturity plus statute of limitations.
   c. Fetal heart monitor records—ten years after infant reaches maturity.
   d. Medicare and Medicaid records—five years.
   e. Register of birth—permanently.
   f. Register of death—permanently.
   g. Register of surgical procedures—permanently.
   h. Immunization records—permanently.
   i. Chemotherapy records—permanently.

TEACHING STRATEGIES

1. Arrange a field trip to the medical records department of a large outpatient clinic. The students should be able to take a guided tour and ask any questions. Have each student develop one question before the field trip.
2. Ask for two student volunteers (one as a physician and one as a healthcare professional) to role-play, asking a physician who is terribly behind in her charting to catch up on this critical task.
3. Ask for two student volunteers (one patient and one healthcare professional) to role-play an angry patient who is demanding that he be given his medical file. The student playing the role of the healthcare professional should be able to defuse the situation while explaining who has ownership of the record.
4. Break the class into small groups frequently for brief periods in which they can analyze, compare, and discuss the elements found in this chapter.
5. Ask students what can happen if medical records get lost. Ask them to brainstorm the issues, and then have one class member summarize them.
6. Have the students prepare flash cards for the key terms (glossary).

Confidentiality in Medical Practice

CHAPTER SYNOPSIS

Patient confidentiality can never be overemphasized for the student. Patients expect that all of their personal medical information is to remain confidential. To assure that electronic transmission of patients' medical information is treated in a confidential manner, the government has placed restrictions on how this information must be treated with the Health Insurance Portability and Accountability Act of 1996 (HIPAA). New instructions regarding this law were enacted in April 2003. This complicated regulation is explained in this chapter along with ethical concerns about information technology.

Chapter Lecture Outline	Instructor's Notes

I. Confidentiality
  A. Confidentiality about sensitive medical information is necessary to preserve the patient's dignity.
  B. In order to receive payment for services from insurers, it is necessary to reveal a patient's name and diagnosis as well as other sensitive Information.
  C. Information regarding the diagnosis of AIDS needs to be communicated carefully to protect the rights of the patient.
II. The Health Insurance Portability and Accountability Act (HIPAA) of 1996
  A. The privacy rule—This rule applies to protected health information (PHI), which includes any identifiable information such as name, age, gender, and diagnosis.
  B. Denial of the request for privacy—Specific institutions, such as nursing homes, have the right to deny access to information in certain situations to protect their residents.
  C. Who is affected?
    1. Covered entities such as physicians, hospitals, skilled nursing facilities, outpatient rehabilitation facilities, home health agencies, hospice programs, private insurers, ambulance companies, and laboratories.
    2. Any entity that submits a bill or receives payment for healthcare or treatment.
  D. Unique identifiers for healthcare providers
    1. Employer Identifier Standard uses an employer's tax ID number.	

Chapter Lecture Outline	Instructor's Notes

2. Employer Identification Number (EIN), a standard code number, is also used.

E. Can public health information (PHI) be de-identified? Yes.

F. What are the obligations to the patient under HIPAA?
   1. Obligation to obtain consent.
   2. Obligation to allow patient to have access to medical information.
   3. Obligation to provide only the minimum necessary standard information.

G. What are the penalties for noncompliance with HIPAA?
   1. Range from civil penalties of up to $100 per person per incident for minor improper disclosures of health information up to $25,000 for multiple violations in a calendar year.
   2. Federal criminal liability carries sanctions (fines) of $50,000 and one year in prison.

H. What are the patients' rights under the privacy standards? Include right to:
   1. A copy of the privacy notice from healthcare provider.
   2. Access their medical records.
   3. Restrict access to others.
   4. Ask provider to limit the way healthcare information is shared.
   5. Ask for an accounting of who the healthcare information is given to.
   6. Ask to be contacted in a certain way (phone or mail).
   7. Examine and copy the health information the provider has recorded.
   8. Complain to the covered entity and the Department of Health and Human Services if patient believes there is a violation of his or her privacy.

I. Special rules relating to research—Researchers must obtain patient authorization that complies with HIPAA rules or request a waiver of authorization from a privacy board or Institutional Review Board from their hospital or university.

J. Problems relating to implementation of HIPAA's privacy rules—The HIPAA regulations have made some healthcare providers reluctant to release information due to fear of civil or criminal action.

K. Misconceptions about HIPAA—The privacy law:
   1. Does not prevent physicians or hospitals from sharing patient information with other physicians or hospitals.
   2. Does not prevent hospitals from disclosing names of patients to clergy or from keeping patient directories.
   3. Allows hospitals or physicians to share information with the patient's spouse, family members, friends, or anyone the patient has identified as involved in their care.
   4. Does not apply to most police and fire departments.

L. Recommendations

III. Ethical Concerns with Information Technology (Informatics)

LEARNING OBJECTIVES

(Student answers may vary.)

1. Define the glossary terms.

   Clearinghouse   a private or public healthcare entity that facilitates the processing of nonstandard electronic transactions into HIPAA transactions (e.g., a billing service).

   Covered entities   healthcare organizations covered under HIPAA regulations such as public health authorities, healthcare clearinghouses, and self-insured employers, life insurers, information systems vendors, and universities.

   Employer Identification Number (EIN)   a number assigned to an employer for purposes of identification.

   Employer Identifier Standard   a standard number based on an employer's tax ID number or EIN that is used for all electronic transmissions.

   Healthcare plan   an individual or group plan that provides or pays for medical care.

   Healthcare Integrity and Protection Data Bank (HIPDB)   a national data bank that collects and reports disclosures of actions taken against healthcare practitioners, providers, and vendors for noncompliance and fraudulent activities.

   Health Insurance Portability and Accountability Act of 1996 (HIPAA)   regulates the privacy of patient's health information.

   HIPAA-defined permissions   permission to use information based on the reason for knowing, or use of, the information.

   Medical informatics   the application of communication and information to medical practice, research, and education.

   Minimum necessary standard   the provider must make a reasonable effort to limit the disclosure of patient information to only the minimum amount that is necessary to accomplish the purpose of the request.

   Notice of privacy practices (NPP)   a written statement that details the provider's privacy practices.

   Office of Civil Rights (OCR)   the federal office that investigates violations of HIPAA.

   Privacy rule   a requirement that all covered entities under HIPAA must be in compliance with the privacy, security, and electronic data provisions by April 14, 2003.

   Protected health information (PHI)   any individually identifiable information that relates to the physical or mental condition or the provision of healthcare to an individual.

   Sanctions   penalties or fines.

   State's preemption   occurs when the state privacy laws are stricter than the privacy standards established by HIPAA.

   Telemedicine   the use of communications and information technologies to provide healthcare services to people at a distance.

   Treatment, payment, and healthcare operations (TPO)   functions that a healthcare provider can perform.

   Wireless Local Area Network (WLAN)   a wireless system that is used by physicians and nurses to access patient information.

2. Identify the problems associated with patient confidentiality.

   The patient is no longer seen by only one physician for the duration of his or her life. There are now a multitude of entities, such as physicians, hospitals, and health agencies, that come into contact with confidential patient medical information. In addition, modern technology means that this medical information can be transmitted via the Internet or by fax. There is a danger of loss of security with both the Internet and the fax machine.

3. Discuss the purpose of the Health Insurance Portability and Accountability Act (HIPAA) of 1996.

   There are four main objectives:

   a. Improve the portability of health insurance.
   b. Combat the fraud, abuse, and waste in healthcare.
   c. Promote the expanded use of medical savings accounts.
   d. Simplify the administration of health insurance.

4. Describe the information to which the privacy rule refers.

   The privacy rule applies to protected health information (PHI), which is any individually identifiable information that relates to all past, present, and future physical or mental conditions or the provision of healthcare to an individual. The disclosures are limited to only the minimum amount of information that is necessary to convey.

5. List which entities are affected by HIPAA.

   a. Physicians
   b. Hospitals
   c. Skilled-nursing facilities
   d. Comprehensive outpatient rehabilitation facilities
   e. Home health agencies
   f. Hospice programs
   g. Ambulance companies
   h. Clinical laboratories
   i. Pharmaceutical companies
   j. Medical device companies

6. Discuss the penalties for noncompliance with HIPAA.

   The penalties include sanctions of both fines and imprisonment. The fines range from $100 to $50,000, depending on the seriousness of the offense. Imprisonment for Medicare fraud carries with it a penalty of up to $250,000 and/or up to ten years in prison.

7. List the patients' rights under the privacy standards.

   Patients have a right to

   a. A copy of the privacy notice from the healthcare provider.
   b. Access their medical records, restrict access by others, request changes, and learn how their records have been accessed.
   c. Ask the provider to limit the way in which healthcare information is shared and to keep disclosures to the minimum needed for treatment and business operations.
   d. Ask for an accounting of who the healthcare information was given to.
   e. Ask to be contacted in a special way, such as by mail or at work.
   f. Examine and copy the health information that the provider has.

g. Complain to the covered entity and the Department of Health and Human Services (HHS) if the patient believes there is a violation of his or her privacy.

8. Discuss the ethical issues concerning information technology.

Healthcare providers are concerned about the security when patient data is transmitted via the Internet. They are also concerned about the credentials of the person who is advising patients about their healthcare problems via the Internet.

THE CASE OF THE NEW MINISTER AND THE ANTIDEPRESSANT

Dawn is an ordained minister in a little church located in a small New England community. She has had to overcome discrimination as the first female clergy member in the town. However, Dawn feels that her church congregation and other members of the community have finally started to accept her in this new role. Dawn has recently been diagnosed with irritable bowel syndrome by a gastroenterologist in the next town. He performed a colonoscopy on Dawn to rule out cancer of the bowel and found nothing more than a few polyps, which he removed. He told Dawn that he wanted her to start taking amitriptyline for three months to see if that would solve her irritable bowel problem. He said that he had success using this antidepressant, also known as Elavil, to treat irritable bowel syndrome. He said that he would call the prescription into Dawn's local pharmacy.

When Dawn went in to pick up her prescription, she met two members of her congregation, who were also picking up their prescriptions. The pharmacist leaned over the front counter and said to Dawn, "Why are you taking this antidepressant?"

Case Questions

1. What rights of Dawn's were violated?

Dawn's rights to privacy and patient confidentiality were violated. A pharmacist operates under the same doctrine of confidentiality that physicians, as well as other healthcare professionals, must practice.

2. Were any laws broken by the pharmacist's statement? If so, what are they?

The Privacy Rule under the Health Insurance Portability and Accountability Act (HIPAA) was violated. There is a severe fine for this violation.

3. How could Dawn's reputation suffer from this brief comment by the pharmacist?

This statement could have affected the reputation of any person, including a local member of the clergy, since many people attach an unwarranted stigma to taking antidepressants. Unfortunately, gossip can spread quickly through a small town.

[Note: This case is based on a true incident.]

POINTS TO PONDER (FROM TEXTBOOK)

Teaching note: The following questions are a starting point for a general class discussion of the impact of HIPAA. Student responses and opinions may vary.

1. Will it be possible to balance the wealth of medical information to the patient via the Internet with the loss of a personal relationship between the patient and caregiver?

2. How can a patient's PHI be maintained when medical information is being faxed from one location to another?

3. Is the high cost of implementing HIPAA in a small medical practice worth the expense?

4. In your opinion, will HIPAA make it more or less difficult for public services such as police, fire, and ambulance services to administer to patients? Explain your answer.

REVIEW QUESTIONS (FROM TEXTBOOK)
Discussion Questions

1. Why has patient confidentiality become more difficult in the present healthcare environment?

   Preserving patient confidentiality is more challenging today because there are so many more persons and entities treating the patient today. It is no longer just one physician seeing one patient. The patient may see a variety of specialists, each of whom has staff members who have access to the patient's medical record. In addition, the inpatient and outpatient facilities, such as MRI centers, have grown in number. Today there are hundreds of opportunities for persons or entities to read patient health information.

2. Why is the implementation of the new privacy rule so expensive?

   The paperwork alone for this regulation has cost physicians and all covered entities both time and money. Blue Cross has estimated spending $43 billion over a five-year period to come into compliance with HIPAA. In addition, each covered entity must have a designated privacy officer. In many cases, an existing staff member can assume this position, but in some large enterprises, a full-time staff person must be hired.

3. Should family members, and even friends, have access to a patient's medical record? Why or why not?

   In some cases, particularly with elderly persons, there is no one to help the patient with difficult healthcare decisions except a family member or friend. If they were denied access to the patient's medical condition and record, the patient would lose a valuable advocate.

4. Should patients be treated via the Internet? Why or why not?

   There are diverging opinions about this form of medical treatment. Many patients are fearful about coming into a physician's office for treatment but will discuss their medical needs with medical personnel via the Internet. A problem arises when the medical provider supplying information is not qualified. Many healthcare professionals are concerned about the lack of regulations concerning this type of medical care.

   The healthcare consumer is also becoming better informed about medical conditions due to the use of technology such as the Internet. Using this technology, consumers can also investigate the alternative treatments for their medical conditions.

Matching

Column A	Column B
1. privacy rule	e. all covered entities must be in compliance
2. WLANs	c. wireless system to send and receive data
3. HIPAA	i. Health Insurance Portability and Accountability Act of 1996
4. EIN	a. number assigned to an employer
5. clearinghouse	g. a billing service
6. healthcare plan	j. individual or group that provides or pays for medical care
7. PHI	b. individually identifiable information
8. telemedicine	h. use of information technologies to treat people at a distance
9. employer identifier standard	d. based on employer's tax ID or EIN
10. HHS	f. Department of Health and Human Services

Multiple Choice

1. The privacy rule is meant to ensure
   a. standardization of health data
   b. standardization of financial data
   c. standardization of medical care
   d. a and b only
   e. a, b, and c

   Answer: d

2. An example of a clearinghouse is
   a. PHI
   b. skilled-nursing facility
   c. a billing service
   d. a government regulation
   e. EIN

   Answer: c

3. The government organization that investigates a violation of a patient's medical privacy is
   a. OSHA
   b. OCR
   c. PHI
   d. HIPAA
   e. none of the above

   Answer: b

4. A network of wireless communication systems used to access patient records is
   a. HIPAA
   b. PHI
   c. WLANs
   d. EIN
   e. ADA

   Answer: c

5. The privacy law
   a. prevents hospitals from sharing medical information with other facilities
   b. prevents hospitals from sharing registered patient names with the clergy
   c. does not apply to most police and fire departments
   d. allows unlimited information to be shared by EMTs
   e. none of the above

   Answer: c

6. A violation of HIPAA
   a. is a criminal offense
   b. does not carry any financial penalty at present
   c. is not reportable
   d. does not affect a physician's reputation, since it is just a document
   e. may have a fine of under $100 for all offenses

   Answer: a

7. When implementing HIPAA, physicians and physician groups should
   a. hire a privacy officer
   b. implement a notice of privacy practices
   c. retain signed authorizations for at least six years
   d. enter into agreements with nonemployee service providers
   e. all of the above

   Answer: e

8. Covered entities include all of the following except
   a. hospice programs
   b. medical device companies
   c. clinical laboratories
   d. police departments
   e. skilled-nursing facilities

   Answer: d

9. Patients' rights under HIPAA include the ability to
   a. examine their medical records
   b. have a full copy of their medical records
   c. complain to the HHS if they believe there is a violation of privacy
   d. a and c only
   e. a, b, and c

   Answer: e

10. When patient information is requested via a subpoena, you must
    a. comply and send the entire record immediately
    b. provide only the "minimum necessary standard" even if more is requested in the subpoena
    c. provide all PHI that is requested in the subpoena
    d. provide PHI only with the consent of the patient
    e. none of the above are correct

    Answer: c

Fill in the Blanks

1. A written statement detailing the provider's privacy practices is called a <u>Notice of Privacy Practices</u>.
2. Electronic transactions of healthcare information that are required under HIPAA are called <u>covered transactions</u>.
3. The <u>minimum necessary</u> standard is the disclosure of the least amount of information that is necessary to accomplish a request for patient information.
4. The application of communication and information to medical practice, research, and education is called <u>medical informatics</u>.
5. A state's <u>preemption</u> occurs when the state's privacy laws are stricter than the privacy standards established by HIPAA.
6. Healthcare organizations that are included under HIPAA regulations, such as public health authorities and self-insured employers, are called <u>covered entities</u>.
7. The abbreviation HIPAA stands for <u>Health Insurance Portability and Accountability Act.</u>
8. The Privacy Rule covers, among other things, the <u>electronic</u> transmission of data.
9. Another term for penalties or fines is <u>sanctions.</u>
10. A person's name, age, and gender are called <u>protected health information</u>.

PUT IT INTO PRACTICE

Request a copy of a notice of privacy practice from your physician's office. What does the notice state about filing a complaint?

WEB HUNT

1. Look under the patient/consumer website *www.healthfinder.gov* to find consumer information on complaints. Click on "all topics"; under C, click on "complaints"; click on "Bureau of Consumer Protection: Online Complaint Form." Do you believe the information is accurate? Why or why not? Do you believe the information is useful? Why or why not? Rate the information on a scale of 1 to 10 with 1 = low usefulness and 10 = high usefulness.
2. Look under the official government Web site relating to HIPAA, *www.hhs.gov/ocr/hipaa*, to find the answers to frequently asked questions about HIPAA. Describe five questions and answers that you believe all health care professionals should know.

CASE STUDY

Mary Smith has just reported for duty and is reviewing the patients she will have during the evening shift. One of them, Ida Monroe, a recovering alcoholic, is in the hospital for some liver function tests. Dr. Jerome comes into the nursing station around 9:00 P.M. after making hospital rounds to see his patients. He tells Mary that he noticed that one of his neighbors, Ida Monroe, is a patient, and he would like to review her medical chart. Mary starts to give him the chart and then realizes that Dr. Jerome is not Ida's physician. Dr. Jerome says not to worry about that, since he has taken care of the rest of Ida's family for years and is sure that Ida will want him to consult on her case. When Mary hesitates to give him the chart, Dr. Jerome says that he will report her to her nursing supervisor. He walks over to pick up the chart.

Case Questions

1. Should Mary give Ida's medical chart to Dr. Jerome? Why or why not?

   No. Mary is required by law to protect patient confidentiality and the right to privacy. Until she has more information about the role Dr. Jerome has in Ida's medical case, she may not give him the medical chart.

2. What should Mary say to Dr. Jerome?

   She should be frank with Dr. Jerome and tell him that she cannot allow anyone, other than physicians and staff who are directly responsible for Ida's medical care, to see her medical chart.

3. What should Mary do if Dr. Jerome continues to insist on seeing Ida's chart?

   If Dr. Jerome will not listen to Mary, then she should call her supervisor and have him or her handle the situation. Mary may have to take dramatic actions such as taking possession of Ida's medical chart so that Dr. Jerome cannot see it.

4. What ethical principles are involved in this case?

   Some of the ethical principles that this case addresses include confidentiality, honesty, integrity, and respect for the patient's rights.

5. What legal regulations are involved in this case?

   The Patient Privacy Act would be violated if Ida's medical chart is turned over to Dr. Jerome.

   HIPAA is violated when electronic transfer of Ida's medical information is inappropriately given to someone. That does not seem to be the situation in this case. However, HIPAA has been more broadly interpreted by many healthcare professionals to cover the release of medical information in any format (oral or written). The Department of Health and Human Services states that "reasonable safeguards" should be taken to protect patient privacy.

SUPPLEMENTAL QUESTIONS

Chapter Review

Cover the terms in the left-hand column with a piece of paper. Read the statement and fill in the blank with the answer before uncovering the correct response.

Confidentiality	_____ about sensitive information is necessary to preserve the patient's dignity. Third-party payers such as
Medicaid	insurance companies, Medicare, and _____ need to have the patient's diagnosis revealed in order to receive
payment	_____. The Health Insurance Portability and
HIPAA	Accountability Act of 1996 is known as _____.
HHS	Congress mandated that _____ is responsible for developing detailed privacy standards. These rules are meant
electronic	to ensure the standardization of _____ patient
unique	health records. They also provide for _____ identifying codes for all healthcare providers. These identifiers
EIN	use the employer's tax ID number, or their _____.

sanctions	The fines or _____ are severe for noncompliance
prison	with the regulation. They include _____ and/or financial penalties.

Multiple Choice

Select the one best answer to the following statements.

1. In order to de-identify a patient's public health information, all the following have to be removed except
   a. telephone and fax numbers
   b. communicable disease
   c. social security number
   d. email address
   e. all of the above have to be removed

   Answer: b

2. The "minimum necessary" standard means that
   a. a copy of the entire medical record can never be sent to anyone
   b. a copy of only the specific information requested from the medical record can be sent, minus the patient's name
   c. does not apply to any health information disclosures that are required by law
   d. electronic transfers of patient's information cannot be made
   e. none of the above

   Answer: c

3. The national data bank that collects reports and disclosures of actions taken against healthcare practitioners for noncompliance and fraudulent activities is
   a. HIPAA
   b. HHS
   c. PHI
   d. HIPDB
   e. EIN
   f. none of the above

   Answer: d

4. Under HIPAA, medical practitioners and other covered entities are required to
   a. use their employer identification number for electronic transfers of patient information
   b. supply all their patients with notice of privacy practices
   c. meet all the notification requirements by the year 2008
   d. a and b only
   e. a, b, and c

   Answer: d

5. Under HIPAA, the rules relating to research must include which of the following?
   a. a waiver from an Institutional Review Board
   b. a waiver from the primary care physician
   c. a notification about the research published in the *Journal of the American Medical Association*
   d. a waiver from the coroner
   e. none of the above

   Answer: a

6. The purpose(s) of HIPAA is/are to
   a. allow patients to have easier access to their health records
   b. protect computerized medical records and billing
   c. prevent the police from accessing a patient's medical record
   d. prevent hospitals from placing patients' names in their directory
   e. a and b only

   Answer: e

7. Signed authorizations from patients restricting disclosure of PHI
   a. must be retained permanently
   b. are not enforceable
   c. should be retained for ten years
   d. should be retained for six years from the date they were created
   e. do not have to be retained

   Answer: d

8. A privacy officer should
   a. be appointed by every covered entity
   b. should be trained to receive complaints
   c. should be trained to provide information concerning the provider's privacy notice materials
   d. a and c only
   e. a, b, and c

   Answer: e

9. Telemedicine is
   a. illegal
   b. considered to be harmful to the general population
   c. is seen by many to be the future of medicine
   d. not to be used for providing continuing education to medical professionals
   e. none of the above

   Answer: c

10. People and organizations that require a patient's health information include
    a. police
    b. selected family members
    c. insurance companies
    d. ambulance services
    e. all of the above

    Answer: e

True/False Questions

1. Under HIPAA, a patient cannot have his or her name removed from a hospital patient registry. (false)

2. Compliance with HIPAA has been relatively inexpensive for the covered entities such as Blue Cross. (false)

3. The privacy rule that went into effect on April 14, 2001, grants a five-year period for compliance. (false)

4. Under HIPAA, nursing homes have the right to deny access to patients' medical information. (true)

5. Medical device companies have no rights under HIPAA to a patient's medical information. (false)

6. Vital healthcare information, such as a patient's case of venereal disease, can be supplied and still be in compliance with HIPAA. (true)

7. The penalties for noncompliance with HIPAA are relatively mild. (false)

8. Under HIPAA, patients can request to be contacted only at work by their physicians. (true)

9. Under HIPAA, patients can examine all of their medical records, with the exception of the physician's written comments. (false)

10. Under HIPAA, patients have the right to restrict the access of their medical file. (true)

Short Answer Questions

1. Who is affected by the Health Insurance Portability and Accountability Act (HIPAA) of 1996?

   Virtually everyone in the U.S. healthcare system is affected by HIPAA.

   - Patients
   - Providers
   - Payers
   - Intermediaries (e.g., pharmacies and medical device companies)

2. What is the purpose of the privacy rule?

   The privacy rule ensures that there is

   - Standardization of electronic patient health, administrative, and financial data, including healthcare claims, healthcare payment and remittance advice, health claim status, enrollment and disenrollment in a healthcare plan, eligibility in a healthcare plan, and healthcare premium payments.
   - Unique identifying codes for all healthcare providers, healthcare plans, employers, and individuals.
   - Security of electronic health information with standards protecting the confidentiality and integrity of individually identifiable health information, past, present, or future.

3. What are examples of entities that may have to deny access to a patient's medical information?

   - Nursing homes
   - Physicians who must protect a patient's mental health records

4. What are the two unique identifiers used under HIPAA?

   - Employer Identification Number (EIN)
   - Employer Identifier Standard—uses an employer's tax ID or EIN

5. What information must be removed from a patient's medical record in order to de-identify it?

   - Patient's name
   - Address, including email
   - Telephone and fax numbers
   - All dates, including birth (except year), admission, discharge, and death
   - Social security numbers

- Medical records numbers
- Healthcare insurance numbers
- License numbers
- Facial photographs such as found on a driver's license
- Any other identifying number or characteristic

6. What are some of the problems with the implementation of HIPAA?

This is an expensive law to implement due to the extensive paperwork. In addition, the covered entity must designate a privacy officer. The penalties for noncompliance are severe, and many covered entities, therefore, overreact with their adherence to the privacy rule.

7. What are some misconceptions about HIPAA?

Some covered entities, such as hospitals and police and fire departments, believe that under HIPAA regulations, they may not provide any information about patients. As a result, some vital patient information, such as a name and address in the case of a fire, is not shared with the proper people. Physicians may share patient information with each other for purposes of treating the patient. Hospitals may maintain a directory of their patients' names. Hospitals and physicians may also share patient information with the patient's spouse, family members, friends, or anyone the patient has identified as involved in their care.

8. What are some practical recommendations for the implementation of HIPAA?

- Appoint and train a privacy officer to receive complaints and provide information about the provider's privacy notice materials.
- Conduct an internal assessment of existing policies and procedures.
- Enter into agreements with all nonemployee service providers that may have access to PHI.
- Adopt procedures for handling patient requests.
- Implement a notice of privacy practices.
- Revise employee manuals regarding HIPAA standards.
- Train all employees on policies and procedures regarding HIPAA.
- Retain signed authorizations for a period of six years.

9. What is the agency that investigates HIPAA violations?

The Office of Civil Rights (OCR).

10. What is the application of communication and information to medical practice, research, and education called?

Medical informatics.

TEACHING STRATEGIES

1. Have the students divide into three teams to discuss how to role-play the following short case scenarios. Have each team select members to portray the characters in the scenarios and present the team's solution to the short case. As each group presents its solution to the case, have the rest of the class critique their presentations in writing. Potential solutions are offered by the author. However, as an instructor who knows the students, you should bring your own experience and insights into the discussion of these scenarios.

a. Jerry Lately has just come out of Dr. Moore's office after having had a complete physical examination. Dr. Moore requests payment at the time of service, and Jerry is loudly refusing to pay his bill. Jerry is complaining that the fee charged for a physical exam is excessive. Other patients in the waiting room can hear Jerry's loud conversation. What do you, as Dr. Moore's receptionist, do to handle the situation?

Teaching note: The student should speak calmly and quietly to Mr. Lately. If he does not immediately become calmer, then he should be asked to accompany the receptionist/student into an empty room where they can discuss the matter in private. Always let the patient know that you are concerned about the problem and wish to find a mutual solution. Never discuss personal matters within hearing distance of other patients. If necessary, ask another staff member to be present during the conversation as a witness. Document the conversation.

b. Dr. Lewis is a well-known general practitioner. He is also homosexual. How should the office personnel, including his nurse, respond when a patient, Rita Anderson, asks "I've heard that Dr. Lewis is gay. Is this correct?"

Teaching note: Dr. Lewis has a right to have his private life respected. An employee should never discuss personal information about his or her employer. It is always a good idea to immediately change the subject from a personal focus to a professional one. In this case, Dr. Lewis's credentials could be mentioned, but the topic of his personal life should be closed immediately.

c. Emma Helm, a 90-year-old patient of Dr. Williams, has recently suffered a stroke. Her breathing has become difficult and labored. She is currently receiving oxygen, but the hospital physician suggests that Emma be placed on a respirator if her breathing becomes more labored. Her family members, a daughter and a son, are in the hospital and wonder what to do. They don't want their mother to suffer needlessly. Emma is barely conscious and has not left any advance directive instructions in writing about her wishes. What should the son and daughter do?

Teaching note: The son and daughter should immediately talk with Dr. Williams. She may have spoken to Emma about her final wishes and documented this information in her medical record. Today, most physicians discuss this matter with their elderly patients. If there is no directive, then the relatives may have to consult with an attorney to obtain a medical power of attorney. If Emma is conscious enough to speak to her relatives, then she should be asked what she wishes in front of a witness such as a nurse or physician.

2. Have the students prepare flash cards for the key terms (glossary).

Ethical and Bioethical Issues in Medicine

CHAPTER SYNOPSIS

The study of healthcare ethics is an applied ethics, which means that it is more than just a study of theory. Students need to understand the role of ethics in the practice of their medical discipline. A critical-thinking approach to ethics requires the student to look for a solution that includes fairness to patients, respect for society, and a concern for the future implications of the decision. This must be a decision in which the dignity of the individual is always respected. This chapter includes a brief history of ethics, codes of ethics, and a discussion of ethics committees. Bioethical issues such as transplant rationing, biomedical research, and conflicts of interest are included. Three models for examining ethical dilemmas are included in Chapter 1.

Chapter Lecture Outline	Instructor's Notes

I. Early History—In 400 B.C., Hippocrates, a Greek physician referred to as "the Father of Medicine," wrote a statement of principles for his medical students to follow that is still important in medicine.
 	
II. Ethical Standards and Behavior
  A. AMA definition—Ethical behavior, according to the AMA, refers to the following:
    1. Moral principles and practices
    2. The customs of the medical profession
    3. Matters of medical policy
  B. *Allege* means "declare without proof."
  C. Censure is a warning issued to a physician who is accused of unethical behavior or conduct in violation of ethical standards.
  D. Expulsion—The AMA Board of Examiners may recommend the expulsion (forcing out) or suspension of a physician from membership in the medical association.
 	
III. Codes of Ethics
  A. People's behavior must match their set of values.
  B. Some codes of ethics developed in direct response to atrocities.
    1. Declaration of Geneva—medical vow adopted by the Second General Assembly in Geneva, Switzerland, September 1948.
    2. Declaration of Helsinki—Recommendations guiding medical doctors in biomedical research involving human subjects, adopted by the Eighteenth World Medical Assembly, Helsinki, Finland, 1964.
    3. The Nuremberg Code—See Appendix A of the text.	

Chapter Lecture Outline	Instructor's Notes

C. American Medical Association (AMA) Principles of Medical Ethics discuss the following:
 1. Human dignity
 2. Honesty
 3. Responsibility to society
 4. Confidentiality (privacy)
 5. The need for continued study
 6. Freedom to choose patients
 7. A responsibility of the physician to improve the community
 8. Responsibility to the patient is of paramount importance
 9. Support access to medical care for all people
 D. Judicial Council Opinions of the AMA
    1. The Council on Ethical and Judicial Affairs of the AMA is comprised of nine members who interpret the Principles of Medical Ethics.
    2. Summary of Opinions of the Council Opinions of the AMA:
     a. Abuse
     b. Accepting patients
     c. Allocation of health resources
     d. Artificial insemination
     e. Confidential care of minors
     f. Euthanasia
     g. Fee splitting
     h. Futile care
     i. Gene therapy
     j. Ghost surgery
     k. HIV testing
     l. Mandatory consent to abortion
     m. Physician-assisted suicide
     n. Quality of life
     o. Withholding or withdrawing life-prolonging treatment
 IV. Codes of Ethics for Other Medical Professionals
 A. Nurses' Code of Ethics—Discusses the role of nurses as they relate to people, their practice, society, their coworkers, and their profession.
 B. Code of Ethics of the American Association of Medical Assistants (AAMA)—"Sets forth principles of ethical and moral conduct as they relate to the medical profession and the particular practice of medical assisting."
 V. Bioethical Issues—Many areas of medical ethics concern problems for which there is no conclusive answer.
 A. Organ and tissue donation—There is a short supply of organs and tissue for donation, which can result in unethical behavior.
 B. The ethics of transplant rationing
 C. Ethical issues and personal Choice
 VI. The Ethics of Biomedical Research
 A. Ethics of the biomedical researcher
 B. Consent
 C. When research can resolve debate over the best treatment
 D. Conflicts of interest	

Chapter Lecture Outline	Instructor's Notes
E. Ethics of randomized test trials F. Problems with the double-blind test—A test conducted when neither the researcher nor the patient knows who is getting the research treatment. G. Human Genome Project—A federal government project determined or "mappel" the sequence of each gene within the 23 chromosomes. VII. Genetic Engineering 　A. Cloning 　B. Gene therapy 　C. Human stem cell research VIII.　Healthcare Reform 　A. Concern for the 46 millions uninsured Americans 　B. Decline in number of physicians caring for the uninsured	

LEARNING OBJECTIVES

(Student answers may vary.)

1. Define the glossary terms.

   Allege　to assert or declare without proof.

   Censure　to find fault with, criticize, or condemn.

   Chromosome　threadlike structures within the nucleus (center) of a cell that transmit genetic information.

   Clone　a group of identical matching cells that come from a single common cell.

   Control group　research subjects who receive no treatment.

   Double-blind test　a research design in which neither the experimenter nor the patient knows who is getting the research treatment.

   Euthanasia　the administration of a lethal agent by another person to a patient for the purpose of relieving intolerable and incurable suffering.

   Expulsion　the act of forcing out.

   Gene markers　list of genes that are responsible for disease.

   Gene therapy　the replacement of a defective or malfunctioning gene.

   Genetics　a science that describes the biological influence that parents have on their offspring.

   Harvest　remove organs or embryos.

   Human genome　the complete set of genes within the 23 pairs of human chromosomes.

   Human Genome Project　a research program funded by the federal government to "map" and sequence the total number of genes with the 23 pairs, or 46 chromosomes.

   Institutional Review Board (IRB)　a hospital or university board of members who oversee any human research in that facility.

   National Organ Transplant Law of 1984　federal law that forbids the sale of organs in interstate commerce.

Nontherapeutic research research conducted that will not directly benefit the research subject.

Posthumous after death.

Revocation the act of taking away or recalling, such as taking away a license to practice medicine.

Social utility method of allocation a method of determining the allocation of organs by giving them to people who will benefit the most.

Stem cells master cells in the body that can generate specialized cells.

Therapeutic research a form of medical research that might directly benefit the research subject.

United Network for Organ Sharing (UNOS) the legal entity in the United States responsible for allocating organs for transplantation.

2. List and discuss at least ten bioethical issues the modern physician and health-care professional faces.

   Answers may include:
   abortion
   allocation of scarce health resources
   determination of death
   euthanasia: active and passive
   fetal tissue research
   genetic counseling
   harvesting of embryos
   HIV, AIDS, and ARC
   in-vitro fertilization
   organ donation and transplantation
   quality-of-life issues
   random clinical trials
   sterilization
   surrogate parenthood
   withdrawing treatment
   withholding lifesaving treatment

3. Describe how an ethical decision-making model can be used when confronted with difficult ethical dilemmas.

   An ethical model, such as the seven-step model, can help the student confronted with an ethical dilemma, to problem solve instead of following a gut reaction. Furthermore, it requires that the student examine all the facts and look at alternative solutions before coming to a conclusion.

4. Discuss ethical issues relating to human stem cell research.

   There is a concern among ethicists that a "slippery slope" could develop, which means that mankind could slip backwards down this slope and find that the uses for stem cells may be outweighed by the ethical dangers of harvesting them. Some religious groups are opposed to stem cell research since it means that embryos are destroyed when the cells are removed for research. New research indicates that embryos may not have to be destroyed since amniotic fluid cells may be used instead.

5. Describe the advances in human stem cell research.

   New information is coming out about stem cell research almost weekly. These master body cells can generate specialized cells that can grow into any cells or tissue in the body. It is believed that the use of stem cells will eventually allow the body to heal itself from diseases such as Parkinson's, diabetes, stroke, and Alzheimer's.

6. Summarize the ethical issues of organ transplantation.

   The ethical concerns for this issue are wide-ranging but include determining who receives a scarce organ, the expense of a transplant, and the sale of organs.

7. Discuss the importance of codes of ethics such as the Nuremberg Code and the Declaration of Helsinki.

   These codes were developed as a direct response to atrocities that occurred during wartime, especially in response to the medical experimentation in Nazi concentration camps during World War II. These codes express concern for the human subject in medical experimentation.

THE CASE OF THE TUSKEGEE SYPHILIS RESEARCH STUDY

In 1929, the U.S. Health Service worked with state and local departments of health in six states to find a method to control venereal disease. The statistical reports that were conducted between 1930 and 1932 demonstrated a high rate of syphilis in Macon County, Alabama, where over 84 percent of the population were black and 40 percent of the men were infected with syphilis. The methods used for treating this disease consisted of the injection of mercury and other toxic chemicals. Some men recovered with this treatment; other were made even more ill; and in some cases in which no treatment was given, the patient was able to live for several decades.

After funding to treat this disease ran out during the Depression, the researchers conducting the Tuskegee Study attempted to discover how severe this disease was if left untreated. For this study, the U.S. Public Health Service selected 600 men. Of these 600 research subjects, 400 of the men had syphilis, and the other 200 non-syphilic men became the control group of research subjects who received no treatment. The infected patients were not told the purpose or nature of the research. In fact, the researchers would refer to procedures such as spinal taps as "treatments" to induce patient participation. When some of the men in the control group developed syphilis over the course of the study, they were transferred into the research group without ever being told they had the disease. No treatment was ever given to any of the men to fight the disease.

In the early 1940s, penicillin was found to be effective against syphilis. The Tuskegee Project could have been discontinued at this time, since there was no longer any need to study the course of this disease without treatment. However, the research project did continue. The researchers were able to track the men and make sure they did not receive antibiotics for any condition. In the 1960s, a researcher working for the U.S. Public Health Service tried to put an end to the project, which was now being conducted by the Centers for Disease Control (CDC) in Atlanta. When he was unsuccessful, he notified the press, and ultimately the project was stopped. The public was outraged that poor black men had been subjected to a research project without their consent and denied treatment for a treatable disease in an attempt to gain what was seen as useless information. In 1973, the surviving patients received an out-of-court settlement of $37,500 for the infected men and $16,000 for the men in the control group. The families of men who had died also received compensation of $15,000 for the infected men and $5,000 for the uninfected men.

In 1997, President Clinton offered a public apology to the men who were involved in this study. The few surviving men are now in their nineties.

This was never a secret project. This project had been well publicized in medical journals. The people who read about the study did nothing to stop it.

Case Questions

1. Could this type of research study be conducted today? Why or why not?

   While there are currently greater controls over large research projects such as the Tuskegee Project, nevertheless, there are still cases of researchers changing the results of their study in order to obtain status or financial gain. Institutional Review Boards in hospitals and universities require stringent documentation of all research conducted on human subjects. However, there must by ongoing review by an oversight group as the study progresses in order to have good control.

2. Taking into account inflation over a period of thirty years, the settlement of $37,500 would now be around $150,000; the $16,000 settlement would now be $75,000; the $15,000 would be $60,000; and, the $5,000 settlement would be $20,000. Was this a fair settlement? Why or why not?

   It's difficult, even impossible, to place a dollar value on a human life. It's interesting to note that the settlement for the men who died was less that the settlement for those who lived.

3. What should the public have done, since they knew about the study?

   Clearly, someone should have questioned the study. It's curious that not even the family members of the men spoke up.

4. Many scientists believe that using data from this type of experiment indirectly condones the experiments. How should the data be used that is obtained in an unethical study?

   Ethical researchers will not use data collected in this manner.

[*Instructor's note:* The students will easily see the horror of this type of research. However, an important reason for studying this case is that this was never a secret project. The public knew about this study. No one did anything to stop the project until thirty years later. An important concept for students to understand is that they must speak out if there is unethical behavior taking place.]

POINTS TO PONDER (FROM TEXTBOOK)

Teaching note: These questions are meant to promote critical thinking and classroom discussion. The student responses will vary.

1. Why do students still learn about codes of ethics such as the Nuremberg Code and the Hippocratic Oath?

2. Why do some healthcare professionals ignore the code of ethics in their particular discipline?

3. Do all physicians follow the guidelines relating to euthanasia as discussed in the Opinions of the Council on Ethical and Judicial Affairs of the AMA? If not, why not?

4. What would you do if you knew that a patient suffering from cancer was part of a control group of research patients who were not receiving a drug that could benefit them?

5. What do you do when you observe unethical behavior by a coworker?

6. What do you do when you make a mistake?

7. In your opinion, what criteria should be used for selecting the recipient of a scarce organ such as a heart or liver? Would you include such factors as the patient's medical need, chance for success of the procedure, and the patient's responsibility for causing the illness? Why or why not?

REVIEW QUESTIONS (FROM TEXTBOOK)
Discussion Questions

1. Explain what the AMA Principles of Medical Ethics statement on "improved community" means.

   The AMA Principles of Medical Ethics is found in Chapter 5 of the text. "Responsibility to improved community" is interpreted to mean that a physician shall recognize a responsibility to participate in activities contributing to an improved community.

2. Discuss the freedom of choice that a physician has about accepting patients, as stated in the AMA's Principles of Medical Ethics.

   Students should explain the statement, "A physician shall, in the provision of appropriate healthcare, except in emergencies, be free to choose whom to serve, with whom to associate, and the environment in which to provide service" (found in Chapter 5 of the text).

3. Discuss the AMA's opinion on euthanasia.

   Students should discuss the statement found in the AMA's summary of opinions (in this chapter) that states, "Instead of engaging in euthanasia, physicians must aggressively respond to the needs of patients at the end of life. Patients should not be abandoned once it is determined that a cure is impossible."

4. What should healthcare professionals do if their ethical values differ from those of their employer? Discuss several options.

   Student responses will vary but may include:
   a. Approach the employer to discuss the problem.
   b. Request permission to refrain from participating in the procedure.
   c. If unable to reach a mutually satisfying solution, the employee may have to resign.

5. Describe several bioethical issues that modern-day healthcare professionals have to face.

   Answers will vary but may include:

   abortion
   allocation of scarce health resources
   determination of death
   euthanasia: active and passive
   fetal tissue research
   genetic counseling
   harvesting of embryos
   HIV, AIDS, and ARC
   in-vitro fertilization
   organ donation and transplantation
   quality-of-life issues

> random clinical trials
> sterilization
> surrogate parenthood
> withdrawing treatment
> withholding lifesaving treatment

6. Why are bioethical issues discussed in codes of ethics?

    Bioethical issues often have no clear right or wrong answer. Modern technology has moved quickly, and the medical professional often needs guidance on how to use this technology to help and not harm patients. The professional codes of ethics present guidelines for members of that profession to follow.

7. Do you agree with Craig Irwin's statement about Oregon's limited resources for transplants? Why or why not?

    Opinions will vary.

8. Do you think that a national health plan, which would provide medical coverage for all citizens, is a good idea in the United States? Why or why not?

    Opinions will vary.

9. Describe a situation in which the "slippery slope" of ethics may be a concern.

    Comments will vary but could include issues such as euthanasia, abortion for rape, stem cells, assisted suicide, cloning, and the allocation of scarce resources.

10. Should whistleblowers be protected by law from losing their jobs if they "blow the whistle" about an illegal or unethical action in their organizations?

    Hopefully, students will understand that there should be protection for whistleblowers who are performing a useful and/or life-saving function.

Matching

Column A

1. revocation
2. expulsion
3. censure
4. allege
5. posthumous
6. fee splitting
7. euthanasia
8. ghost surgery
9. double-blind test
10. medical etiquette

Column B

e. take away; recall
g. force out
a. condemn
i. to assert
c. after death
h. illegal referral payment
j. aiding in the death of another person
f. one physician substituting for another
d. research design
b. standards of professional behavior

Multiple Choice

1. Nontherapeutic research
    a. will always benefit the research subject
    b. does not directly benefit the research subject
    c. is unethical
    d. should be justified with the benefits outweighing the risks
    e. b and d only

    Answer: e

2. A double-blind test means that
   a. the control group may not receive any benefit from the experimental drug
   b. the participants are visually impaired
   c. the results will not be gained from an objective method for testing
   d. the control group will eventually benefit from being in the experiment
   e. there is an unethical practice taking place

   Answer: a

3. Many professional codes of ethics are based on
   a. current laws
   b. mandates from the government
   c. early writings of Hippocrates
   d. outdated value systems
   e. none of the above

   Answer: c

4. The practice of fee splitting
   a. is legal but unethical
   b. is both unethical and illegal
   c. results in benefit for the patient
   d. is advised by the American Medical Association
   e. is addressed in the code for nursing

   Answer: b

5. The Declaration of Helsinki and the Declaration of Geneva are
   a. authored by the World Medical Association
   b. meant as guidelines for medical researchers
   c. a response to Nazi experimentation during World War II
   d. a and c only
   e. a, b, and c

   Answer: e

6. The Summary of Opinions of the Council on Ethical and Judicial Affairs of the AMA
   a. describes fee splitting as an accepted practice
   b. admonishes the surgeon against "ghost surgery."
   c. admonishes the physician to be sensitive to the need to assist patients in suicide
   d. describes gene therapy as acceptable as long as it is for the purpose of altering human traits
   e. all of the above

   Answer: b

7. Taking away a license to practice medicine is called
   a. revocation
   b. censure
   c. expulsion
   d. a and c only
   e. a, b, and c

   Answer: d

8. Medical issues relating to bioethics include
   a. harvesting embryos
   b. DRGs
   c. withdrawing treatment
   d. HMOs
   e. a and c only

   Answer: e

9. Conflicts of interest occur
   a. when there are financial interests present
   b. if stock is owned by the physician in the company that sponsors the research
   c. if the researcher can control the results of the research
   d. if the patient's needs are not considered
   e. all of the above

   Answer: e

10. A model for making ethical decisions requires that
    a. the potential consequences are not revealed in order to provide objectivity
    b. the alternative of "not doing anything" is not an appropriate consideration
    c. the ethical issues be defined in vague terms in order to look at all the dimensions of the problem
    d. the facts be determined by asking who, what, where, when, and how
    e. all of the above

    Answer: d

Fill in the Blanks

1. A research design in which neither the researcher nor the patient knows who is getting the research treatment is called a double-blind test.

2. Therapeutic research is a form of medical research that might directly benefit the research subject.

3. The legal entity in the Unites States that is responsible for allocating donor resources is the United Network for Organ Sharing also known as UNOS.

4. To take away a physician's license to practice is called revoking the license.

5. A hospital or university board to oversee human research in that facility is the Institutional Review Board.

6. Something that occurs after the death of an individual is known as posthumous.

7. The threadlike structure within the nucleus (center) of a human cell that transmits genetic information is called a chromosome.

8. A complete set of genes is called a human genome.

9. A type of research that will not directly affect or benefit the research subject is called nontherapeutic research.

10. The Nuremberg Code, developed as a result of World War II trials, addresses the issues of performing involuntary research on human subjects.

PUT IT INTO PRACTICE

Select a newspaper article relating to a medical ethics or bioethical issue. Summarize the article. Discuss the people who could be adversely affected by this issue.

WEB HUNT

1. Using the website of the National Association for Healthcare Quality (*www.nahq.org*), discuss the Code of Ethics for Healthcare Quality Professionals.

2. Using the website of the Department of Health and Human Services (*www.hhs.gov*), examine the statement on National Organ and Tissue Donation Initiative. Click on the site for organ donation and discuss the steps that you would need to take in order to become an organ and tissue donor.

3. Using the information on the website of the United Network for Organ Sharing (UNOS) (*www.unos.org*), summarize the purpose of this organization.

4. Using the website for the National Kidney Foundation (www.kidney.org), click on "patients" to learn about Medicare drug coverage for kidney patients.

HISTORICAL CASE STUDY

Mickey Mantle, Baseball Hall of Fame center fielder for the New York Yankees, received a liver transplant in 1995 after a six-hour operation. It took only two days for the Baylor Medical Center's transplant team to find an organ donor for the 63-year-old former baseball hero when his own liver was failing due to cirrhosis and hepatitis. Mantle was a recovering alcoholic who also had a small cancerous growth that was not believed to be spreading or life-threatening.

There is usually a waiting period of about 130 days for a liver transplant in the United States. A spokesperson for the United Network for Organ Sharing located in Richmond, Virginia, stated that there had been no favoritism in this case. She based her statement on the results of an audit conducted after the transplant took place. However, veteran transplant professionals were surprised at how quickly the transplant liver became available.

Doctors estimated that due to Mantle's medical problems, he had only a 60 percent chance for a three-year survival. Ordinarily liver transplant patients have about a 78 percent three-year survival rate. There are only about 4,000 livers available each year with 40,000 people waiting for a transplant of this organ. According to the director of the Southwest Organ Bank, Mantle was moved ahead of others on the list due to a deteriorating medical condition. The surgery was uneventful and Mantle's liver and kidneys began functioning almost immediately. His recovery from surgery was fast.

There were mixed feelings about speeding up the process for an organ transplant for a famous person. However, Kenneth Micetich, an ethicist at Loyola University in Chicago, stated, "People should not be punished just because they are celebrities." The ethics of giving a scarce liver to a recovering alcoholic was debated in many circles. University of Chicago ethicist Mark Siegler said, "First, he had three potential causes for his liver failure. But he also represents one of the true American heroes. Many people remember how he overcame medical and physical obstacles to achieve what he did. The system should make allowances for real heroes."

Mickey Mantle died a few years later from cancer.

Case Questions

1. As in the case of the liver transplant for Mickey Mantle, should the system make allowances for real heroes? Why or why not?

   Student responses will vary. However if the term *hero* is used to determine who will receive a scarce organ for transplantation, then who will determine the definition of hero? Should all war heroes be placed ahead of everyone else for a scarce organ? Many ethicists believe that it is better to use more objective criteria, such as ability to recover and the age of the patient. Another approach might be the justice-based approach to rationing, which means that everyone should have an equal chance to the available organs. The seniority method and a lottery approach have also been suggested and used in the United States. These are difficult ethical questions to answer, and students should know that there is no one right answer.

2. Analyze the Mickey Mantle case using the seven-step model found in Chapter 1 for examining ethical dilemmas.

Answers will vary.

Seven-step model
    I. Determine the facts.
    II. Define the precise ethical issue.
    III. Identify the major principles, rules, and values.
    IV. Specify the alternatives.
    V. Compare values and alternatives.
    VI. Assess the consequences.
    VII. Make a decision.

SUPPLEMENTAL QUESTIONS

Chapter Review

Cover the terms in the left-hand column with a piece of paper. Read the statement and fill in the blank with the answer before uncovering the correct response.

censure suspension/expulsion	When a physician is accused of unethical behavior, the AMA Board of Examiners can issue a _____ and recommend _____ or _____.
Ethical/Judicial	The Council on _____ and _____ Affairs of the AMA is a group of nine members who interpret the principles. One such interpretation is the practice of a physician accepting money from another physician for re-
fee splitting	ferrals and is called _____ _____.
Nontherapeutic	_____ research does not directly benefit the research subject. The justification for all medical research is
benefits/risks	that the _____ must outweigh the _____.
increasing knowledge conflict of interest	Merely _____ _____ is not considered an adequate justification for taking a risk. A _____ _____ _____ can arise if medical researchers place their interests above the patient's.
unethical double/blind informed	Many scientists believe it is _____ to use a control group when conducting medical experiments. In a _____-_____ test, neither the experimenter nor the patient knows who is getting the research treatment. In these tests, an ethical question arises about the process of _____ consent, because patients are not fully aware that they are receiving treatment.
objective ethical/alternatives values	The decision maker must always be _____ when making ethical decisions. A model that aids in decision making includes the following steps: define the precise _____ issues, specify _____, compare _____ and alternatives, and make a decision.

Multiple Choice

Select the one best response to the following questions.

1. If a physician is accused of unethical behavior in violation of AMA standards, the AMA Board of Examiners can

   a. censure
   b. recommend expulsion
   c. recommend suspension
   d. bring legal action against the physician
   e. a, b and c only

   Answer: e

2. The American Medical Association's Principle of Ethics discusses all of the following except

   a. human dignity
   b. confidentiality
   c. responsibility to society
   d. sanctions for unethical behavior
   e. honesty

   Answer: d

3. The replacement of a defective or malfunctioning gene refers to

   a. euthanasia
   b. gene therapy
   c. therapeutic
   d. revocation
   e. cloning

   Answer: b

4. Nontherapeutic research

   a. does not directly benefit the research subject
   b. is considered to be unethical
   c. requires a fee
   d. will directly benefit the research subject
   e. refers to DRGs

   Answer: a

5. Medical issues relating to bioethics include

   a. abortion
   b. surrogate parenthood
   c. genetic counseling
   d. a and c only
   e. a, b, and c

   Answer: e

6. Ideally, people with personal, religious, or ethical reasons for not wishing to be involved in a particular procedure should state these wishes

   a. when the situation arises
   b. never—it is not work related and should not be mentioned
   c. before being hired
   d. after the procedure has started
   e. immediately, since physicians must participate in all AMA-approved procedures

   Answer: c

7. Problems with the double-blind test include
   a. the researcher has a bias toward a specific treatment
   b. only the experimenter is aware of who is receiving treatment
   c. the patients are not fully aware of whether they are receiving treatment
   d. only implied consent is necessary
   e. it is not considered an objective test

   Answer: c

8. The term "slippery slope"
   a. is considered an ethical dilemma
   b. is used to discuss stem cell research
   c. means that the uses for a new research development can be outweighed by the ethical dangers
   d. is meant to warn people about ethical dangers in biomedical research
   e. all of the above

   Answer: e

9. The World Medical Association authorized
   a. the Declaration of Geneva
   b. the Code of Ethics of the AAMA
   c. the Declaration of Helsinki
   d. a and c only
   e. a, b, and c

   Answer: d

10. Many ethicists believe the use of control groups is
    a. ethical
    b. a double-blind test
    c. unethical
    d. a conflict of interest
    e. a bioethical issue

    Answer: c

True/False Questions

1. An institutional review board oversees the sale of organs in interstate commerce. (false)

2. The social utility method of allocation of organs uses the criteria that there is a strong chance that the recipient will survive. (false)

3. The seven-step ethical decision-making model provides a subjective method for solving ethical dilemmas. (false)

4. Since nontherapeutic research will not directly benefit the research subjects, it is not necessary to obtain informed consent. (false)

5. The entire healthcare team is responsible for explaining to the patient the risks involved in a research project. (false)

6. In a double-blind test, neither the researcher nor the patients know who is receiving the treatment. (false)

7. Medical etiquette is the same as medical ethics. (false)

8. Posthumous means occurring after the death of a person. (false)

9. Euthanasia is the self-inflicted death of a person. (false)

10. Censure is the same as condemnation of an individual. (false)

Short Answer Questions

1. The World Medical Association is the authoring body of what codes?
    a. Declaration of Geneva
    b. Declaration of Helsinki

2. What are the steps in the seven-step decision-making model?
    a. Determine the facts by asking the questions.
    b. Define the precise ethical issue.
    c. Identify the major principles, rules, and values.
    d. Specify the alternatives.
    e. Compare values and alternatives.
    f. Assess the consequences.
    g. Make a decision.

3. What alternatives does the AMA Board of Examiners have if a physician is accused of unethical behavior?
    a. Censure
    b. Suspension
    c. Expulsion

4. What does the National Organ Transplant Law of 1984 control?

   It forbids the sale of organs in interstate commerce.

5. What is the United Network for Organ Sharing (UNOS)?

   It is a legal entity that is responsible for allocating organs for transplantation.

6. What happens if someone alleges that a physician has committed a criminal act such as fee splitting?

   The American Medical Association is required to report the accusation to the state licensing board or governmental agency. If, upon examination of the claim, the physician is convicted of a crime, it may result in a fine, imprisonment, and/or revocation of his or her medical license.

7. Why do we have codes of conduct in the medical profession?

   Some of our codes of conduct, such as the Declaration of Geneva and the Declaration of Helsinki, are a direct result of atrocities that occurred during wartime. There is a concern for human experimentation in the Nuremberg Code. Modern-day codes, such as the AMA's, Nurses' and the AAMA's codes of ethics, are meant to serve as a moral guide for those professions.

8. What is the purpose of the Uniform Anatomical Gift Act?

   This act, which has been adopted in all states, permits competent adults to either allow or forbid the posthumous (after death) use of their organs. A written document or donor card, signed by the patient, is required.

9. What should an employee do if he or she has a religious, moral, or personal reason for not wishing to participate in a particular procedure?

   The employee can request to refrain from participating in a procedure such as a therapeutic abortion. However, the employee's wishes should be clearly stated ahead of time, even at the time of hiring, so as not to jeopardize the health and safety of the patient. The employee is justified in asking for these considerations.

However, a problem arises when an employee refuses to provide normal medical care for a patient, such as a patient with AIDS. This can be considered insubordination, since the AIDS patient is not only protected by law (Americans with Disabilities Act) but also requires treatment and care that any other patient with a life-threatening illness would require.

10. What is the purpose of an institutional review board?

This board is required by law in any institution that receives federal funding. It oversees any human research in that facility.

TEACHING STRATEGIES

1. Have the class review the AMA's Principles of Medical Ethics found in Chapter 5 that govern gene therapy. Break the class into small groups (four or five) and ask them to critique this opinion, then summarize the opinions of the group members for a general class discussion.
2. Have the students work in small groups (four or five) to develop a code of classroom conduct. They should use the various codes found within this chapter as models for format and style. Ask each group to present its code of conduct to the class for discussion. Have the class vote on the issues from each group's code that should be incorporated into one code for the class.
3. Working in small groups, have the students develop a list of ways that a physician and his or her staff can participate in activities contributing to an improved community, as stated in the AMA's Principles of Medical Ethics.
4. Have the students describe the difference between ethics and applied ethics in their own words.
5. Review the Nurses' Code of Ethics by reading each item and then describing or acting out an application of each.
6. Have the students prepare flash cards for the key terms (glossary).

Ethical Issues Relating to Life

CHAPTER SYNOPSIS

Ethical issues relating to birth and life are especially difficult because they carry the extra burden of the students' and the instructor's own personal values. Nevertheless, all healthcare professionals must be willing to understand the topics and issues discussed by patients, physicians, and the federal court system. This chapter includes a discussion of fetal development, contraception, sterilization, abortion, assisted or artificial conception, conscience clauses, genetic counseling and testing, wrongful-life suits, the human genome project, genetic engineering, gene therapy, and stem cell research.

Chapter Lecture Outline	Instructor's Notes

I. Fetal Development—When Does Life Begin?
   A. *Embryo* is the name given to an unborn child between the second and twelfth weeks after conception.
   B. *Fetus* is the term used when the embryo reaches the third month of development, starts to develop organs, and has a pronounced heartbeat and a functioning brain.
   C. The gestational period is the time period before birth occurs, which is usually around forty weeks.
 II. Assisted or Artificial Conception
   A. Artificial insemination (AI) is the injection of seminal fluid that contains male sperm into the female's vagina from her husband, partner, or donor by some means other than sexual intercourse.
   B. Artificial insemination by husband (AIH) is a procedure in which sperm from the woman's husband or partner is used.
   C. Artificial insemination by donor (AID) is a procedure in which a donor's sperm is used. A man donates his semen for insemination of a woman who is not his wife.
   D. Legal status of offspring—The most common legal and ethical concern relates to the legitimacy of the child and the determination of who is responsible for the child's support.
   E. In-vitro fertilization is a process in which ovum and sperm cells are combined outside the woman's body.
   F. Surrogate motherhood
     1. A surrogate mother is a woman who agrees to bear a child for a couple using the husband's viable sperm.	

Chapter Lecture Outline	Instructor's Notes

      2. The Baby M case resulted from a surrogate parenting contract between Mary Beth Whitehead and Mr. and Mrs. Stern. Mrs. Whitehead was inseminated with Mr. Stern's sperm in 1985. On March 7, 1986, baby M was born.

  G. Fertility drugs

      1. Increase the female hormones and the production of ova, thus enhancing the ability to conceive and become pregnant.

      2. Harvesting is a procedure performed by entering the uterus and removing some of the embryos, leaving only two or three.

      3. Fertility drugs enhance a woman's ability to conceive. However, the use of these drugs increases the woman's chance of having a multiple birth, as many as eight embryos at a time. Miscarriages, stillbirths, infant deaths, and disabled children can result from the use of fertility drugs.

III. Contraception—Any action taken to prevent a pregnancy from occurring.

IV. Sterilization—The process of medically altering reproductive organs so as to terminate the ability to produce offspring.

  A. Voluntary sterilization

  B. Consent for sterilization—A patient, even if a criminal, must grant consent for the surgical procedure of sterilization.

  C. Therapeutic sterilization—May be necessary if the mother's life or mental health is threatened.

  D. Eugenic sterilization—Eugenic, or involuntary, sterilization is the sterilization of certain categories of persons, such as those who are insane, mentally-retarded, cognitively disabled, or epileptic, in order to ensure that they won't pass on the defective gene to their children.

  E. Negligence suits related to sterilization

  F. Ethical issues surrounding sterilization and birth control

V. Abortion

  A. Abortion is the termination of a pregnancy before it is viable (able to survive outside the uterus).

  B. A spontaneous abortion is one that occurs naturally without any interference.

  C. An induced abortion, or one that is caused by artificial means such as medications or surgical procedures, is used to save the life of the mother.

  D. In *Roe v. Wade*, the U.S. Supreme Court declared a Texas criminal abortion law that prohibited all abortions not necessary to save the life of the mother to be a violation of the woman's right to privacy under the Fourteenth Amendment of the Constitution.

  E. Historical progression of cases affecting abortion—Since *Roe v. Wade*, a steady progression of abortion cases has reached the Supreme Court to challenge that ruling.

  F. Partial birth abortion—Abortions occurring late in the pregnancy when the fetus is considered to be viable outside of the uterus (at about 24 weeks). This practice causes much controversy.

  G. Incompetent persons and abortion—Difficult ethical issues surround situations in which incompetent persons may be subjected to unplanned or unwanted pregnancies.

Chapter Lecture Outline	**Instructor's Notes**

H. Opposition to abortion
I. Employee's rights to refuse to participate in abortions—Hospital employees have the right to refuse to participate in performing an abortion, and a hospital cannot dismiss employees for insubordination.
J. Funding for abortion—Funding for abortions has been another area of great controversy.
K. Ethical issues surrounding abortion—Abortion raises a multitude of ethical issues, even for those who believe abortion, in general, should be legal.
  1. One of the most vocal opponents of induced abortion is the Catholic Church.
  2. Many private citizens do not wish their tax money to be spent on funding abortions for women on Medicaid.
  3. Does the fetus have rights?
  4. Abortion is always a moral decision, since it results in the loss of human life.
  5. Should abortion be used as a means of gender selection of children?
VI. Genetic Counseling and Testing
  A. Genetics is the study of heredity and its variations. It describes the biological influence that parents have on their offspring.
  B. Genetic counseling involves investigation and counsel through interview and conferencing with perspective parents to determine potential for passing on genetic traits to their offspring.
  C. Prenatal testing—The most common means of testing during pregnancy is amniocentesis, a surgical procedure to withdraw amniotic fluid from the pregnant uterus for testing.
  D. Genetic testing of newborns—Routine genetic screening on newborns has become a standard in many hospitals.
  E. Ethical questions regarding genetic testing
VII. Wrongful-life suits—In general, the courts have rejected wrongful-life lawsuits brought against hospitals or physicians by children with genetic defects who claim they were injured by the action of being born.	

LEARNING OBJECTIVES

(Student answers may vary.)

1. Define the glossary terms.

   Amniocentesis   a test for the presence of genetic defects in which a needle is used to withdraw a small amount of amniotic fluid that surrounds the fetus in the uterus.

   Anencephaly   missing a brain and spinal cord.

   Artificial insemination   the injection of seminal fluid that contains male sperm into the female's vagina from her husband, partner, or donor by some means other than sexual intercourse.

   Artificial insemination donor (AID)   a procedure in which a donor's sperm is used.

Artificial insemination husband (AIH)   a procedure in which sperm from the woman's husband or partner is used.

Contraception   birth control.

Embryo   unborn child between the second and twelfth week after conception.

Eugenic (involuntary) sterilization   sterilization of certain categories of persons, such as the insane and mentally retarded (cognitively disabled), in order to prevent them from passing on defective genes to their children.

Eugenics   the science that studies methods for controlling certain characteristics in offspring.

Fetus   unborn child from the third month after conception until birth.

Gestational period   time before birth during which the fetus is developing; usually nine months.

Induced abortion   an abortion caused by artificial means such as medications or surgical procedures.

In-vitro fertilization (IVF)   the process of combining ovum and sperm outside of a woman's body.

Preimplantation genetic diagnosis (P.G.D.)   genetic testing on embryos for genes that cause untreatable or severe diseases.

Spontaneous abortion   termination of pregnancy that occurs naturally before the fetus is viable.

Sterilization   the process of medically altering reproductive organs so as to terminate the ability to produce offspring.

Surrogate mother   a woman who agrees to bear a child for another couple. The husband's sperm is implanted into this woman's uterus.

Therapeutic sterilization   sterilization undertaken to save the mother's life or protect her health.

Viable   in the case of a fetus, ability to survive outside of the uterus.

2. Discuss the ethical considerations relating to artificial insemination.

   Responses will vary but could include:

   a. The confidentiality of AID records
   b. The method for handling the sperm donation
   c. The husband's acceptance of a child conceived in this manner
   d. The child's wish to know the identity of the father

3. Describe the Baby M case.

   Baby M was the result of a surrogate parenting contract between the surrogate mother, Mary Beth Whitehead, and Mr. and Mrs. Stern. The baby was conceived from Mr. Stern's sperm and Mrs. Whitehead's egg. The baby was turned over to the Sterns after birth, but a few months later, Mrs. Whitehead and her husband escaped to Florida with the baby. The baby was returned to the Sterns. A court ruled that the natural mother should have parental rights to see the child, but the Sterns were granted custody.

4. Discuss the ethical considerations relating to surrogate motherhood and contraception.

Student responses will vary. The students might discuss the following questions:

Is it right to ask the surrogate mother to give up all rights to the baby she has carried for nine months?

Does, or should, the child have an emotional or physical link to the surrogate mother?

Will the relationship between the husband and wife be altered if the husband's sperm is implanted into another woman?

What is the sibling relationship toward the surrogate baby?

Can the contract between the surrogate mother and the couple be enforced?

5. List several ethical issues surrounding sterilization and contraception.

   a. Eugenic sterilization is abhorrent to many people. It carries the stigma of determining who shall live and who shall die.
   b. Many people question the ethics of public schools, which receive federal and state funding, dispensing contraceptive devices such as condoms and birth control pills.
   c. Many people question the ethics of suggesting that violent sex offenders be ordered to undergo sterilization.
   d. Some people believe that women who receive public funds such as Medicaid should not continue to have children by unknown fathers because, by so doing, they increase the welfare rolls.
   e. What is the ethical implication when hospitals refuse to allow sterilization procedures on their premises if they are the only hospital in the area?
   f. Should mentally incompetent women be sterilized to prevent a pregnancy from occurring if a man takes advantage of them?
   g. Are children being treated as property?
   h. Is human life being destroyed to achieve birth (harvesting of embryos)?
   i. Some people believe that issues of contraception can interfere with the relationship between husband and wife.

6. Explain the importance of *Roe v. Wade.*

   In *Roe v. Wade,* the Supreme Court declared a Texas criminal abortion law that prohibited all abortions not necessary to save the life of the mother to be a violation of the woman's right to privacy under the Fourteenth Amendment of the Constitution. It gave strength to the argument that a woman should be allowed the right to have privacy over matters related to her own body.

THE CASE OF KAREN'S BABY

Dale and Karen were excited to learn they were expecting their first child. However, their joy turned to sorrow when a sonogram (record taken from an ultrasonography test using high frequency sound waves) revealed that their daughter was missing a brain and spinal cord (anencephaly). They were told that most babies with this condition are stillborn or only survive for a few hours. There seemed to be few options for treating this baby even if she would be born alive. All of the specialists that Karen and Dale consulted recommended that Karen have an abortion since she was still in her first trimester of pregnancy. But Dale and Karen decided that Karen would carry their baby until full term, if possible, and then donate her organs to help other sick infants. Her personal obstetrician said that he would honor her wishes no matter what her decision was. He advised that Karen have a cesarean section (C-section) in order to give the baby a chance to survive the birth. Their daughter, who they named Jessica, was born alive and was immediately placed onto a ventilator to assist her breathing and help to maintain the quality of her internal organs, which appeared to be normal.

A legal problem immediately arose when the doctors had to declare that Jessica was brain-dead in order to remove her organs for transplant. She did not possess a brain that could be connected to electrodes to determine if there was a cessation of brain function. According to the lawyers hired by the hospital, a court would have to make the determination that the baby was brain dead. After a hearing, the court denied the parents' petition to turn off the ventilator and declare their baby dead. An appeals court upheld that decision. Even though the courts acted quickly, a week had passed and Jessica's organs were no longer usable.

She died quietly while still connected to a ventilator.

[*Note:* The following questions are meant to stimulate discussion. There is not a perfect answer to some of these questions.]

Case Questions

1. Who should make the life and death decisions of severely disabled babies?

   It is difficult, if not impossible, to determine if the life of a disabled baby should be terminated. In many cases, even the most severely handicapped individuals have led meaningful lives that provided great comfort to those people around them.

2. Is it ever proper to hasten the death of a severely disabled baby?

   There have been legal cases in which a physician or a parent tried to withhold care from a handicapped newborn. This is illegal.

3. If a genetic screening indicated there was a certainty that a couple would conceive a severely disabled child, should the government ever intervene and recommend an abortion?

   The U.S. Constitution provides protection for the human rights of all its citizens—including the disabled. A couple who wish to abort a severely disabled fetus may do so during the first trimester under the ruling of *Roe v. Wade.* However, the government cannot mandate an abortion.

4. What are the ethical implications for a society that wishes to eliminate persons who are disabled or are considered defective?

   From an ethical perspective, that society would be no better than during Hitler's regime in Germany when, in addition to eliminating the Jewish population, he also attempted to eliminate all handicapped persons. The world still considers his actions to be heinous. From a practical standpoint, a society that eliminates its handicapped members would not have the benefit of the many handicapped scientists, artists, musicians, teachers, and other persons who enrich life for all of us.

POINTS TO PONDER (FROM TEXTBOOK)

Teaching note: These questions are meant to promote critical thinking and classroom discussion. The student responses will vary.

1. What do you say to a patient who asks for family planning advice?

2. How would you react to a coworker who tells you she has recently had an abortion?

3. Can you relate to the dilemma faced by a surrogate mother who is giving up her baby to the contractual parents? Why or why not?

4. What would you say to a person who does not share your religious or moral views concerning abortion?

5. What are some of the daily issues faced by parents who have children born with hereditary disorders?

REVIEW QUESTIONS (FROM TEXTBOOK)
Discussion Questions

1. Discuss the ethics of minors having the same access to contraceptives as adults.

   Student responses will vary.

2. Should there be mandatory testing for genetically transmitted diseases? Why or why not?

   Students need to question the term *mandatory* in this statement. They may also relate mandatory testing for genetically transmitted diseases to eugenics, since the purpose of the testing may be to terminate the pregnancy if the test results are positive.

3. List and describe six hereditary disorders discussed in this chapter.

   Responses may include:
   a. Cooley's anemia
   b. Cystic fibrosis
   c. Down syndrome
   d. Duchenne's muscular dystrophy
   e. Hemophilia
   f. Huntington's chorea
   g. Phenylketonuria (PKU)
   h. Retinoblastoma
   i. Sickle-cell anemia
   j. Tay-Sachs disease

4. Discuss the history of U.S. Supreme Court decisions relating to abortion since *Roe v. Wade.*
   a. In a 1976 case, the Supreme Court ruled that requiring girls under the age of 18 to obtain parental consent in writing before they could obtain an abortion was unconstitutional.
   b. In 1977, the Supreme Court examined a Connecticut statute that denied Medicaid payment for first-trimester, medically necessary abortions. The Court voted six to three that states may refuse to spend their public funds to provide nontherapeutic abortions.
   c. In 1980, the Supreme Court upheld the Hyde Amendment, which prohibits the use of federal funds to pay for Medicaid abortions.
   d. In 1981, the Supreme Court upheld a Utah statute requiring the physician to notify, if possible, the parents or guardian before an abortion is performed on a minor.
   e. In 1990, the Supreme Court upheld the federal statute that prohibited federally funded family planning clinics from giving abortion advice.
   f. In 1992, the Supreme Court examined Pennsylvania's law that restricted a woman's right to abortion. The Court rejected the trimester approach used in *Roe v. Wade* and ruled that it placed an undue burden on the mother to seek spousal consent.

5. What are the ethical implications relating to abortion?

   Student responses will vary but might include:
   a. Concerns of private citizens who do not want tax money spent on abortions for women on Medicaid.
   b. A rights-based question about an incompetent person submitting to an abortion.
   c. Appropriateness of the government to deny spousal consent for abortion.
   d. Moral issues, since it always involves the loss of a human life.

e. Using abortion as a means for gender selection of children.

f. Concerns voiced by religious organizations.

6. Discuss some of the ethical implications relating to sterilization.

The discussion may involve the following:

a. Eugenic sterilization is abhorrent to many people. It carries the stigma of determining who shall live and who shall die.

b. Many question the ethics of suggesting that violent sex offenders be ordered to undergo sterilization.

c. Some people believe that women who receive public funds such as Medicaid should not continue to have children by unknown fathers because, by so doing, they increase the welfare rolls.

d. What is the ethical implication when hospitals refuse to allow sterilization procedures on their premises if they are the only hospital in the area?

e. Should mentally incompetent women be sterilized to prevent a pregnancy from occurring if a man takes advantage of them?

7. What are some of the ethical implications relating to fertility drugs?

- Concern for multiple births with little chance of all the babies surviving or being normal.
- The ethics of harvesting multiple embryos that result from the use of fertility drugs.

8. Discuss the ethical implications relating to artificial insemination donor (AID).

a. The confidentiality of AID records

b. The method for handling the sperm donation

c. The husband's acceptance of a child conceived in this manner

d. The child's wish to know the identity of the father

9. Do you feel that abortion is an appropriate method to use for birth control?

Student responses will vary.

10. How is the traditional notion of family challenged by the new reproductive technologies?

Issues such as surrogate motherhood, in-vitro fertilization, and artificial insemination with donor sperm have raised concerns about the difficulty that children born as a result of these technologies may have in the future. For example, a child might raise questions about his or her "true" parent, siblings, grandparents, and other relatives.

11. Should genetic counseling include recommendations by the medical personnel?

Parents can be given options for treatment but should be told, or receive recommendations, of what to do. Most parents wish to be fully informed about their child's options for life in order to make an informed decision.

Matching

Column A

1. fetus
2. embryo
3. in-vitro fertilization

4. anencephaly

Column B

j. third month of development until birth

f. second to twelfth week of development

h. ovum and sperm combined outside of the mother's body

c. born without a brain and spinal cord

5. genetics   e. biological influence of parents on their offspring

6. AID   g. artificial insemination by donor

7. AIH   b. artificial insemination by husband

8. surrogate   i. substitute

9. gestational period   a. time before birth during the development of the fetus

10. viable   d. able to survive

Multiple Choice

1. The current laws relating to artificial insemination
   a. do not forbid artificial insemination
   b. state that the donor father must provide a portion of the child's support
   c. provide for the records that relate to the donor to remain open
   d. clarify the child's illegitimacy
   e. all of the above

   Answer: a

2. The Baby M case is an example of
   a. problems encountered with fertility drugs
   b. problems relating to the practice of eugenics
   c. problems encountered as a result of the use of a surrogate
   d. problems encountered due to involuntary sterilization
   e. problems encountered as a result of genetics

   Answer: c

3. Ethical issue(s) relating to contraception is/are
   a. dispensing contraceptives in schools receiving federal funds
   b. requiring sex offenders to undergo sterilization
   c. providing contraceptives for women on Medicaid
   d. sterilization of mentally incompetent women
   e. all of the above

   Answer: e

4. A miscarriage is the same thing as a/an
   a. induced abortion
   b. spontaneous abortion
   c. drug-induced abortion
   d. conscience clause
   e. eugenics

   Answer: b

5. A genetic disorder that causes severe joint pain, chronic weakness, and infections and is more prevalent in people of African heritage is
   a. Tay-Sachs disease
   b. hemophilia
   c. cystic fibrosis
   d. sickle-cell anemia
   e. Cooley's anemia

   Answer: d

6. Genetic testing of the newborn is required by law for
   a. Tay-Sach's disease
   b. phenylketonuria
   c. retinoblastoma
   d. Down syndrome
   e. Cooley's anemia

   Answer: b

7. A disease that could cause serious birth defects for an unborn child if the pregnant mother is exposed to it during her pregnancy is
   a. down syndrome
   b. huntington's disease
   c. cystic fibrosis
   d. rubella
   e. retinoblastoma

   Answer: d

8. Withdrawing a small amount of amniotic fluid from the uterus for genetic testing is called
   a. induced abortion
   b. eugenics
   c. amniocentesis
   d. spontaneous abortion
   e. drug-induced abortion

   Answer: c

9. A person appointed by the court to defend a lawsuit on behalf of an incapacitated person is
   a. conscience clause
   b. surrogate
   c. AID
   d. AIH
   e. *guardian ad litem*

   Answer: e

10. Tay-Sachs disease
    a. results from an enzyme deficiency
    b. is more common among people of Eastern European descent
    c. is curable if diagnosed early
    d. a, b, and c
    e. a and b only

    Answer: e

Fill in the Blanks

1. The terms abortion and <u>miscarriage</u> are used interchangeably.
2. A common method for genetic testing during pregnancy is <u>amniocentesis.</u>
3. <u>Anencephaly</u> refers to an infant born without a brain and spinal cord.
4. An <u>embryo</u> is the stage of development between the second and eighth week of gestation.
5. A <u>fetus</u> is the stage of gestational development that occurs at about the ninth week of gestation.

6. The third three months of life during a mother's gestational period is known as the third <u>trimester</u>.

7. The law stating that federal funds cannot be used for an abortion except to save the life of the mother or in a case of rape or incest is called the <u>Hyde Amendment.</u>

8. An infertile couple who does not wish to adopt has the option of <u>surrogate</u> motherhood.

9. In some cases in which a baby is born with severe defects that greatly affect the quality of life, a <u>wrongful-birth</u> claim is brought by the parents.

10. A <u>viable</u> infant is one who is able to survive after birth.

PUT IT INTO PRACTICE

Contact your local chapter of Planned Parenthood and a right-to-life organization and request information on their organizations and services. Compare the philosophies and missions of the two organizations as stated in their printed materials. What do they have in common? What are the differences?

WEB HUNT

Using the Web site of the National Institute of Health (www.nih.gov), click on the Office of Rare Diseases heading. Using the list provided by the office, determine which of the hereditary disorders in Table 12-2 are considered rare diseases.

CASE STUDY

A physician was recently convicted of using his own sperm for artificially inseminating his patients. He told the court that he didn't see anything wrong with this practice because these women came to him wanting to have a child. However, his patients were unaware that he was using his own sperm for the procedure. Some of his office staff became suspicious of the physician's methods, but failed to report their suspicions immediately. Many children were conceived as a result of this physician's sperm having been implanted into the mothers.

Case Questions

1. Is this a legal, ethical, or bioethical issue? Explain your answer.

   It is a legal, ethical, and bioethical issue. It is a legal issue because the patients had a contract with the physician based on the physician–patient relationship. The physician violated this contract and therefore was negligent. The ethical issue concerns dishonesty to the patient. The bioethical issue concerns the ability of modern biological technology to artificially inseminate women. The AID process requires following certain standards of protocol that this physician abused.

2. Was the office staff at fault?

   Yes. The staff has a responsibility and a duty to the patients to report any suspicious behavior. In this case, the staff should have brought the issue to the physician's attention. If he was unwilling to declare his wrongdoing, then the staff had a responsibility to report the behavior to the proper authorities.

3. What is the potential long-term effect for this physician's patients and members of the surrounding community?

There is a grave concern about the long-term effect that this will have on the local community, since the identity of some of the children is unknown. Some of these children, who are related by having the same father, could marry. There is a higher incidence of genetic disorders in children whose parents are related by birth.

4. What should happen to this physician?

In this case, he violated his profession's medical code of ethics as well as the law. His patients had an implied contract with him to provide them with artificial insemination. The women did not expect, nor wish, to have this elderly physician's sperm implanted. He faced criminal prosecution as well as losing his medical license to practice.

HISTORICAL CASE STUDY: THE WILLOWBROOK STATE HOSPITAL CASE

Willowbrook State Hospital, an institution for mentally retarded children on Staten Island, experienced a large number of infectious diseases among its patients. Conditions at the hospital were not good, and most children suffered from hepatitis, measles, and parasitic and respiratory infections. Hepatitis, in particular, was a problem, since many of the children were not toilet-trained and the disease was spread through an oral-intestinal route. Researchers determined that nearly all susceptible children became infected with hepatitis during their first year at the hospital.

Between the years 1956 and 1970, 10,000 children were admitted to Willowbrook Hospital. Of those children, almost 800 were entered into a research project to gain information about the disease with the hopes of eventually developing an immunization against the disease. All the parents of the children in the research project granted written consent. The children were injected with the same strain of hepatitis that was already prevalent at the hospital.

The physicians–researchers in charge of the project received intense criticism by subjecting the children to this research. The researchers defended their actions by stating that

a. The children that were used as subjects were unharmed or, at least, not made any more ill than they already were.
b. The children may have even benefited, since they were placed on an isolated unit and thus were not exposed to other infectious diseases.
c. The children in the study may have had a subclinical infection, which would render them immune to the hepatitis virus.
d. The children may have been better off as a result of the research, since the study added to the growth of information about the disease.
e. All the parents had given their informed consent.

The medical community was outraged about the experiment and raised the following objections:

a. Mentally retarded persons, especially children, should not be used for research experimentation
b. The children were unable to defend or speak for themselves
c. There is a greater possibility of abuse with children than with adults
d. The parents may have been coerced to grant consent, since the hospital was full and there was only space to admit children into the hepatitis unit
e. The experiment did not appear to be therapeutic
f. The benefits to the hospital and the community at large were minimal
g. The experiments were designed to confirm *existing* studies about the effects of gamma globulin immunization for hepatitis

   h. Researchers withheld from the nonresearch children (control group) an inoculation that may have been effective against hepatitis.

Since 800 children were isolated from other children, they did not acquire infectious diseases prevalent at the time. Ultimately, the claim that the children in the research study benefited from the project was upheld in court.

[*Note*: The following answers are examples of potential solutions to the questions. There may be many other suggestions made by the instructor and students.]

Case Questions

1. What are the pros (positives) of this study?

The children placed into this special unit did benefit since they were not exposed to other infectious diseases. However, this was not purpose of placing the children on the special unit—it was an unexpected benefit.

2. What are the cons (negatives) of this study?
> The children could not voice their consent.
> The parents were coerced to have their mentally retarded children placed into this study since that was the only way the children could be admitted into Willowbrook.
> The most important negative of this study is that the children were injected with the hepatitis virus.

3. Is society ever justified in permitting this type of research when the outcome benefits some members of society? Why or why not?

If by "this type of research" we mean testing mentally retarded children without their own consent, then the answer must be a resounding NO.

4. Should public funds be used to pay for this type of research on children? Why or why not?

This question is similar to the rationale behind the Hyde Amendment relating to abortion. Public funds, which are from U.S. taxpayers, should not be used for procedures that many oppose.

5. Some say that the final outcome of the Willowbrook case falls into a "gray area" of ethics in which there is no one clear answer. If this is the case, then, in your opinion, where do we draw the line on testing children?

Suggested responses:
> The answer does not seem to lie with "parental consent" since the children in this case all had the consent of their parents.
> The federal government may have to step in and provide the legal grounds for experimentation on children since the children cannot voice their own consent.

SUPPLEMENTAL QUESTIONS

Chapter Review

Cover the terms in the left-hand column with a piece of paper. Read the statement and fill in the blank with the answer before uncovering the correct response.

Artificial insemination

In-vitro fertilization

surrogate

Baby M

_____ _____ is the injection of seminal fluid that contains sperm into the female's vagina from her husband or donor. _____ _____ _____ occurs when ovum and sperm cells are combined outside of the woman's body and then implanted into the woman's uterus. An infertile couple who does not wish to adopt has the option of _____ motherhood. The option has raised several ethical questions, such as in the famous _____ _____ case in which the New Jersey Supreme Court ruled against the enforceability of the agreed-upon contract.

Sterilization

Therapeutic

eugenic

involuntary

_____ is the process of termination of the ability to produce offspring. _____ sterilization may be necessary if the mother's life or mental health is threatened. In some cases, the procedure is performed to certain categories of people, such as the insane, and is referred to as _____ or _____ sterilizations.

viable

spontaneous

induced

Abortion is the termination of a pregnancy before the fetus is _____, or able to survive outside the uterus. A(n) _____ abortion is one that occurs naturally without interference, whereas a(n) _____ abortion is caused by artificial means.

Hyde

Funding for abortion is limited by the _____ Amendment.

genetics

eugenics

Cooley's anemia

cystic fibrosis

hemophilia

amniocentesis

The science of _____ is the study of heredity and its variations, in contrast to _____, which is the science that studies methods for controlling certain characteristics in offspring. The study of this science can aid in identifying hereditary disorders such as _____ _____, which is a rare form of anemia; _____ _____, a disorder of exocrine glands; and _____, a bleeding disorder. The most common means of genetic testing during pregnancy is through _____.

wrongful

birth

In some cases in which a baby is born with severe defects that greatly affect the quality of life, a _____-_____ claim is brought by the parents.

Multiple Choice

Select the one best response to the following questions.

1. For most surgical procedures, federal law requires
   a. patients' written consent
   b. implied consent
   c. spousal consent
   d. a and c
   e. a, b, and c

   Answer: a

2. A spontaneous abortion is
   a. caused by artificial means
   b. one that occurs naturally
   c. referred to as a miscarriage
   d. b and c
   e. a, b, and c

   Answer: d

3. All of the following are hereditary disorders except
   a. cooley's anemia
   b. cystic fibrosis
   c. huntington's chorea
   d. hemophilia
   e. all of the above are hereditary disorders

   Answer: e

4. The most common means of genetic testing during pregnancy is through
   a. stem cell research
   b. amniocentesis
   c. phenylketonuria
   d. human genome project
   e. in-vitro fertilization

   Answer: b

5. In *Roe v. Wade,* the U.S. Supreme Court ruled
   a. the state may not regulate medical conditions under which an abortion procedure is performed
   b. the state can regulate abortion during the first three months of pregnancy
   c. induced abortion is illegal under the Fourteenth Amendment
   d. the state may not prohibit abortions during the third trimester of pregnancy
   e. the state could not prohibit abortions that save the mother's life

   Answer: e

6. Parents of a healthy baby, after an unsuccessful tubal ligation, may sue the physician for
   a. wrongful conception
   b. eugenics
   c. wrongful life
   d. conscience clause
   e. *guardian ad litem*

   Answer: a

7. In-vitro fertilization involves
   a. ethical issues dealing with what happens to unused cells
   b. ovum and sperm cells combined outside the woman's body
   c. the injection of seminal fluid into the female's vagina
   d. a and b
   e. a, b, and c

   Answer: d

8. Funding for abortion
   a. can only be regulated by the state legislature
   b. is limited by the Hyde Amendment
   c. is covered by the Medicaid program in all situations
   d. is unconstitutional
   e. is not controlled by the government

   Answer: b

9. A cancerous tumor of the eye that is fatal if untreated is
   a. hemophilia
   b. retinoblastoma
   c. sickle-cell anemia
   d. phenylketonuria
   e. cystic fibrosis

   Answer: b

10. Ethical dilemmas relating to surrogate motherhood include
    a. reducing birth to a legal arrangement and the exchange of money
    b. potential court battles over custody of the child
    c. future emotional distress for the child
    d. potential embarrassment for the gestational mother
    e. all of the above

    Answer: e

True/False Questions

1. The Hyde Amendment forbids all abortions using federal funds. (false)

2. One-fourth of all hospitalizations and deaths among babies are due to hereditary or congenital disorders. (true)

3. A spontaneous abortion is caused by the illegal ingestion of chemicals. (false)

4. A viable fetus is unable to survive outside of the uterus. (false)

5. The gestational mother is a woman who requests a surrogate mother to carry a child for her. (false)

6. The term *embryo* is used for a baby during its last three months before birth. (false)

7. It is legal for a man to allow his semen to be used to impregnate a woman other than his wife or mate. (true)

8. In the Baby M case the surrogate mother was granted custody of the child by the court. (false)

9. The abbreviation AIDS stands for artificial insemination donor. (false)

10. In recent years many children born as a result of fertility drugs have survived. (true)

Short Answer Questions

1. Name the three most recent methods of assisted conception.
   a. artificial insemination
   b. in-vitro fertilization
   c. surrogate motherhood

2. What are the different types of sterilization?
   a. voluntary
   b. therapeutic
   c. incidental
   d. involuntary

3. Describe a surrogate mother.

   A surrogate mother is a woman who agrees to bear a child for another couple.

4. What was the result of the *Griswold v. Connecticut* case?

   The U.S. Supreme Court struck down the Connecticut law that made it illegal for a physician to prescribe contraceptives for a woman. The Court declared that it is a woman's constitutional right to privacy to use contraceptives if she wishes.

5. What was the result of the *Skinner v. Oklahoma* case?

   The court held that a law permitting sterilization of habitual criminals violates the equal protection clause of the Fourteenth Amendment. The court further stated that the right to bear children is one of the basic civil rights of mankind and is fundamental to the existence of the human race.

6. What are two categories of abortion?
   a. Spontaneous abortion occurs naturally, without interference. It can result from an illness or injury of the mother, her physical inability to bear a child, or other causes.
   b. Induced abortion is caused by artificial means such as medications or a surgical procedure. It can be performed to save the life of the mother (therapeutic) or to cause the death of the fetus.

7. What are the three divisions of life during the mother's gestational period?
   a. First trimester—first three months
   b. Second trimester—second three months
   c. Third trimester—third three months

8. What are some of the recommendations regarding abortion that result from the *Roe v. Wade* decision?
   a. First trimester abortions should be performed in hospitals.
   b. The approval process for abortions should include other physicians in addition to the woman's attending physician.
   c. Viability of the fetus needs to be carefully defined.
   d. The woman should wait for a designated period of time before having the abortion and should receive counseling.
   e. Certain medical procedures, such as partial-birth abortion, cannot be used.
   f. The father's consent should be obtained.

9. What is the Hyde Amendment?

   This bill, sponsored by Rep. Henry Hyde (R-Ill.), is now a law stating that federal funds cannot be used for an abortion except to save the life of the mother or in the case of incest or rape.

TEACHING STRATEGIES

1. Ask students to research the laws governing artificial insemination donation. Instruct students to prepare a short presentation about the most eye-opening aspect of the law that they encountered.
2. Have the class discuss whether there should be a ruling that requires mandatory parental consent to abortion. Break students into small groups (four or five) and ask them to present their group opinion, and then summarize the opinions of the group members for a general class discussion.
3. Ask students to search the newspaper for articles about issues discussed in this chapter. Have each student bring an article to class and then lead a class discussion about the article.
4. Have the students prepare flash cards for the key terms (glossary).

Death and Dying

CHAPTER SYNOPSIS

The ethical issues relating to death and dying are especially sensitive. The one point of agreement that people have when discussing these sensitive issues is that the dying patient must be treated with dignity. This chapter includes information on the dying process, definitions of death, the stages of dying, quality-of-life issues, the use of medications for the dying patient, hospice care, palliative care, viatical settlements, advance directives, choices of life and death, the death certificate, and medical examiner cases.

Chapter Lecture Outline	**Instructor's Notes**
I. The Dying Process 　A. *Expired* means "died." 　B. Modern medicine has enabled people to live longer and survive illnesses that once caused death. This has created some ethical and moral dilemmas. 　C. Legal definition of death 　　1. The actual determination of death has also become critical in the past few decades due to advances in medicine such as organ transplantation and life-support systems. 　　2. Karen Ann Quinlan Case (1975) 　　　a. Represented the first time a family requested the court to approve the removal of a respirator from a permanently comatose patient and won the case. 　　　b. *Comatose* is a word used to refer to a person who is in a permanently vegetative state. 　　　c. EEG—an electroencephalogram is a test that measures brain activity. 　　3. Criteria for death—Certain criteria or standards assist in the determination that death has occurred. 　　　a. Rigor mortis or stiffness that occurs in a dead body. 　　　b. Loss of heartbeat. 　　　c. Loss of body color. 　　4. Debate over using cardiac definition or brain-oriented definition of death. 　　　a. Cardiac death occurs when the heart has stopped functioning. 　　　b. However, many people believe that a cardiac-oriented definition of death is inadequate.	

Chapter Lecture Outline	Instructor's Notes

5. Brain-oriented death
  a. Means that death occurs when there is irreversible cessation of all brain function.
  b. Also found in irreversible coma.
  c. Harvard Criteria used for a definition of irreversible coma includes consideration of the following:
    i. Whether the patient is unreceptive and unresponsive with a total unawareness of externally applied, and even painful, stimuli.
    ii. Whether the patient has no spontaneous movements or breathing, as well as an absence of response to stimuli such as pain, touch, sound, or light.
    iii. Whether the patient has no reflexes with fixed dilated pupils, lack of eye movement, and lack of deep tendon reflexes.
6. Uniform Determination of Death Act
  a. Many groups object to the brain-death criterion.
  b. This act says that an individual is dead if the individual has sustained either
    i. Irreversible cessation of circulatory and respiratory function, OR
    ii. Irreversible cessation of all function of the entire brain, including the brain stem.
D. Withdrawing versus withholding treatment
  1. Withdrawing life-sustaining treatment means to discontinue it after it has started.
  2. Withholding life-sustaining treatment never starting treatment.
E. Active euthanasia versus passive euthanasia
  1. Active euthanasia, the intentional killing of the terminally ill such as by a lethal dose of medication, is illegal in all jurisdictions in the United States, with the possible exception of Oregon.
  2. Passive euthanasia, or allowing a patient to die naturally, is legal everywhere. Includes withholding basic needs such as artificial hydration and artificial nutritional needs.
F. The slippery slope argument of assisted suicide
  1. Some ethicists argue that if society allows assisted suicide, it could lead to legalized murder.
  2. The "slippery slope" might eventually allow us to "slip back" and have a diminished respect for life.
G. Direct versus indirect killing
  1. The double-effect doctrine recognizes that an action may have two consequences: one desired (and intended) and one undesired (and unintended).
  2. An "act" can be an act of omission.
H. Ordinary versus extraordinary means
  1. Ordinary means—The term *ordinary* refers to a treatment or procedure that is morally required, such as fluids and comfort measures.
  2. *Extraordinary measures* refer to those procedures and treatments that are morally expendable (do not serve any useful purpose, such as using further chemotherapy in the final days of a cancer patient's life).	

Chapter Lecture Outline	Instructor's Notes

I. Right to die legislation or right to refuse treatment—Courts have rules that patients must be mentally competent in order to make their own decisions.

J. Stages of dying—Dr. Elisabeth Kübler-Ross devoted much of her life to studying the dying process. She divided the process into five stages that she believed the patient, family members, and caregivers all go through.

    1. Denial

    2. Anger

    3. Bargaining

    4. Depression

    5. Acceptance

II. Quality-of-Life Issues

  A. General health

  B. Physical functioning

  C. Role limitations

  D. Pain

  E. Social function

  F. Vitality

  G. Mental health

III. Use of Medications

  A. Physicians reluctant to prescribe heavy doses of narcotics for terminal patients due to fear of addiction.

  B. New belief that dying patient's pain should be controlled with adequate medication.

IV. Hospice Care

  A. Originated in France to keep a terminal patient as pain free as possible

  B. Called "death with dignity."

  C. Focus on comfort measures, emotional support, and pain-free environment.

V. Palliative Care

  A. The total care of patients whose disease is no longer responsive to curative therapy.

  B. Care for the terminally ill patient consisting of comfort measures and symptom control.

VI. Viatical Settlements—Allow people with terminal illnesses, such as AIDS, to obtain money from their life insurance policies by selling them.

VII. Advance Directives—Also known as living wills.

VIII. Choices of Life and Death

  A. Suicide

  B. The case of the conjoined twins

IX. Mechanical Heart Recipient—First mechanical heart was implanted into a 59-year-old man, Robert Tools, in 2002.

LEARNING OBJECTIVES

(Student answers may vary.)

1. Define the glossary terms.

   Active euthanasia   actively ending the life of or killing a patient who is terminally ill.

   Brain death   an irreversible coma from which a patient does not recover; results in the cessation of brain activity.

   Cardiopulmonary   heart and lung function.

   Comatose   vegetative condition.

   Electroencephalogram (EEG)   test to measure brain activity.

   Expired   died.

   Hypothermia   state in which body temperature is below normal range.

   Mercy killing   another term for voluntary euthanasia.

   Palliative care   care for terminally ill patients consisting of comfort measures and symptom control.

   Passive euthanasia   allowing a patient to die by forgoing treatment.

   Quality of life   the physiological status, emotional well-being, functional status, and life, in general, of the individual.

   Rigor mortis   stiffness that occurs in a dead body.

   Substitute judgment rule   used when decision must be made for a person who cannot make his or her wishes known.

   Terminally ill   one whose death is determined to be inevitable.

   Viatical settlements   allow people with terminal illnesses, such as AIDS, to obtain money from their life insurance policies by selling them.

   Withdrawing life-sustaining treatment   discontinuing a treatment or procedure, such as artificial ventilation, after it has started.

   Withholding life-sustaining treatment   failing to start a treatment or procedure, such as artificial ventilation.

2. Discuss the difference between cardiac and brain-oriented death.

   Cardiac death, or the legal definition of death, occurs when the heart has stopped functioning.

   Brain-oriented death occurs when there is an irreversible cessation of all brain function. This does not necessarily mean that the heart has stopped functioning.

3. Describe the Harvard criteria for a definition of irreversible coma.

   Based on this criteria, the considerations include whether the patient

   a. Is unreceptive and unresponsive, with a total unawareness of externally applied, and even painful, stimuli.
   b. Has no spontaneous movements or breathing as well as an absence of response to stimuli such as pain, touch, sound, or light.
   c. Has no reflexes, with fixed dilated pupils, lack of eye movement, and lack of deep tendon reflexes.

4. Discuss the pros and cons of euthanasia.

Responses may vary but could include the following:

Arguments made by people in favor:

a. Respect for patient self-determination.
b. Provides a means for harvesting viable organs.
c. Provides relief for the family of a patient with an irreversible condition or terminal disease.
d. Provides a means to end a terminally ill person's suffering.

Arguments made by people in opposition:

a. There is no certainty regarding death.
b. Modern technology may find a cure for a terminal disease.
c. Families undergoing financial strain due to the burden of a dying relative may use euthanasia to relieve the financial burden.
d. Euthanasia might be used indiscriminately.
e. It is not good for society to allow physicians to kill patients or patients to kill themselves.
f. There is value and dignity in human life.
g. The sick and dying may have a fear of involuntary euthanasia if euthanasia is legalized.
h. Only God has domination over life.

5. Provide examples of ordinary versus extraordinary means used in the treatment of the terminally ill.

Ordinary means include fluids, pain-reducing medications, and comfort measures such as turning patients.

Extraordinary means include respirators, feeding tubes, chemotherapy, and intravenous therapy.

6. List and discuss the five stages of dying as described by Dr. Kübler-Ross.

a. Denial—a refusal to believe that dying is taking place.
b. Anger—at this stage, the patient may be angry with everyone and may express an intense anger toward God and even healthcare professionals.
c. Bargaining—this involves attempting to gain time by making promises to God in return for a cure.
d. Depression—there is a deep sadness over the loss of health, independence, and eventually life.
e. Acceptance—this stage is reached when there is a sense of peace and calm.

7. Discuss eleven treatments that might be ordered for the critically or terminally ill.

a. Cardiopulmonary resuscitation (CPR)—a lifesaving technique for accident and heart attack victims when their hearts have stopped beating. It consists of applying chest compressions and ventilation into the mouth until the heart begins to beat again.
b. Mechanical breathing or respirator—a mechanical device used for artificial ventilation of the lungs.
c. Tube feedings—nutritional support that consists of placing a tube within the patient's stomach either through the nose or directly into the gastrointestinal system.
d. Kidney dialysis—a medical treatment in which impurities or waste matter are removed from the patient's blood when the kidneys fail to function.
e. Chemotherapy—the use of chemicals that have a toxic effect on disease-producing organisms, such as cancer.

   f. Intravenous therapy—the administration of fluids by means of a tube inserted into the vein.

   g. Surgery—an invasive procedure, usually conducted under a general anesthetic, to remove a diseased organ or tissue, to repair the body, or as a diagnostic tool.

   h. Diagnostic tests—medical tests that help to determine the cause of a disease or abnormality.

   i. Antibiotics—medications used to fight disease and ward off illnesses such as pneumonia.

   j. Transfusions—the replacement of blood for ailments such as severe anemia or hemorrhage.

   k. Pain medications and palliative care—care used to relieve pain and discomfort.

THE CASE OF ROBERT W. AND LIFE SUPPORT

In September 1993, 50-year-old Robert W. was involved in a pickup truck accident that left him brain-damaged and unable to eat, drink, talk, or communicate his wishes. Two years later, his wife, Ruth, requested that her husband's doctors remove the feeding tubes that kept him alive. She stated that long before the accident, he had indicated that he would not wish to live in a helpless condition.

Robert's mother and sister objected to having his tubes removed and stated that he was minimally conscious and not comatose. The state Supreme Court ruled in favor of the mother and sister in August 2001. The court finding stated that families have no right to stop life support for conscious patients who are not terminally ill and who have left no explicit written instructions regarding the issue. Ironically, the patient died of pneumonia, with the feeding tubes still in place, one month before the court's ruling on the case. The Court, in a six to zero decision, stated "absent clear and convincing evidence" that Ruth's decision was in accordance with her husband's own wishes or best interests, it would not have allowed the removal of life support.

Courts had previously allowed the removal of life support in cases in which the patient is terminally ill or in a coma-like state. But the law is unclear on how families can proceed when patients are conscious but unable to express their wishes.

Case Questions

1. What should Robert have done before he became ill?

   This case and the Terri Schiavo case discussed in this chapter are both relating to the same issue—the lack of a written statement regarding their wishes if they should become incapacitated. These cases demonstrate the need for people to have clearly written and witnessed advance directives before they become patients.

2. Should the wishes of his wife to have his feeding tube removed or the wishes of his mother and sister to have left it in place be given priority?

   There is no simple and correct answer to this dilemma. This is an ethical case much like the biblical story of King Solomon and the two women who both claimed that they were the mother of the same baby. The women went to the wise Solomon for him to determine who the rightful mother of the baby was. He said that they should cut the baby in half and each woman could have exactly one-half of the baby. One mother spoke up immediately and said that the other woman could have the entire baby. Solomon declared that the mother who spoke up to save the child's life was the rightful mother.

3. Since Robert was brain-damaged and semi-conscious when he died of pneumonia, could he have been considered terminally ill? Why or why not?

Pneumonia is not considered to be a terminal illness since it can be treated with antibiotics. However, when a patient is debilitated because of another disease or physical condition, then pneumonia can result in death. The fact that Robert was semi-conscious made this a difficult decision for the court. The same was true of the Terri Schiavo case.

POINTS TO PONDER (FROM TEXTBOOK)

Teaching note: These questions are meant to promote critical thinking and classroom discussion. The student responses will vary.

1. What do you say to a dying patient who asks you, "Why me?"

2. What are some major concerns of family members of a dying patient?

3. Does an individual have the right to determine when he or she wishes to die? Why or why not?

4. What are the benefits of hospice care for the terminally ill?

5. What is your opinion regarding Jack Kevorkian's behavior?

6. Why is the ability to determine when death has occurred so critical in today's healthcare environment?

7. What is cardiac death?

8. Can a patient write an advance directive requesting maximum care?

REVIEW QUESTIONS (FROM TEXTBOOK)
Discussion Questions

1. Explain the statement, "Healthcare practitioners often find it more difficult to withdraw treatment after it has started than to withhold treatment."

   It is very difficult, both emotionally and legally, to remove a patient from a life-support system. Many healthcare professionals who work with the terminally ill prefer that a decision about using life support be made by the patient and the family before the need arises.

2. What attributes do you think a *guardian ad litem* should possess?

   Responses will vary. Answers might include objectivity, intelligence, compassion, and honesty.

3. Describe a situation in which passive euthanasia might be acceptable.

   Answers may vary. Some students may believe that passive euthanasia is never acceptable. One example of passive euthanasia might be to remove painful intravenous (IVs) tubes from a dying patient. Another example is discontinuing chemotherapy for a terminally ill cancer patient if it is found to be ineffective and burdensome.

4. Discuss reasons against the practice of euthanasia.
   a. There is no certainty regarding death.
   b. Modern technology may find a cure for a terminal disease.
   c. Families undergoing financial strain due to the burden of a dying relative may use euthanasia to relieve the financial burden.
   d. Euthanasia might be used indiscriminately.

    e. It is not good for society to allow physicians to kill patients or patients to kill themselves.

    f. There is value and dignity in human life.

    g. The sick and dying may have a fear of involuntary euthanasia if euthanasia is legalized.

    h. Only God has domination over life.

5. How would you describe the following advance directives to a patient: durable power of attorney for healthcare, Uniform Anatomical Gift Act, and a DNR order?

    a. Durable power of attorney for healthcare is a legal document that empowers another person, or proxy, to make healthcare decisions for an incompetent patient. It goes into effect after the patient becomes incompetent and only pertains to healthcare decisions.

    b. Uniform Anatomical Gift Act allows persons 18 years of age or older and of sound mind to make a gift of any part of their body for purposes of medical research or transplantation.

    c. A DNR order is placed into patients' charts or medical records to indicate that they do not wish to be resuscitated if they stop breathing.

6. What are the pros and cons of a viatical settlement?

The advantage of a viatical settlement is that persons with a terminal illness, such as AIDS, can obtain money from their life insurance policies by selling the policy. The rationale is that the person needs the money while he or she is still alive and does not wish to leave it to a survivor.

The disadvantage is that there is no clear knowledge of exactly how long a person, even a terminally ill person, will live. Consequently, the relatively small amount of money the person receives from the viatical settlement may not take care of his or her needs until death occurs. In addition, there are tax liabilities associated with receiving a cash settlement that would further reduce the amount of money received. A one-time-only cash payment received in a viatical settlement could disqualify a person who needs to receive a means-based entitlement (based on the amount of income one has), such as Medicaid.

Matching

Column A	Column B
1. proxy	b. person acting on behalf of another person
2. expired	h. died
3. mercy killing	d. euthanasia
4. comatose	f. vegetative condition
5. rigor mortis	e. stiffness that occurs in death
6. hypothermia	a. body temperature is below normal
7. stages of dying	j. Kübler-Ross' reflection on the dying process
8. cardiac death	c. legal definition of death
9. brain death	i. irreversible coma
10. active euthanasia	g. legal term for killing a patient

Multiple Choice

1. The practice of allowing a terminally ill patient to die by foregoing treatment is called
   a. active euthanasia
   b. passive euthanasia
   c. mercy killing
   d. a and c
   e. b and c

   Answer: e

2. An electroencephalogram is used to
   a. reverse a coma patient's condition
   b. measure cardiopulmonary function
   c. measure brain function
   d. reverse the condition of hypothermia
   e. reverse the condition of rigor mortis

   Answer: c

3. The Uniform Determination of Death Act
   a. provides a definition of active euthanasia
   b. provides a definition of brain death
   c. is also called the doctrine of double effect
   d. mandates that everyone entering a nursing home must provide a written document stating the care he or she wishes to receive
   e. discusses the treatments that might be used for a comatose patient

   Answer: b

4. Criteria or standards for death include
   a. rigor mortis
   b. hypothermia
   c. loss of body color
   d. biological disintegration
   e. all of the above

   Answer: e

5. What is the ethical term that is used to morally justify the removal of a cancerous uterus from a pregnant patient?
   a. mercy killing
   b. extraordinary means
   c. ordinary means
   d. doctrine of double effect
   e. advance directive

   Answer: d

6. Another term meaning death is
   a. comatose
   b. expired
   c. proxy
   d. terminally ill
   e. hypothermia

   Answer: b

7. A hospice provides for
   a. palliative care
   b. pain medications
   c. in-patient care
   d. home care
   e. all of the above

   Answer: e

8. Extraordinary care means that when caring for a comatose patient, one should include
   a. CPR and mechanical breathing
   b. chemotherapy
   c. turning and hydration
   d. a and b only
   e. a, b, and c

   Answer: e

9. The Karen Ann Quinlan case involved
   a. mercy killing
   b. removal of hydration from a comatose patient
   c. removal of a respirator from a comatose patient
   d. a heart transplant
   e. court order for a surgical procedure on an incompetent patient

   Answer: c

10. Terms referring to heart and pulmonary function include
    a. cardiac
    b. comatose
    c. hypothermia
    d. cardiopulmonary
    e. none of the above

    Answer: d

Fill in the Blanks

1. The substitute judgment rule is used when decisions must be made for a person who cannot make his or her wishes known.
2. DNR stands for Do Not Resuscitate.
3. A term that refers to both heart and lung function is cardiopulmonary.
4. The care given to terminally ill patients that consists of comfort measures and symptom control is referred to as palliative care.
5. A type of settlement that allows people with terminal illnesses, such as AIDS, to obtain money from their insurance policies by selling them is a viatical settlement.
6. A terminally ill person is one whose death is inevitable.
7. A test used to measure brain activity in a comatose patient is the electroencephalogram.
8. When a person has died, he or she is said to have expired.
9. The set of conditions that must be present to determine if a patient is in a irreversible coma is known as the Harvard Criteria.
10. Allowing a patient to die by foregoing any further treatment is known as passive euthanasia.

PUT IT INTO PRACTICE

Find a recent obituary in your local newspaper. What information does it give about the deceased person?

WEB HUNT

1. Using the website *www.iom.edu*, search for the report "Improving Palliative Care for Cancer." This is a report by the National Cancer Policy Board of the Institute of Medicine and National Research Council. Summarize the report findings.
2. Search the website of the National Hospice and Palliative Care Organization (*www.nhpco.org*) and look under "find a hospice program." Using this listing, find a hospice in your area.

CASE STUDY

Glenn Ross, a 55-year-old man, was diagnosed with inoperable pancreatic cancer. His prognosis was poor; he was given about six months to live. He underwent several series of chemotherapy treatments, but they were of no benefit. He continued to lose weight, suffered from nausea, and became weaker. After three months of chemotherapy treatments, he stated that he wanted no further treatment. He became bedridden and was admitted into a nursing home for terminal care. Glenn's son, who lived in another state, arrived at the nursing home and demanded that his father's physician be called immediately. The son wanted his father to be hospitalized and placed on chemotherapy immediately. When the physician explained that there was little hope for the father's recovery, the son threatened to sue the physician for withdrawal of care.

Case Questions

1. Identify the ethical issues in the case.

   A major ethical issue is that the son is attempting to overturn the father's wishes to discontinue chemotherapy. The physician has a duty to respect the patient's wishes if at all possible. Therefore, the physician is ethically correct in withdrawing the chemotherapy.

2. In your opinion, does the son have a legitimate reason to sue the physician? Why or why not?

   Glenn, who is still alive and able to make decisions on his behalf, has already made his wishes clear to the physician. All physicians should document such conversations in the patient's medical record so that the entire healthcare team can comply with the patient's wishes. In addition, this provides a protection for the physician if the son should sue him. The son has very little basis for a lawsuit, since Glenn is still alive to state his wishes. However, anyone can institute a lawsuit. The son may still sue the physician, but probably will not win the case.

3. What are the possible solutions to this case?

   With the father's permission, the healthcare team, including clergy, could speak with the son and explain what treatment has already been given to the father. Perhaps if the son had a better understanding of the progression of the father's disease and treatment, he would be more open to agreeing with his father's wishes.

The father has already made his decision. He is being cared for in a nursing home without the use of chemotherapy. If the son wishes to further challenge this decision, he will have to take the matter to court.

4. What might the physician have done to prevent the confrontation with Glenn's son?

The physician cannot discuss the father's case with the son unless the father has given his consent. Therefore, the physician should have asked for this consent. He could then have spoken with the son to prepare him for the father's decision. The physician should explain to the son that since his father is still coherent, he is able to make decisions about his own care and treatment. Better communication might have prevented some of the problems in this case.

5. Using Dr. Kübler-Ross's five stages of dying or grief, what stage is Glenn in? What stage is his son in?

From the information we have in the case, we can surmise that Glenn is in the acceptance stage while his son appears to be at the denial or even anger stage.

SUPPLEMENTAL QUESTIONS

Chapter Review

Cover the terms in the left-hand column with a piece of paper. Read the statement and fill in the blank with the answer before uncovering the correct response.

expired
corpse

A person who dies, or is said to have _____, is no longer treated the same way as a living human being. This in no way means that the body of the deceased person, also known as a _____, can be handled in a disrespectful way.

cardiac
irreversible

hypothermia

A _____ death defines a person as deceased when there is an _____ cessation of respiratory and circulatory functions. Sometimes, the cessation of breathing and pulse are reversible, such as in the case of _____ (a state in which the body temperature is below normal range).

brain oriented

brain

The _____-_____ definition of death has gained favor in many countries. This definition of death means that there is an irreversible cessation of all _____ functions.

Active euthanasia

euthanasia

_____ _____ is actively ending the life of the terminally ill, such as by injection of a lethal dose of medication. However, passive _____ is allowing a patient to die naturally.

five/denial

depression

Dr. Kübler-Ross has divided the dying process into _____ stages. These stages include _____, a refusal to believe that dying is taking place; anger; bargaining; _____ or a deep sadness, and acceptance.

Advance directives

limit

incompetent

mercy killing

Suicide

_____ _____ are popularly known as living wills. The reason for a living will is to _____ the type and amount of treatment that patients will receive if they should become _____ and have a poor prognosis.

Voluntary euthanasia, or _____ _____, is the action of a second person to hasten the death of a patient who wishes to die. _____ involves only the actions of the person seeking death.

Multiple Choice

Select the one best response to the following questions.

1. The Karen Ann Quinlan case is an example of
   a. withholding treatment
   b. active euthanasia
   c. withdrawing treatment
   d. physician-assisted suicide
   e. b and d

   Answer: c

2. The unintended death of a fetus caused by the removal of a cancerous uterus is considered
   a. an action fitting within the double-effect doctrine
   b. indirect killing
   c. unethical by groups such as the AMA and Catholic Church
   d. a and b only
   e. a, b, and c

   Answer: d

3. The stage of dying in which the patient may indicate a need to talk is
   a. denial
   b. depression
   c. bargaining
   d. acceptance
   e. anger

   Answer: c

4. People who are in favor of euthanasia offer the following reason(s):
   a. there is no certainty regarding death
   b. it is a means for harvesting viable organs
   c. there is value and dignity in every human life
   d. modern technology may find a cure for terminal disease
   e. all of the above

   Answer: b

5. A legal document that goes into effect after the person becomes incompetent and only pertains to healthcare decisions is a
   a. uniform Anatomical Gift Act
   b. passive euthanasia
   c. DNR order
   d. mercy killing
   e. durable power of attorney for healthcare

   Answer: e

6. Suspicious cases include death

   a. caused by criminal abortion
   b. of a violent nature
   c. of a child under the age of 2 if death results from an unknown cause
   d. a and b
   e. a, b, and c

   Answer: e

7. Advice regarding the course of medical treatment can be given by

   a. any healthcare professional
   b. no one; it is unethical for anyone to give advice to a terminally ill patient
   c. healthcare professionals familiar with the patient
   d. a physician
   e. none of the above

   Answer: d

8. Ordinary means refer to procedures

   a. that do not serve a useful purpose
   b. that are morally required
   c. not morally justified
   d. such as administering chemotherapy to a cancer patient in the final days of life
   e. that involve a great burden but prolong life

   Answer: b

9. A person is legally dead only after

   a. cardiac death
   b. irreversible coma
   c. brain-oriented death
   d. laws vary from state to state
   e. irreversible cessation of respiratory and circulatory functions

   Answer: d

10. A living will

    a. is an advance directive
    b. can be verbal if the instructions are given to a physician
    c. must be approved by a physician
    d. a and c
    e. a, b, and c

    Answer: a

True/False Questions

1. Another term for voluntary euthanasia is suicide. (false)

2. A comatose patient is said to be in a vegetative state. (true)

3. Withdrawing life-sustaining treatment may require a court order. (true)

4. Death by prescription is legal only in the state of Nevada. (false)

5. Passive euthanasia is legal in all states. (true)

6. Nancy Cruzan's parents sought help from the American Civil Liberties Union with her case. (true)

7. Ordinary care, or means, of taking care of a dying patient, refers to the administration of fluids, nutrition, and frequent turning of the patient. (true)

8. Artificial means of nutrition, such as a feeding tube, are considered within the context of ordinary means. (false)

9. Research surveys suggest that cancer patients are receiving adequate pain medications. (false)

10. Palliative care is given in order to try to save a patient's life. (false)

Short Answer Questions

1. What are Kübler-Ross's five stages of dying?
   a. Denial
   b. Anger
   c. Bargaining
   d. Depression
   e. Acceptance

2. What seven things must be included on the death certificate?
   a. Name and address of decedent
   b. Age
   c. Place and date of birth
   d. Name of parents (including mother's maiden name)
   e. Birthplace of parents
   f. Race
   g. Decedent's occupation

3. What are the Harvard Criteria for a Definition of Irreversible Coma?
   a. Unreceptive and unresponsive, with a total unawareness of externally applied, and even painful, stimuli.
   b. No spontaneous movements or breathing, as well as an absence of response to stimuli.
   c. No reflexes, with fixed dilated pupils, lack of eye movement, and lack of deep tendon reflexes.

4. What is active euthanasia?

   Active euthanasia is actively ending the life of or killing a patient who is terminally ill.

5. What are the two definitions of death?
   a. Cardiac death
   b. Brain-oriented death

6. In addition to the loss of a heartbeat, what are some indications of death?
   a. Significant drop in body temperature
   b. Loss of body color
   c. Rigor mortis
   d. Biological disintegration

7. What are four ethical considerations when dealing with a critically ill person?
   a. Withdrawing versus withholding treatment
   b. Active euthanasia versus passive euthanasia
   c. Direct versus indirect killing
   d. Ordinary versus extraordinary means

8. What are some of the measures to assess quality of life?
   a. General health
   b. Physical functioning
   c. Role limitations, such as within the family
   d. Pain
   e. Social function
   f. Vitality
   g. Mental health

9. What measures does palliative care include?
   a. Frequent turning and bathing
   b. Oral fluids
   c. Listening to the patient
   d. Controlling symptoms such as shortness of breath
   e. Treating depression
   f. Massage

10. Why did the surgeons attempt to separate conjoined twins Ladan and Laleh Bijani when the chances for survival were apparently very slim?

    The surgeons stated that the women were adults and thus capable of making decisions about their medical treatment. There was an expectation that the women had a chance of survival. In addition, the twins had left instructions with their next-of-kin that they wished to be separated no matter what the surgeons encountered once they started the surgery.

TEACHING STRATEGIES

1. Invite a hospice nurse into class to discuss the hospice concept. Ask him or her to give examples of patients who might benefit from this type of care.
2. Invite an attorney who is familiar with advance directives to talk to the students in depth about living wills.
3. Have students research the Karen Ann Quinlan case. Ask them to provide another possible solution to the case. Have the class discuss these various options.
4. Have small groups of students research humane and inhumane methods of execution that have been used throughout history and then report their findings to the class.
4. Conduct a "kangaroo court" trying Dr. Jack Kevorkian, a physician who was convicted and sent to prison for practicing assisted euthanasia. Half of the class can represent the state, and the other half can represent the defendant. Go to this website to learn more about the pathologist, Jack Kevorkian: http://en.wikipedia.org/wiki/Jack_Kevorkian.
5. Have the students prepare flash cards for the key terms (glossary).

Test Bank

CHAPTER 1: INTRODUCTION TO MEDICAL LAW, ETHICS, AND BIOETHICS

1. Which definition most accurately describes applied ethics?
   a. Legal application of moral standards that concern benefiting the public.
   b. Practical application of moral standards that concern benefiting the patient.
   c. Legal application of moral standards that benefit the patient.
   d. Legal application of moral standards that benefit the public.

2. Illegal actions are
   a. usually unethical.
   b. seldom unethical.
   c. not unethical.
   d. not related to ethics.

3. Laws are rules or required actions that are
   a. written by the people to control the actions of criminals.
   b. moral decisions about how the population should live.
   c. ethical considerations of the cultural beliefs of the population.
   d. prescribed by an authority and have a binding legal force.

4. The purpose of law is to
   a. provide a way of measuring our actions.
   b. punish us when our actions break the law.
   c. provide moral decision-making standards.
   d. a and b.

5. The study of a branch of philosophy related to morals, moral principles, and moral judgments is called
   a. ethics.
   b. law.
   c. medical practice acts.
   d. utilitarianism.

6. The quality of being virtuous is called.
   a. sympathy.
   b. utilitarianism.
   c. morality.
   d. empathy.

7. Unethical acts are
   a. not always illegal.
   b. always illegal.
   c. not related to the law.
   d. uncommon in society.

8. Which definition is correct for medical practice acts?
   a. The practice of medicine in all fifty states.
   b. The practice of medicine in a particular state, including the requirements and methods of licensure.
   c. The practice of medicine in all 50 states and what constitutes unprofessional conduct.
   d. The practice of medicine in a particular state, including the requirements and methods of certification.

9. Medical practice acts may include laws regarding
   a. conviction of a felony.
   b. unlicensed persons practicing medicine.
   c. improper record keeping.
   d. b and c.

10. The study of ethics includes the use of
    a. moral principles.
    b. moral judgments.
    c. logic.
    d. all of the above.

11. The mandate of medical ethics is the
    a. welfare and confidentiality of the patient must be of least concern.
    b. welfare and confidentiality of the patient must be of most concern.
    c. principle of the greatest good for the greatest number must be of most concern.
    d. principle of formal consideration of the interests of others must be of most concern.

12. Which definition best describes utilitarianism?
    a. Ethical theory based on the principle of the greatest good for the greatest number
    b. Legal ruling based on the principle of the greatest good for the greatest number
    c. Legal ruling based on small portions of society
    d. Based on moral entitlements by virtue of being human

13. An example of utilitarianism might include
    a. an organ for transplant going to the person needing it the most.
    b. providing Medicare for only those who need medical coverage.
    c. a duty to provide healthcare to all Americans.
    d. all of the above.

14. Rights-based ethics emphasizes the
    a. individual rights of persons.
    b. rights of society as a whole.
    c. duty of persons to adhere to laws.
    d. character traits of persons.

15. The purpose of medical professional organizations is to
    a. define the laws of the profession.
    b. punish medical professionals for breaking the law.
    c. set ethical standards for practice within the profession.
    d. determine salaries and benefits for medical professionals.

16. The purpose of a cost/benefit analysis in relation to medical care is to
    a. justify the cost of a treatment as compared to the benefit.
    b. justify only the benefit of a treatment.
    c. provide an estimate of the cost of a treatment.
    d. make sure no one "falls through the cracks" for treatment.

17. Empathy requires the ability to
    a. feel sorry for someone else.
    b. feel a sense of commitment to a person.
    c. understand the feelings of another person.
    d. have a distant and unemotional attitude toward the patient.

18. Which of the following is the best definition of confidentiality?
    a. Right of all employees to have certain procedures followed when they believe their rights are in jeopardy
    b. One person exerting power over another
    c. Faithfulness or commitment to a person or persons
    d. The ability to safeguard another person's information

19. Due process in the workplace refers to
    a. the right of all employers to certain procedures when their rights are in jeopardy.
    b. the responsibility of employers to provide a safe work environment.
    c. the right of all employees to certain procedures when their rights are in jeopardy.
    d. all of the above.

20. The *best* definition of sexual harassment is a form of sex discrimination in which
    a. males exert power over females.
    b. any one person exerts power over another.
    c. any one male exerts power over males.
    d. females exert power over males.

21. Extending equal pay requirements to all persons who are doing equal work is
    a. due process.
    b. cost/benefit analysis.
    c. comparable worth.
    d. fidelity.

22. A three-step model developed by Kenneth Blanchard and Norman Vincent Peale is used to evaluate
    a. alcoholism.
    b. legal issues.
    c. comparable worth.
    d. an ethical dilemma.

23. The best definition for ethics is
    a. sincerity and feeling.
    b. religious beliefs.
    c. moral principles.
    d. emotional responses.

24. A branch of applied or practical ethics is called
    a. medical ethics.
    b. biomedical ethics.
    c. bioethics.
    d. both b and c.

25. Bioethicists are
    a. specialists in the field of medical law.
    b. specialists who give thought to ethical concerns as they pertain to medicine and medical research.
    c. researchers in medical technology.
    d. all of the above.

CHAPTER 2: THE LEGAL SYSTEM

1. The Congress is the _____ branch of the federal government for the United States.
    a. executive
    b. legislative
    c. judicial
    d. constitutional

2. The individual states
    a. may vary on how they interpret and implement state laws.
    b. may vary on how they interpret and implement federal laws.
    c. must administer federal law the same.
    d. a and c.

3. The purpose of a constitution is to
    a. set up a government.
    b. define the power of the government to act.
    c. set limits on the government's power.
    d. all of the above.

4. Statutes are laws passed by
    a. the state legislature.
    b. Congress.
    c. the President.
    d. Congress or the state legislature.

5. A rule or law made by an agency is called a/an
    a. bill.
    b. regulation.
    c. statute.
    d. act.

6. Common law is established
    a. through court decision.
    b. federal law.
    c. state decision.
    d. municipal decisions.

7. Which definition is the best for precedent?
    a. The ruling of a current case that is applied to a current case when the facts are different
    b. The ruling in an early case that is applied to a subsequent case when the facts are the same
    c. *Let the decision stand*
    d. Liability for an injury to another person even if there was no intent to harm the other person

8. Civil law includes
    a. torts.
    b. contracts.
    c. medical malpractice.
    d. all of the above.

9. A civil injury or wrongful act committed against another person or property that results in harm and is compensated by money damages is
   a. civil law.
   b. tort law.
   c. contract law.
   d. administrative law.

10. Civil law is commonly handled and settled
    a. by the judge.
    b. by the governor.
    c. outside the courtroom.
    d. by the federal government.

11. Intentional torts include
    a. assault and battery.
    b. defamation.
    c. false imprisonment.
    d. all of the above.

12. Action taken to confine a patient against his or her will is
    a. defamation.
    b. false imprisonment.
    c. assault.
    d. battery.

13. Which is the best definition of libel?
    a. Speaking false and malicious words concerning another person, which brings injury to his or her reputation
    b. Making false and/or malicious statements about another person
    c. Any publication in print, writing, pictures, or signs that injures the reputation of another person
    d. Attempts to deceive another person

14. Professional exercise of the type of care that a reasonable person would use in a similar circumstance is
    a. standard of care.
    b. negligence.
    c. breach.
    d. unintentional tort.

15. Failure or omission to perform professional duties to an accepted level is called
    a. fraud.
    b. negligence.
    c. unintentional tort.
    d. consideration.

16. Which is the best definition of an expressed contract?
    a. Agreement is shown through inference by signs, inaction, or silence.
    b. Agreement is entered into orally (clearly stated) or in writing.
    c. Failure to comply with the terms of the agreement.
    d. All of the above.

17. A contract between the patient and the physician can be terminated for
    a. failure to follow instructions on the part of the patient.
    b. missed appointments by the patient.
    c. failure to pay for services.
    d. all of the above.

18. The result of breaking a criminal law may be
    a. a fine.
    b. imprisonment.
    c. loss of a medical license.
    d. all of the above.

19. Which carries the punishment of fines or imprisonment in jail for up to a year?
    a. Misdemeanor
    b. Felony
    c. Negligence
    d. Battery

20. The federal court has jurisdiction over cases when
    a. the case relates to federal law.
    b. the dispute occurred on or in international waters.
    c. another country's citizen and a U.S. citizen are in dispute with a monetary value of over $75,000.
    d. all of the above.

21. Which of the following is the lowest to highest division of the state courts?
    a. Municipal, circuit, supreme
    b. Circuit, municipal, supreme
    c. Supreme, circuit, municipal
    d. Municipal, supreme, circuit

22. The person being sued in a court of law is the
    a. plaintiff.
    b. jury.
    c. defendant.
    d. litigator.

23. A court order for a witness and certain documents to appear in court is a
    a. deposition.
    b. *subpoena duces tecum.*
    c. discovery.
    d. subpoena.

24. An expert witness is considered to have
    a. knowledge of the crime committed.
    b. a legal background (for example, a lawyer).
    c. knowledge or experience beyond the jury.
    d. all of the above.

25. When testifying in court, it is important to
    a. tell the truth.
    b. state the facts.
    c. include your opinion.
    d. a and b only.

CHAPTER 3: IMPORTANCE OF THE LEGAL SYSTEM FOR THE PHYSICIAN

1. The purpose of the medical practice acts is to protect the
   a. healthcare worker.
   b. physician.
   c. general public.
   d. state.

2. The medical practice acts are established by
   a. the state legislature.
   b. state medical board.
   c. federal government.
   d. licensed physicians of a state.

3. The medical practice acts
   a. provide for a medical examining board in each state.
   b. establish the baseline for practice of medicine in each state.
   c. forbid the practice of medicine without a license.
   d. all of the above.

4. The board of examiners in each state grants licensure through
   a. examination.
   b. endorsement.
   c. reciprocity.
   d. all of the above.

5. Requirements for medical licensure may include
   a. proof of a successfully completed approved internship/residency program.
   b. information about any past convictions or history of drug or alcohol abuse.
   c. proof of medical malpractice insurance.
   d. a and b.

6. Successful completion of the National Board Medical Examination (NBME) provides
   a. reciprocity.
   b. endorsement.
   c. registration.
   d. certification.

7. Reciprocity is the practice of
   a. cooperation by which a state grants a license to practice medicine to a physician already licensed in another state.
   b. granting a license to applicants who have successfully passed the National Board Medical Examination.
   c. requiring a set number of continuing medical education units in a designated time period to ensure currency in the field of practice.
   d. withdrawing the right to practice for severe misconduct, commission of a crime, or personal incapacity to perform one's duties.

8. Medicare/Medicaid fraud, rape, murder, larceny, and narcotics convictions are examples of crimes that could lead to
    a. reciprocity of a license.
    b. a license being endorsed.
    c. a license being revoked.
    d. all of the above.

9. An example of a person practicing without a medical license is
    a. a physician signing Dr.
    b. a licensed practical nurse signing RN.
    c. a registered nurse renewing a license as an RN.
    d. a paramedic performing CPR.

10. A voluntary process in which an agency requests an official review of its operation is called
    a. examination.
    b. endorsement.
    c. accreditation.
    d. reciprocity.

11. Accreditation of allied health educational programs is provided by
    a. JCAHO.
    b. CAAHEP.
    c. FLEX.
    d. HIPAA.

12. The ordinary skill and care that medical practitioners must use is called
    a. prudent person rule.
    b. confidentiality.
    c. standard of care.
    d. statute of limitations.

13. The provision of information to a patient that a reasonable person would want before making a decision about treatment is
    a. standard of care.
    b. statute of limitations.
    c. confidentiality.
    d. prudent person rule.

14. Confidentiality involves
    a. keeping private all information about a person and not disclosing it to a third party.
    b. disclosing private information about a person to a third party only when a patient's written consent is given.
    c. providing information by phone when requested by a consulting physician.
    d. b and c.

15. The period of time that a patient has to file a lawsuit is the
    a. Medical Patients Rights Act.
    b. statute of limitations.
    c. statute of limitations for murder.
    d. medical practice acts.

16. An adult who acts in the court on behalf of a child in litigation is called
    a. good samaritan.
    b. *respondeat superior.*
    c. *guardian ad litem.*
    d. prudent person.

17. *Let the master answer* refers to
    a. the physician who assists in an emergency situation outside the workplace.
    b. the employer who assumes responsibility for the actions of employees.
    c. the medical assistant who unsuccessfully performs CPR.
    d. scope of practice.

18. Guidelines for the practice of a profession are called
    a. *respondeat superior.*
    b. *guardian ad litem.*
    c. scope of practice.
    d. all of the above.

19. The ultimate decision for healthcare rests with the
    a. insurance company.
    b. physician.
    c. licensed caregiver.
    d. *guardian ad litem.*

20. The purpose of a *chain of command* for healthcare decisions is to
    a. provide decision making by the most qualified person.
    b. avoid lawsuits.
    c. make the physician responsible for all decisions.
    d. eliminate the need for decision making by employees.

21. Insurance coverage of employees who handle financial statements, records, and cash is called
    a. chain of command.
    b. *respondeat superior.*
    c. bonding.
    d. malpractice.

22. The practice used to control or minimize the incidence of problem behavior that might result in injury to patients and employees is
    a. bonding.
    b. risk management.
    c. confidentiality.
    d. *guardian ad litem.*

23. The legal theory that provides that the statute of limitations begins to run at the time of recognition of an injury is
    a. *respondeat superior.*
    b. endorsement.
    c. discovery rule.
    d. medical practice acts.

24. A physician practicing in a Veteran's Administration hospital
    a. may hold a valid license from any state.
    b. must hold a valid license from the state where the hospital is located.
    c. does not need a license.
    d. is licensed by the federal government.

25. Complaints about physicians from patients, employees, or other physicians
    a. are not considered valid.
    b. are handled by the state board of registration.
    c. are handled by the state board of examiners.
    d. b and c.

CHAPTER 4: MEDICAL PRACTICE AND ALLIED HEALTH PROFESSIONALS

1. A fixed-payment plan of health insurance offers coverage for
   a. hospital care.
   b. physicians visits.
   c. complete medical care.
   d. dental care.

2. Third-party payers are
   a. physicians.
   b. insurance companies.
   c. patients.
   d. hospitals.

3. The purpose of the *gatekeeper* is to
   a. approve all nonemergency services.
   b. approve hospitalizations.
   c. approve tests before they are given.
   d. all of the above.

4. In a managed care organization, financial risk is shared by the
   a. organization.
   b. hospital.
   c. physician.
   d. all of the above.

5. A *gag clause* in contracts between physicians and managed care organizations
   a. prohibits the physician from discussing the income of the organization.
   b. allows the physician to share financial incentives only with patients.
   c. prohibits the physician from discussing financial incentives given by the organization.
   d. allows the managed care organization to refuse to pay for care given by the physician.

6. Managed care organizations may attempt to limit
   a. choice of hospitals.
   b. referrals to specialists.
   c. length of stay in a hospital.
   d. all of the above.

7. A health maintenance organization provides
   a. healthcare services available for a predetermined fee per member by a limited group of providers.
   b. no preventive care services.
   c. healthcare services by requiring a large copayment.
   d. healthcare services through a nonrestricted group of providers.

8. Capitation is
   a. a fixed monthly fee paid to the healthcare provider for providing patient services.
   b. an additional payment for services paid directly by the patient at time of service.
   c. limitation of all services for care to a fixed dollar amount.
   d. a fixed amount the managed care organization may charge the patient for membership in the organization.

9. Medicare is a federal program of
   a. healthcare coverage for the poor and indigent.
   b. healthcare coverage in which rationing of care may occur.
   c. healthcare coverage for the elderly and disabled.
   d. b and c.

10. Medicaid is a
    a. federally implemented program of indigent care.
    b. state-funded program of indigent care.
    c. federal program of care for the poor implemented by states.
    d. locally implemented program of indigent care.

11. A Medicare-instituted method of hospital payment is
    a. HMO.
    b. DRG.
    c. PPO.
    d. EPO.

12. Diagnostic related groups refers to
    a. classification of patients of illness by diagnosis.
    b. persons without funds.
    c. limiting care to a certain number of persons with a diagnosis.
    d. limiting care to a set number of days.

13. Those persons most likely to receive the best care under a managed care system are
    a. the wealthy.
    b. the poor and ignorant.
    c. those who understand the system.
    d. all of the above.

14. Medicare and Medicaid prohibit physicians from
    a. referring to services they own.
    b. charging a reasonable fee for service.
    c. referring to rehabilitation or long-term care.
    d. ordering expensive tests.

15. Different methods of medical practice, such as partnerships and corporations, are the result of
    a. increased insurance coverage costs.
    b. increased desire by physicians to have time off.
    c. increase in patient-initiated malpractice lawsuits.
    d. all of the above.

16. A practice in which the physician employs other physicians and pays them a salary is called
    a. solo practice.
    b. sole proprietorship.
    c. partnership.
    d. associate practice.

17. An associate practice is a legal agreement in which the physicians
    a. share a facility and staff.
    b. share the loss and profits.
    c. share responsibility for legal actions of each other.
    d. all of the above.

18. A business operation of a medical practice in which two or more physicians are responsible for the actions of each, including debts, is called a/an
    a. associate practice.
    b. solo practice.
    c. partnership.
    d. group practice.

19. A medical practice consisting of three or more physicians who practice the same specialty and share expenses and income is a(n)
    a. group practice.
    b. partnership.
    c. associate practice.
    d. corporation.

20. The members of a professional corporation are known as
    a. board of directors.
    b. shareholders.
    c. physicians.
    d. lawyers.

21. Benefits of a corporation include all except
    a. profit-sharing for its members.
    b. pension plans for its members.
    c. insurance for its members.
    d. protection from lawsuits for the corporation.

22. Which form of medical practice ends with the death of the owner?
    a. Corporation
    b. Partnership with several partners.
    c. Associate practice
    d. Solo practice

23. Fee splitting occurs when
    a. a hospital is paid in proportion to business received for holders of the franchise.
    b. one physician pays another physician for the referral of patients.
    c. income in a group practice is shared.
    d. a physician receives payment from both the insurance company and the patient.

24. Allied health professionals who are certified include the following except
    a. medical assistants.
    b. physician assistants.
    c. medical transcriptionists.
    d. pharmacists.

25. A person with the appropriate education who practices as a doctor of medicine or doctor of osteopathy is called a/n
    a. allied health professional.
    b. physician.
    c. dentist.
    d. all of the above.

CHAPTER 5: THE PHYSICIAN–PATIENT RELATIONSHIP

1. The contract for services with a physician includes
   a. an agreement to pay for services for as long as they are received by the patient.
   b. truthful disclosure of conditions by the patient.
   c. an agreement to provide services by the doctor.
   d. all of the above.

2. Physicians may
   a. refuse to treat patients, except in emergencies.
   b. not refuse to treat patients.
   c. withdraw from a contract if the patient is uncooperative.
   d. a and c.

3. An increase in malpractice insurance premiums has caused
   a. physicians to refuse more patients.
   b. physicians to charge more for services than in the past.
   c. physicians to withdraw from caring for more patients.
   d. none of the above.

4. A physician can turn away patients that
   a. are emergencies.
   b. they have not agreed to treat.
   c. are indigent.
   d. have AIDS.

5. An indigent patient is one who
   a. is abandoned by the physician.
   b. has AIDS.
   c. is unable to pay for medical care.
   d. has an emergency.

6. Abandonment can be avoided by
   a. giving informal notice of withdrawal from a case.
   b. giving formal notice of withdrawal from a case.
   c. writing to another doctor about the case.
   d. declaring the patient indigent.

7. Infections responsible for life-threatening illness in the AIDS patient are called
   a. opportunistic infections.
   b. systemic infections.
   c. macrophages.
   d. a syndrome.

8. The physician who believes that his or her AIDS patient may place in jeopardy the health of others has an ethical obligation to
   a. notify the patient's partner.
   b. call the local health department.
   c. persuade the patient to inform his or her partner(s).
   d. notify the local police department.

9. Testing for HIV first requires
   a. a physician's order for the test.
   b. the patient's informed consent.
   c. the lab's acceptance of the sample.
   d. all of the above.

10. A report of an HIV or AIDS diagnosis must be completed by the
    a. physician.
    b. patient.
    c. local health department.
    d. patient's family.

11. Patient confidentiality does not apply in the case of
    a. HIV/AIDS.
    b. any communicable disease.
    c. allied health professionals.
    d. life or safety of the patient.

12. Medical ethicists currently encourage healthcare providers to
    a. maintain falsehoods to protect the patient or family.
    b. focus on the consequences of an action while protecting the patient.
    c. apply the principles of justice.
    d. b and c.

13. The patient has a right to
    a. deny any treatment.
    b. give informed consent for any treatment.
    c. expect the appropriate standard of care.
    d. all of the above.

14. Minor children may receive life-saving treatment
    a. even though the parents refuse.
    b. if they choose to receive it.
    c. when grandparents override the wishes of the parents.
    d. none of the above.

15. A breach of confidentiality is considered unethical and illegal, and is prohibited by
    a. DRGs.
    b. HIPAA.
    c. Medicare.
    d. Medicaid.

16. Confidential information that has been told to a physician by the patient is called
    a. advance directives.
    b. informed consent.
    c. privileged communication.
    d. self-determination.

17. A statement of the patient's intentions for health ???care–related decisions is called
    a. advance directives.
    b. implied consent.
    c. *loco parentis.*
    d. consent.

18. A patient request to either use or not use life-sustaining treatments and artificial nutritional support is
    a. durable power of attorney.
    b. Uniform Anatomical Gift Act.
    c. living will.
    d. PSDA.

19. The authority of a health care agent to act on behalf of the patient
    a. continues even if the patient cancels it.
    b. continues even if the patient is physically or mentally incapacitated.
    c. only includes the elderly.
    d. only includes minors.

20. A minor is one who
    a. is less than 18 years of age (in most states).
    b. is not considered competent to give consent for most treatments.
    c. may have a child.
    d. a and b.

21. The patient's signature on an informed consent form indicates
    a. understanding of the treatment options.
    b. expressed consent.
    c. understanding of the limits or risks in the pending treatment.
    d. all of the above.

22. Patients who indicate by their behavior that they will accept a procedure are providing
    a. informed consent.
    b. expressed consent.
    c. implied consent.
    d. none of the above.

23. Exceptions to obtaining consent may include
    a. commonly known risks.
    b. when the physician does not want to tell the patient the outcome of the treatment.
    c. when a cure is possible.
    d. when a physician guarantees that the treatment will be successful.

24. Refusal for medical or surgical treatment by the patient must be honored if
    a. the patient is concerned about the success of the procedure.
    b. the patient is not confident in the physician.
    c. religious beliefs against the procedure are expressed.
    d. all of the above.

25. One of the best ways to prevent medical errors is for the patient to
    a. be a better informed consumer of medical services.
    b. sue the physician if he or she does not like the outcome of a procedure.
    c. keep quiet and let the physician handle all aspects of the care.
    d. use herbal remedies before calling the physician.

CHAPTER 6: PROFESSIONAL LIABILITY AND MEDICAL MALPRACTICE

1. Failure to perform an action that a reasonable person would have committed in a similar situation is
   a. assumption of risk.
   b. negligence.
   c. *respondeat superior.*
   d. malfeasance.

2. Performing a wrong and illegal act is considered
   a. misfeasance.
   b. nonfeasance.
   c. malfeasance.
   d. feasance.

3. Professional misconduct or demonstration of an unreasonable lack of skill with the result of injury, loss, or damage to the patient is
   a. nonfeasance.
   b. feasance.
   c. malpractice.
   d. misfeasance.

4. Negligence is composed of four elements:
   a. malpractice, misfeasance, nonfeasance, and malfeasance.
   b. duty, dereliction of duty, direct or proximate cause, and damages.
   c. malpractice, misfeasance, dereliction of duty, and damages.
   d. duty, dereliction of duty, nonfeasance, and malfeasance.

5. The *reasonable person standard* refers to the
   a. dereliction of duty.
   b. damages.
   c. duty of due care.
   d. proximate cause.

6. The standard of care for physicians and other health care professionals is determined by
   a. the AMA.
   b. the local hospital.
   c. a board of physicians appointed by the local chapter of the AMA who practice in the same medical specialty.
   d. what members of the same profession would do in a similar situation within the same geographic area.

7. To prove dereliction of duty, a patient would have to prove the physician
   a. did not carry malpractice insurance.
   b. did not conform to the acceptable standard of care.
   c. took additional risks in performing the treatment.
   d. none of the above.

8. *The thing speaks for itself* applies to the law of negligence and is the doctrine of
   a. *res ipsa loquitur.*
   b. *respondeat superior.*
   c. preponderance of evidence.
   d. compensatory damages.

9. Monetary awards by a court to a person who has been harmed in an especially malicious or willful way are
   a. compensatory damages.
   b. nominal damages.
   c. punitive damages.
   d. wrongful damages.

10. To win a *wrongful-death* case, the plaintiff must prove
    a. *proximate* cause of death.
    b. malpractice.
    c. nominal damages.
    d. negligence.

11. The most common defense provided by the defendant in a case is called
    a. affirmative defense.
    b. denial defense.
    c. assumption of risk.
    d. borrowed servant.

12. Assumption of risk is the legal defense
    a. used by the defendant in a case to prove innocence from injury.
    b. that prevents the plaintiff from recovering damages if he or she accepts a risk associated with the activity.
    c. that determines that the patient was fully or partly at fault for the injury, and no damages may be recovered.
    d. that bases the recovery of damages by the plaintiff on the amount of fault of the defendant.

13. When an employer lends an employee to someone else, this is called
    a. comparative negligence.
    b. *respondeat superior.*
    c. borrowed servant doctrine.
    d. fraud.

14. The statute of limitations for a case begins to *run*
    a. when the injury occurs.
    b. two years after the injury.
    c. when the plaintiff sues the defendant.
    d. when the injury is discovered.

15. Deliberate concealment of the facts from a patient is
    a. comparative negligence.
    b. fraud.
    c. liability.
    d. contributory negligence.

16. *Res judicata* means
    a. the thing has been decided.
    b. let the master answer.
    c. borrowed servant doctrine.
    d. the thing speaks for itself.

17. The legal relationship formed between two people when one person agrees to perform work for another person is
    a. promise to cure.
    b. liability.
    c. law of agency.
    d. all of the above.

18. Protection for the physician/employer by the health care professional is best accomplished by
    a. having a job description with clearly defined responsibilities, duties, and necessary skills.
    b. using extreme care when performing his or her job.
    c. carrying out only those procedures for which he or she is trained.
    d. all of the above.

19. Responsibility for action in employment is ultimately assigned to the
    a. employee.
    b. employer.
    c. agency.
    d. supervisor.

20. A contract by which one person promises to compensate or reimburse another if he or she suffers a loss from a specific cause or a negligent act is
    a. a rider.
    b. arbitration.
    c. liability insurance.
    d. malpractice insurance.

21. Coverage of the insured party for all injuries and incidents that occurred while the policy was in effect, regardless of when they are reported, is
    a. occurrence insurance.
    b. claims made insurance.
    c. malpractice insurance.
    d. rider insurance.

22. A general liability policy that covers any negligence on the part of the physician's staff would include
    a. claims-made insurance.
    b. occurrence insurance.
    c. malpractice policy.
    d. a rider on the malpractice policy.

23. Submitting a dispute to a person other than a judge is called
    a. mediation.
    b. arbitrator.
    c. arbitration.
    d. liability.

24. An important reason for arbitration of civil cases is to save
    a. court appointments.
    b. time.
    c. money.
    d. time and money.

25. The only health professional who is not usually employed by the physician is the
    a. nurse.
    b. pharmacist.
    c. medical assistant.
    d. radiology technician.

CHAPTER 7: PUBLIC DUTIES OF THE PHYSICIAN

1. Data, such as birth and death dates, are used by the government to
   a. determine the tax base for a community.
   b. determine population trends and needs.
   c. encourage planning and zoning in a community.
   d. provide health care professionals in a city.

2. Public duties for the physician includes reporting
   a. births and still births.
   b. deaths and injuries.
   c. communicable illnesses or diseases.
   d. all of the above.

3. The live birth certificate must be signed by the
   a. county medical officer.
   b. physician who delivered the child.
   c. person in attendance in a home birth.
   d. b and c.

4. A death certificate must include
   a. date and time of death.
   b. name of parents of the deceased.
   c. location of the place of death.
   d. all of the above.

5. A coroner or medical examiner must sign the death certificate of the deceased when
   a. no physician was present at the time of death.
   b. a violent death occurred.
   c. the death occurred when the deceased was in jail or prison.
   d. all of the above.

6. A medical examiner is a
   a. physician.
   b. nurse practitioner.
   c. physician's assistant.
   d. lawyer.

7. Which of the following is not a reportable communicable disease?
   a. tetanus
   b. tuberculosis
   c. chickenpox
   d. gonorrhea

8. Which of the following are required by the National Childhood Vaccine Injury Act of 1986?
   a. polio virus vaccine, live
   b. hepatitis A vaccine
   c. measles, mumps, and rubella
   d. a and c

9. A physician reporting possible child abuse
    a. may be sued by the parents of the child for defamation.
    b. may not be sued by the parents of the child for defamation.
    c. may file an initial oral report followed by a written report.
    d. b and c.

10. Failure to report a suspected case of child abuse may result in a charge of
    a. manslaughter.
    b. misdemeanor.
    c. felony.
    d. child abuse.

11. Elder abuse may legally include the following except
    a. physical abuse.
    b. exploitation.
    c. verbal abuse.
    d. abandonment.

12. Injuries, fractures, pain in the genital area, and weight loss may be signs of
    a. exploitation.
    b. abandonment.
    c. psychological abuse.
    d. physical abuse.

13. Evidence gathered in an abuse case may include
    a. pictures of bruises or injuries.
    b. urine specimens.
    c. clothing.
    d. all of the above.

14. Chain of evidence refers to all of the following except
    a. clearly labeled evidence with name, date, and time.
    b. documentation in the medical record of date and time evidence was obtained.
    c. clothing evidence that is clean and dry.
    d. evidence that has been kept in locked storage until required.

15. Conditions such as cancer, epilepsy, and congenital disorders of the newborn are often reported to government agencies in order to
    a. receive additional funding from insurance companies.
    b. maintain accurate public health statistics.
    c. receive funding through Medicare.
    d. prevent malpractice lawsuits.

16. Enforcement of drug sales and distribution is through the
    a. local pharmacy.
    b. Drug Enforcement Administration.
    c. Food and Drug Administration.
    d. Bureau of Narcotics and Dangerous Drugs.

17. The purpose of the DEA is to
    a. regulate the Controlled Substances Act of 1970.
    b. ensure the safety of food items sold in the United States.
    c. regulate drug dealers.
    d. keep physicians from prescribing controlled substances.

18. Registration for physicians who administer controlled substances must be renewed every
    a. two years.
    b. three years.
    c. four years.
    d. five years.

19. The proper method of destroying a controlled substance that needs to be wasted is to
    a. return it to the original container to be counted.
    b. pour it down a drain or flush it down a toilet by two individuals.
    c. place it in a locked container to be removed by the hazardous waste disposal personnel.
    d. all of the above.

20. Penalty for violation of the Controlled Substances Act is
    a. a fine.
    b. loss of license to practice medicine.
    c. a jail sentence.
    d. all of the above.

21. DEA registration numbers are available to
    a. physicians.
    b. medical assistants.
    c. nurses.
    d. pharmacists.

22. Prescriptions for Schedule II controlled substances can
    a. be refilled every six months.
    b. be refilled over the phone in a non emergency.
    c. not be refilled.
    d. be refilled up to two years.

23. A program of management-financed and confidential counseling and referral service designed to help employees and/or their family members assess a problem is the
    a. EAP.
    b. DEA.
    c. FDA.
    d. CSA.

24. Personal problems related to alcohol and/or drug abuse cost the U.S. economy more than _____ of its $70 billion budget yearly.
    a. 25 percent
    b. 33 percent
    c. 50 percent
    d. 75 percent

25. Hazardous medical waste includes
    a. solid waste from administration.
    b. infectious waste from body fluid contact.
    c. radioactive waste.
    d. b and c.

CHAPTER 8: WORKPLACE LAW AND ETHICS

1. Laws regulating employment relationships, recruitment, placement, pay plans, benefits, penalties, and terminations are based primarily on
   a. longevity with the organization.
   b. job performance.
   c. desire to succeed in the organization.
   d. education for the job.

2. Employment-at-will allows the
   a. employee to quit at any time.
   b. employer to terminate the employee at any time.
   c. a and b.
   d. none of the above.

3. Discrimination in the form of unfair treatment in employment based on race, color, religion, sex, or national origin is covered through
   a. Title V.
   b. Title VI.
   c. Title VII.
   d. Title VIII.

4. Medicare and Medicaid forbid discrimination in _____ through Title VI.
   a. patient-care institutions
   b. religious-affiliated colleges
   c. employment
   d. pregnancy

5. Sexual harassment includes
   a. unwelcome sexual advances.
   b. requests for sexual favors.
   c. verbal or physical conduct of a sexual nature.
   d. all of the above.

6. The Civil Rights Act of 1991 permits the court to award _____ to mistreated employees.
   a. compensatory damages
   b. punitive damages
   c. prison sentences
   d. a and b

7. The Age Discrimination in Employment Act of 1967 protects persons _____ or older against employment discrimination.
   a. 30 years
   b. 40 years
   c. 50 years
   d. 60 years

8. The Americans with Disabilities Act of 1990 requires the employer to make
   a. every possible accommodation for disabled employees.
   b. no accommodations for disabled employees.
   c. reasonable accommodations for disabled employees.
   d. accommodations even if they are a hardship to the employer.

9. OSHA represents the
   a. Occupational Security and Hiring Act.
   b. Operational Safety and Harassment Agency.
   c. Occupational Safety and Health Act.
   d. Organization for Statutes and Health Agency.

10. Rules to protect health care workers from bloodborne pathogens are regulated by the
    a. OSHA.
    b. EPA.
    c. HMO.
    d. EEOC.

11. The Health Maintenance Organization Act of 1973 requires that any company with 25 employees must provide
    a. free health care to all employees.
    b. childcare facilities for employees.
    c. an HMO alternative to regular group insurance.
    d. bi-yearly physical exams and mammograms for employees.

12. COBRA of 1985 provides that a company with 20 or more employees must provide extended health care insurance to terminated employees for up to
    a. 18 months usually at the employee's expense.
    b. 1 year usually at the employee's expense.
    c. 18 months at the employer's expense.
    d. 1 year at the employer's expense.

13. Through the Drug-Free Workplace Act, employers contracting to provide goods or services to the federal government must certify that
    a. a drug support service is provided for employees.
    b. a drug-free workplace is maintained.
    c. employees may not use drugs on the premises.
    d. employees will be notified of violations before termination.

14. The Fair Labor Standards Act of 1938 regulates employee benefits such as
    a. minimum wage.
    b. payment for overtime work.
    c. hours that may be worked.
    d. a, b, and c.

15. The origin of the current unemployment insurance program for employees who are unable to work through no fault of their own is the
    a. Fair Labor Standards Act.
    b. Consolidated Omnibus Budget Reconciliation Act.
    c. Social Security Act.
    d. Federal Insurance Contribution Act.

16. The Equal Pay Act of 1963 makes it illegal for an employer to discriminate on the basis of
    a. age.
    b. race.
    c. nationality.
    d. gender.

17. A fine imposed by the federal government for employers not contributing to Social Security for their employees is mandated by the
    a. Workers' Compensation Act.
    b. Federal Insurance Contribution Act.
    c. Employee Retirement Income Security Act.
    d. Equal Pay Act.

18. The Workers' Compensation Act protects workers and their families from financial problems resulting from
    a. employment-related injury, disease, or death.
    b. termination of employment due to drug use.
    c. downsizing the organization of employment.
    d. strikes or workplace action by employees.

19. The Family and Medical Leave Act of 1994 allows
    a. the father to take a leave of absence of up to 12 weeks in any 12 month period when a baby is born.
    b. the mother to take a leave of absence of up to 12 weeks in any 12 month period when a baby is born.
    c. unpaid medical leave for up to 12 weeks for leave for their own or a family member's medical or family-related situation.
    d. all of the above.

20. Guidelines for use of an individual's credit information are established by the
    a. Equal Credit Opportunity Act of 1975.
    b. Fair Credit Reporting Act of 1971.
    c. Truth in Lending Act of 1969.
    d. Fair Debt Collection Practices Act of 1978.

21. The Fair Debt Collection Practices Act prohibits phone calls for the purpose of debt collection
    a. after 8:00 A.M.
    b. after 7:00 P.M.
    c. except on the weekends.
    d. before 8:00 A.M.

22. The portion of a paycheck that may be paid directly to an employee's creditors is established by the
    a. Fair Debt Collection Practices Act.
    b. Federal Wage Garnishment Law.
    c. Wagner Act.
    d. Federal Trade Commission Act.

23. Under the Family and Medical Leave Act the employee
    a. must have worked for the employer for six months to be eligible.
    b. must be returned to the same or equivalent position when he or she returns.
    c. may have some loss of employment benefits when he or she returns.
    d. all of the above.

24. The Wagner Act of 1935 (NLRA) gives employees the right to
    a. Form and join unions, bargain individually, and strike for better benefits and working conditions.
    b. form and join unions, bargain collectively, and strike for better benefits and working conditions.
    c. force the employers to discriminate against employees who are not union members.
    d. picket to coerce unionization without seeking an election by workers.

25. An unfair dislike or preference against someone is called
    a. ethnocentric.
    b. bias.
    c. stereotyping.
    d. autonomy.

CHAPTER 9: THE MEDICAL RECORD

1. A medical record ordered by the court to be available during a malpractice case is
   a. disclosed.
   b. subpoenaed.
   c. disclosed only to the judge.
   d. disclosed only to the jury.

2. Medical record management requires
   a. accuracy.
   b. confidentiality.
   c. proper filing and storage.
   d. all of the above.

3. The purpose of a medical record is to
   a. provide the billing record of the patient from admission to the practice.
   b. provide the medical picture and record of the patient from birth to death.
   c. provide data and statistics on health matters.
   d. b and c.

4. Patient information in the medical record should include
   a. date of birth.
   b. date of marriage.
   c. record of divorces.
   d. date of spouse's birth.

5. The medical record must include information about patient care such as
   a. admitting diagnosis.
   b. physician examination report and documentation of complications.
   c. discharge summary and follow-up care.
   d. all of the above.

6. The disadvantage of chronological documentation is
   a. subjective data may be missing.
   b. objective data may be missing.
   c. medical problems may go undiscovered.
   d. vital signs are not done.

7. The accepted method of correcting medical record errors is
   a. erase and write the correction.
   b. draw a line through the error and write the correction underneath.
   c. draw a line through the error and write the correction above with the date and initials of the person making the correction.
   d. erase and write the correction, adding the date and initials of the person making the correction.

8. Federal reimbursement guidelines require that all medical records be completed within
   a. 15 days following the patient's discharge from a hospital.
   b. 30 days following the patient's discharge from a hospital.
   c. 45 days following the patient's discharge from a hospital.
   d. 60 days following the patient's discharge from a hospital.

9. An incomplete medical record may
   a. not be a problem, as the remainder of the entry could be discussed during a court hearing.
   b. make it impossible for the health care provider to defend allegations in court.
   c. allow only part of a bill to be paid.
   d. not be able to be subpoenaed to court.

10. For the court's purpose, if documentation does not appear in the medical record,
    a. it did not occur.
    b. it can be documented at a later date without harm.
    c. the court will not use the medical record against the health care provider.
    d. all of the above.

11. To protect patient confidentiality, medical records can be released
    a. to an attorney.
    b. to a judge.
    c. to the patient's family members.
    d. only with the patient's written consent.

12. Ownership of the medical record usually remains with the
    a. physician.
    b. patient.
    c. court.
    d. all of the above.

13. When preparing a copy of a medical record for a third party,
    a. keep the copy and send the original.
    b. make two copies and send the original.
    c. keep the original and send a copy.
    d. make a copy of the complete record and send it even when one part is requested.

14. The Privacy Act of 1974 protects private citizens from distribution of information about themselves by the federal government except
    a. from hospitals.
    b. Veteran's Administration hospitals.
    c. from privately owned clinics.
    d. Medicare or Medicaid.

15. Medical records are usually exempt from state open-record laws except when
    a. the benefit of disclosure for the public interest (safety) outweighs confidentiality.
    b. requested by a family member to be disclosed to the public.
    c. mental health records are to be disclosed to the public.
    d. an attorney requests the records to be made public.

16. All medical records should be stored for
    a. 5 years from the date of the last entry.
    b. 7 years from the date of the last entry.
    c. 10 years from the date of the last entry.
    d. 23 years from the date of the last entry.

17. Older records of former patients
    a. need to be kept in the physician's office indefinitely.
    b. can be stored in a clean, dry storage space.
    c. can be destroyed after five years.
    d. need to be kept in the physician's office at least seven years.

18. Computerized medical records
    a. pose problems of confidentiality.
    b. make record maintenance and retrieval more efficient.
    c. should be accessed on a need-to-know basis.
    d. all of the above.

19. Confidential medical record information that can be disclosed to a health department without the patient's consent includes
    a. HIV cases.
    b. AIDS cases.
    c. abortions.
    d. a and b.

20. Physicians who wish to disclose confidential medical record information should
    a. first discuss it with the patient's family.
    b. discuss it with the patient first.
    c. discuss the risks involved with his or her lawyer.
    d. first discuss the problem with the patient's contact person.

21. Laws regarding medical records
    a. are mandated by the federal government.
    b. apply to individual health care facilities.
    c. vary from state to state.
    d. are the same from state to state.

22. Health care providers and health care institutions who disclose confidential health information may
    a. do so without consequences.
    b. face civil or criminal liability for disclosure.
    c. face civil liability for disclosure.
    d. face criminal liability for disclosure.

23. Immunization records should be kept
    a. 10 years.
    b. permanently.
    c. 5 years.
    d. until the age of maturity.

24. A written order requiring a person to appear in court, give testimony, and bring the records described is called
    a. *res ipsa loquitor.*
    b. *subpoena duces tecum.*
    c. *respondeat superior.*
    d. subpoena.

25. A subpoenaed medical record should alert the medical staff that
    a. the physician and the patient are to be told that a subpoena has been served.
    b. the physician's attorney should be notified of the subpoena being received.
    c. the records must be turned over to the judge on the specified date.
    d. all of the above.

CHAPTER 10: CONFIDENTIALITY IN MEDICAL PRACTICE

1. A private or public health care entity that facilitates the processing of nonstandard electronic transactions into HIPAA transactions is a
   a. health care plan.
   b. clearinghouse.
   c. covered entity.
   d. wireless local area network.

2. A health care organization covered under HIPAA regulations is a
   a. health care plan.
   b. HMO.
   c. covered entity.
   d. PPO.

3. A number assigned to an employer for purposes of identification is the
   a. social security number.
   b. employer identifier standard.
   c. privacy number.
   d. employer identification number.

4. The individual or group that provides or pays for the patient's medial care is the
   a. health care plan.
   b. covered entity.
   c. Office of Civil Rights.
   d. patient.

5. A national source of reports of actions taken against health care providers, practitioners, and vendors who are in noncompliance or performing fraudulent activities is the
   a. Office of Civil Rights.
   b. wireless local area networks.
   c. Healthcare Integrity and Protection Data Bank.
   d. Health Insurance Portability and Accountability Act.

6. The use of communication and information in medical practice, research, and education is called
   a. sanctions.
   b. covered entities.
   c. the privacy rule.
   d. medical informatics.

7. The reasonable effort that a health care provider uses to limit disclosure of patient information is referred to as
   a. privacy rule.
   b. minimum necessary standard.
   c. confidentiality.
   d. all of the above.

8. The objective of the Health Insurance Portability and Accountability Act of 1998 is to
   a. combat fraud, abuse, and waste in health care.
   b. promote medical savings accounts.
   c. simplify the administration of health insurance.
   d. a, b, and c.

9. The federal office that investigates violations of HIPAA is the
   a. National Institutes of Health.
   b. Healthcare Integrity and Protection Data Center.
   c. Social Security Administration.
   d. Supreme Court.

10. Which Title of HIPAA most affects confidentiality issues for health care providers?
    a. Title I: Insurance Portability
    b. Title II: Administrative Simplification
    c. Title III: Medical Savings and Tax Deduction
    d. Title IV: Group Health Plan Provisions
    e. Title V: Revenue Offset Provisions

11. The *privacy rule* is meant to ensure that there is/are
    a. security of electronic transfer of information.
    b. disclosure of only the necessary information.
    c. no longer a need for patient consent.
    d. a and b only.

12. Protected health information relates to
    a. past individually identifiable health information.
    b. present individually identifiable health information.
    c. future individually identifiable health information.
    d. all of the above.

13. Those who would be covered under HIPAA include
    a. life insurers.
    b. information systems vendors.
    c. universities.
    d. a, b, and c.

14. Health care fraud alerts are issued by the
    a. Inspector General of the HHS.
    b. Attorney General of the United States.
    c. Surgeon General of the United States.
    d. Postmaster General of the United States.

15. Researchers who wish to obtain individually identifiable medical information must
    a. pay the patient for the information that is obtained for the research.
    b. obtain a patient authorization that complies with the rules set by HIPAA.
    c. use the information only after the patient is deceased.
    d. pay the institution that has initially obtained the information from the patient.

16. An exception to the release of information policy under HIPAA would allow information to be released to
    a. a priest or minister for the purpose of religious counseling.
    b. a news reporter reporting a crime.
    c. the police investigating a crime.
    d. the military on induction of a service person.

17. Violation of HIPAA is a
    a. misdemeanor.
    b. local criminal offense.
    c. state criminal offense.
    d. federal criminal offense.

18. The *original* intent of HIPAA is to
    a. protect medical records and billing.
    b. protect computerized medical records and billing.
    c. provide easier access of medical records for the patient.
    d. b and c.

19. HIPAA allows all of the following except
    a. physicians or hospitals to share patient information with each other to treat the patient.
    b. complete disclosure of patient information by an EMT.
    c. disclosure to clergy of patient admission to a facility.
    d. all of the above.

20. HIPAA law stipulates that the patient
    a. may sue over privacy violations.
    b. may not sue over privacy violations.
    c. may register a complaint to the government.
    d. a and c.

21. Suggestions for physicians and physician groups when implementing HIPAA include
    a. appoint and train a privacy officer.
    b. adopt procedures for handling patient requests.
    c. implement a notice of privacy practices.
    d. a, b, and c.

22. Signed authorizations and any agreements with patients restricting disclosure of PHI should be retained for a period of
    a. five years.
    b. six years.
    c. ten years.
    d. the lifetime of the patient.

23. Wireless local area networks are used by physicians and nurses to
    a. access bank accounts for patients who are hospitalized.
    b. access patient records from central databases.
    c. add patient observations and assessments to databases.
    d. b and c.

24. The application of communication and information to medical practice, research, and education is called
    a. telemedicine.
    b. informatics.
    c. clearinghouse.
    d. sanctions.

25. The use of communications and information technologies to provide health care services to people at a distance is known as
    a. computer technology.
    b. clearinghouse.
    c. family practice.
    d. telemedicine.

CHAPTER 11: ETHICAL AND BIOETHICAL ISSUES IN MEDICINE

1. The branch of philosophy relating to morals or moral principles is
   a. bioethics.
   b. law.
   c. ethics.
   d. applied ethics.

2. Applied ethics relates to
   a. religious beliefs.
   b. health care professions.
   c. common sense.
   d. social utility.

3. Issues discussed in the context of advanced medical technology are called
   a. bioethics.
   b. telemedicine.
   c. ethics.
   d. informatics.

4. Illegal acts are
   a. always ethical.
   b. frequently ethical.
   c. usually unethical.
   d. all of the above.

5. The earliest code of ethics governing the conduct of those practicing medicine is
   a. the Hippocratic Oath.
   b. Code of Hammurabi.
   c. American Medical Association Code of Ethics.
   d. the Declaration of Geneva.

6. The *father of medicine,* who wrote a statement of principles for his medical students to follow, is
   a. Semmelweis.
   b. Hammurabi.
   c. Hippocrates.
   d. Nuremberg.

7. The issue of a warning or censure by the American Medical Association to a physician occurs when the physician
   a. is accused of unlawful behavior.
   b. criticizes the AMA.
   c. does not renew his or her license to practice.
   d. is accused of unethical behavior or conduct.

8. An allegation of a criminal act by a physician requires that the
   a. act be reported to the state licensing board or governmental agency
   b. physician be expelled from the AMA.
   c. physician be arrested for the crime.
   d. all of the above.

9. The loss of a physician's license is called
   a. expulsion.
   b. disbarment.
   c. allegation.
   d. revocation.

10. The concern for the human subject in medical experimentation is the result of the
    a. Nuremberg Code.
    b. Code of Hammurabi.
    c. Declaration of Geneva.
    d. Declaration of Helsinki.

11. The AAMA has developed a code of ethics for the
    a. anesthesiologist.
    b. nurse.
    c. medical assistant.
    d. information technologist.

12. The ethics committee of a hospital serves in an advisory capacity to patients, families, and staff to
    a. decide who gets donated organs.
    b. review difficult ethical issues.
    c. determine when care will be discontinued.
    d. all of the above.

13. The Uniform Anatomical Gift Act
    a. permits minors to allow posthumous use of organs through a type of written document.
    b. permits competent adults to have organs donated by their parents.
    c. permits competent adults to allow posthumous use of their organs through a written document.
    d. requires all persons to be organ donors.

14. Giving organs to patients who will benefit the most is called
    a. social utility.
    b. justice.
    c. lottery.
    d. first-come, first served.

15. The National Organ Transplant Law of 1984
    a. allows the sale of organs.
    b. developed an allocation formula.
    c. forbids the sale of organs.
    d. funds organ transplantation.

16. Kidney transplants are fully funded by
    a. medical insurance.
    b. Medicare.
    c. Medicaid.
    d. United Network for Organ Sharing.

17. An employee should state a preference for not wishing to be involved in assisting with a procedure
    a. when the situation arises.
    b. after the situation arises.
    c. before being hired.
    d. only if absolutely necessary.

18. Research that will not directly benefit the research subjects is
    a. therapeutic.
    b. nontherapeutic.
    c. unethical.
    d. unlawful.

19. An institutional review board in a hospital or university receiving federal research funds
    a. oversees any human research in the facility.
    b. regulates any animal research in the facility.
    c. permits genetic research on humans without consent.
    d. all of the above.

20. Medical research that may directly benefit the research subject is
    a. illegal.
    b. unethical.
    c. nontherapeutic.
    d. therapeutic.

21. Placing the researcher's interests above the patient's interests is considered
    a. nontherapeutic.
    b. conflicts of interest.
    c. therapeutic.
    d. personal choice.

22. In a double-blind test
    a. the experimenter knows who is getting the research treatment.
    b. the patient knows who is getting the research treatment.
    c. neither the experimenter nor the patient knows who is getting the research treatment.
    d. both the experimenter and the patient know who is getting the research treatment.

23. Standards of professional behavior practiced by physicians in their relationships or conduct with other physicians is called
    a. code of ethics.
    b. medical code.
    c. medical etiquette.
    d. problem solving.

24. A decision model for helping resolve ethical issues includes asking
    a. what do we know?
    b. who is involved?
    c. where and when does the situation occur?
    d. all of the above.

25. The administration of a lethal agent by another person to a patient for the purpose of relieving intolerable and incurable suffering is
    a. censure.
    b. gene therapy.
    c. euthanasia.
    d. posthumous.

CHAPTER 12: ETHICAL ISSUES RELATING TO LIFE

1. In the stage of human development between the second and twelfth week, the developing life is
   a. an embryo.
   b. a fetus.
   c. a zygote.
   d. viable.

2. The gestational period is the
   a. time before conception.
   b. time after birth.
   c. time from conception to birth.
   d. all of the above.

3. AID is the same as
   a. acquired immune deficiency syndrome.
   b. artificial insemination donor.
   c. artificial insemination disorder.
   d. autoimmune disorder.

4. The most common legal and ethical concern related to AID is
   a. legitimacy of the procedure.
   b. legitimacy of the child and its support.
   c. the possibility of battery by the parent.
   d. lack of consent by the potential mother.

5. AID records are
   a. confidential.
   b. not a public record.
   c. handled the same as adoption papers.
   d. all of the above.

6. In-vitro fertilization occurs as a result of
   a. ovum and sperm combining inside the female body.
   b. growth of the fertilized ovum in the laboratory.
   c. implantation of the fertilized ovum in the uterus.
   d. b and c.

7. Surrogate motherhood allows the
   a. surrogate mother to keep the child.
   b. parents to pay for the child.
   c. surrogate mother to be paid for medical expenses.
   d. all of the above.

8. The use of fertility drugs
   a. decreases the chance of multiple births.
   b. increases the chance of multiple births.
   c. does not change the chance of multiple births.
   d. rarely increases the chance of a pregnancy.

9. Any action taken to prevent pregnancy from occurring is
    a. sterilization.
    b. conception.
    c. fertilization.
    d. contraception.

10. A woman's right to privacy, including the right to an abortion, is guaranteed by
    a. *Griswold v. Connecticut.*
    b. *Roe v. Wade.*
    c. *Roe v. Texas.*
    d. *Griswold v. Roe.*

11. The process of medically altering reproductive organs to prevent the possibility of producing children is
    a. hysterectomy.
    b. vasectomy.
    c. contraception.
    d. sterilization.

12. Sterilization requires
    a. written consent.
    b. a mentally competent adult.
    c. consent from the spouse.
    d. a and b.

13. Voluntary sterilization of unmarried minors is
    a. common in most states.
    b. forbidden in many states.
    c. allowed with authorization of the minor and parent or guardian in some states.
    d. b and c.

14. Eugenic sterilization is
    a. sterilization of certain persons to assure they will not pass defective genes to their children.
    b. sterilization of criminals, especially those who are incarcerated for life.
    c. the common practice of sterilization of the mentally retarded.
    d. all of the above.

15. Castration or sterilization of another person without legal permission is considered to be
    a. a misdemeanor.
    b. legal.
    c. assault and battery.
    d. an automatic life sentence.

16. The termination of a pregnancy before the fetus is viable is called
    a. stillbirth.
    b. induced abortion.
    c. spontaneous abortion.
    d. b and c.

17. Initially, *Roe v. Wade* said that during the third trimester of pregnancy, the state
    a. did not require the physician performing an abortion to be licensed.
    b. only regulated the medical conditions under which an abortion may be performed.
    c. prohibited all abortions except to save the life of the mother.
    d. did not require a viable fetus to be protected until the seventh month.

18. Recommendations from the *Roe v. Wade* decision included all of the following except
    a. first semester abortions should be performed in hospitals.
    b. viability of the fetus is not required.
    c. the woman should receive counseling before having the abortion.
    d. the father's consent should be obtained.

19. A person appointed by the court to speak on behalf of an incapacitated party is called the
    a. *respondeat superior.*
    b. *guardian ad litem.*
    c. guardian.
    d. conscience.

20. An employee can abstain from assisting in an abortion procedure as a matter of
    a. conscience.
    b. religious conviction.
    c. opinion.
    d. a and b.

21. Pro-choice advocates believe that
    a. women have the right to choose what to do with their bodies.
    b. legalized abortions are safer for the woman.
    c. a woman has the right to an abortion when she is the victim of rape or incest.
    d. all of the above.

22. Right-to-life advocates argue that
    a. no one has the right to deny a life.
    b. the embryo is a human life.
    c. it is morally wrong to take a human life.
    d. the right of the unborn child takes precedence over the right of the mother.
    e. all of the above.

23. The conscience clause refers to
    a. hospitals not choosing to perform sterilization procedures.
    b. physicians and hospital personnel not being required to participate in sterilizations.
    c. a and b.
    d. none of the above.

24. The study of heredity and its variations was discovered by
    a. George Aryan.
    b. Adolf Hitler.
    c. Gregor Mendel.
    d. Tay-Sachs.

25. A means to detect couples who are at risk of passing on a genetic disease to their offspring is called
    a. genetic manipulation.
    b. genetic counseling.
    c. eugenics.
    d. amniocentesis.

CHAPTER 13: DEATH AND DYING

1. Criteria or standards that assist in the determination of death include
   a. significant drop of body temperature.
   b. loss of consciousness.
   c. rigor mortis.
   d. a and c.

2. A legal death is a
   a. respiratory death.
   b. brain death.
   c. cardiac death.
   d. thermal death.

3. Prolonged absence of oxygen can result in
   a. neurological damage.
   b. brain death.
   c. cardiac death.
   d. all of the above.

4. According to the brain-oriented death definition, death occurs when
   a. there is irreversible cessation of all brain function.
   b. the brain stem is the only portion continuing to function.
   c. breathing is the only remaining function.
   d. heart action is the only remaining function.

5. Discontinuing ventilation support for a patient who is brain dead will result in
   a. respiratory death.
   b. cardiac death.
   c. neurological damage.
   d. all of the above.

6. Irreversible coma includes all of the following criteria except
   a. unreceptive and unresponsive to painful stimuli.
   b. spontaneous movements or breathing.
   c. no reflexes, with fixed dilated pupils.
   d. lack of eye movement and deep tendon reflexes.

7. The use of Harvard Criteria for declaration of an irreversible coma includes an
   a. EKG.
   b. EEG.
   c. EKG with repeat in twenty-four hours.
   d. EEG with repeat in twenty-four hours.

8. Before terminating a life-support system, a physician should
   a. seek the advice of the family.
   b. seek an outside medical opinion.
   c. seek the advice of a lawyer.
   d. talk with the religious counselor.

9. Ethical considerations of the terminally ill patient include
   a. withdrawing versus withholding treatment.
   b. active euthanasia versus passive euthanasia.
   c. ordinary versus extraordinary means.
   d. all of the above.

10. Withdrawing life-sustaining treatment refers to
    a. not starting artificial methods of maintaining life.
    b. discontinuing artificial methods of maintaining life.
    c. gradually discontinuing feeding.
    d. gradually discontinuing ventilation.

11. Patients have the legal right to
    a. refuse treatment.
    b. refuse food.
    c. refuse fluids.
    d. all of the above.

12. The intentional killing of the terminally ill person is called
    a. passive euthanasia.
    b. active euthanasia.
    c. patient-assisted suicide.
    d. b and c.

13. Justifications for euthanasia include
    a. individuals should have the right to determine the outcome of their lives.
    b. there is no certainty regarding death.
    c. modern technology may find a cure for a terminal disease.
    d. there is value and dignity to every human life.

14. Active euthanasia
    a. is illegal.
    b. violates the medical profession's ethics.
    c. both a and b.
    d. none of the above.

15. Advice regarding the course of action taken for a dying loved one can be given by
    a. any health care worker.
    b. the physician.
    c. a nurse.
    d. all of the above.

16. The double-effect doctrine recognizes that an action may have
    a. only one consequence: undesired.
    b. two consequences, both desired.
    c. two consequences, both undesired.
    d. two consequences: one desired, one undesired.

17. A treatment or procedure that is morally required is considered
    a. extraordinary.
    b. ordinary.
    c. appropriate.
    d. b and c.

18. Dr. Elisabeth Kübler-Ross is known for her study of
    a. quality-of-life issues.
    b. stages of death and dying.
    c. functional living index.
    d. hospice care.

19. A facility with a homelike atmosphere where terminally ill patients find comfort until death is called a
    a. hospital.
    b. hostel.
    c. hospice.
    d. all of the above.

20. The focus of hospice care is
    a. comfort measures.
    b. emotional support.
    c. relief from pain.
    d. all of the above.

21. The total care of patients whose disease is no longer responsive to curative therapy is
    a. palliative care.
    b. preventive care.
    c. hospice care.
    d. euthanasia.

22. Viatical settlements allow terminally ill persons to
    a. borrow money from a loan company.
    b. obtain money from their life insurance policies.
    c. obtain money from the federal government for experimental treatments.
    d. obtain money through Medicaid without paying taxes.

23. Health care facilities, in order to receive Medicare or Medicaid funding, must ask patients if they have
    a. life insurance.
    b. health insurance.
    c. long-term care insurance.
    d. an advance directive.

24. Persons who cannot exercise the fundamental right to self-determination include
    a. persons with a head injury who are coherent.
    b. persons who suffer irreversible brain damage, such as those with Alzheimer's disease.
    c. persons who are unable to provide health insurance.
    d. all of the above.

25. A DNR order can be placed on the medical chart of a patient by the
    a. physician.
    b. nurse.
    c. EMT.
    d. pharmacist.

COMPREHENSIVE EXAM

Multiple Choice Questions

Select the one best answer to the following questions.

1. Professional liability is covered under what branch of law?
   a. civil law
   b. criminal law
   c. administrative law
   d. constitutional law
   e. probate law

2. The legal nature of a physician–patient relationship is considered to be a(n)
   a. *in loco parentis.*
   b. agent.
   c. *respondeat superior.*
   d. contract.
   e. felony.

3. Any physician who administers a controlled substance must register with the
   a. Bureau of Narcotics and Dangerous Drugs.
   b. Food and Drug Administration.
   c. Drug Enforcement Administration.
   d. Employee Assistance Program.
   e. none of the above.

4. Which of the following situations is a reason for the revocation of a physician's license?
   a. receiving drug samples from pharmaceutical companies
   b. reporting unethical conduct of another physician
   c. refusal to accept a new patient
   d. betrayal of patient confidentiality
   e. acquittal of a crime

5. The authority that can revoke or suspend a physician's medical license is the
   a. U.S. Department of Education.
   b. federal government.
   c. state medical board that granted the license.
   d. National Board Medical Examination.
   e. American Medical Association.

6. A physician who removes a patient's appendix, without permission, during a surgical procedure for a hysterectomy for which he or she had permission commits a(n)
   a. invasion of privacy.
   b. assault and battery.
   c. misdemeanor.
   d. professional courtesy.
   e. none of the above.

7. A nurse who provides support for a physician–employer's felonious action
   a. is innocent under the doctrine of *respondeat superior*
   b. may still be liable even though covered under the doctrine of *respondeat superior.*
   c. is acting within the scope of practice for a nurse.
   d. is supportive of the bond between an employer and employee and thus not guilty of the felony.
   e. should countersue his or her employer.

8. When a patient's reputation is injured as a result of a statement made to another person about a patient's medical condition, this is called
   a. libel.
   b. slander.
   c. embezzlement.
   d. discovery.
   e. *stare decisis.*

9. The Human Genome Project
   a. is funded by the federal government.
   b. relates to court-appointed guardians for minors.
   c. maps the sequence of chromosomes.
   d. studies the gestational period of a pregnancy.
   e. a and c.

10. An institutional review board oversees violations of
    a. the Equal Employment Opportunity Act.
    b. the Civil Rights Act of 1991.
    c. research in hospitals or universities.
    d. OSHA.
    e. the Fair Labor Standards Act.

11. The medical record is
    a. a legal document.
    b. owned by the physician.
    c. owned by the patient.
    d. immune to subpoena.
    e. a and b.

12. The employer identification standard is
    a. used for purposes of writing prescriptions for controlled substances.
    b. based on an employer's tax ID number.
    c. based on an EIN.
    d. b and c.
    e. all of the above.

13. Vesting occurs when
    a. an employee leaves a company.
    b. an employee obtains a medical leave of absence.
    c. an employee waives his or her rights to receive benefits.
    d. the employee completes ten years of employment.
    e. none of the above.

14. A method for resolving a civil dispute that does not involve going to court is called a(n)
    a. affirmative defense.
    b. claims-made insurance.
    c. alternative dispute resolution.
    d. settlement.
    e. c and d.

15. The purpose for the statute of limitations is to
    a. provide a fixed period of time or a deadline for initiating a legal action.
    b. protect the physician from a lawsuit.
    c. place a cap on the amount of money awarded in a malpractice lawsuit.
    d. protect the physician from frivolous lawsuits.
    e. none of the above.

16. Spoken words about a person that bring injury to his or her reputation is called
    a. assault.
    b. slander.
    c. libel.
    d. feasance.
    e. b and c.

17. An example of *res ipsa loquitur* is
    a. a surgeon leaving a surgical sponge in a patient.
    b. vomiting after receiving a dose of ipecac.
    c. intestinal bleeding shortly after receiving a large dose of aspirin.
    d. inability to flex an arm after having blood drawn.
    e. all of the above.

18. The four Ds of negligence include all of the following except
    a. duty.
    b. disability.
    c. dereliction.
    d. damages.
    e. direct cause.

19. The elements of a contract are
    a. consideration.
    b. offer.
    c. acceptance.
    d. both parties are competent.
    e. all of the above.

20. Ways to avoid a malpractice suit include all of the following except
    a. act within your scope of practice.
    b. provide training for staff members after they have completed their professional education.
    c. prescribe medications over the telephone only for patients who you know well.
    d. never make a promise of a cure.
    e. identify all patients by name even if you know who they are.

21. Physicians can refuse to do all of the following except
    a. perform abortions.
    b. treat AIDS patients.
    c. accept new patients.
    d. treat emergency patients.
    e. b and d.

22. A contract is not valid if
    a. it is not in writing.
    b. the patient does not have a complete understanding of all parts of it.
    c. there is nothing offered by the patient in return.
    d. b and c.
    e. a, b, and c.

23. To take a blood sample without the consent of the patient, except in the case of an emergency, is
    a. invasion of privacy.
    b. assault.
    c. battery.
    d. false imprisonment.
    e. all of the above.

24. A coroner's report must be filed for the death
    a. occurring in a hospital setting.
    b. from a gunshot wound.
    c. of an elderly person with dementia.
    d. of a cancer patient who dies in a hospice.
    e. all of the above.

25. Good Samaritan laws encourage
    a. lawsuits.
    b. insurance fraud.
    c. health care professionals to provide aid in emergency situations.
    d. onlookers to stop at an auto accident.
    e. none of the above.

26. An informed consent must be signed for all of the following except
    a. chemotherapy.
    b. electroconvulsive therapy.
    c. minor surgery.
    d. organ donation.
    e. All of the above need an informed consent.

27. An informed consumer should do all the following except
    a. self-medicate with over-the-counter medications whenever possible.
    b. store medications away from children.
    c. carry a list of all medications being taken.
    d. read the label every time a medication is taken.
    e. All of the above are correct.

28. Prescription pads should
    a. be readily available in every exam room for the physician's use.
    b. not be left in exam room.
    c. kept in the physician's locked car.
    d. kept in a physician's locked bag.
    e. b and d.

29. One of the most common contracts used in the medical office is a(n)
    a. subpoena.
    b. signed contract.
    c. implied contract.
    d. living will.
    e. Anatomical Uniform Gift Act.

30. SOAP charting provides
    a. a health care employee's subjective assessment of the patient.
    b. the patient's subjective statements.
    c. a nurse's diagnosis.
    d. the patient's requested plan of treatment.
    e. all of the above.

31. Health care professionals should
    a. discuss a patient's medical condition with others as often as possible to gain other perspectives about the patient.
    b. never promise a cure.
    c. avoid contact with the patient's family members.
    d. hide when a process server attempts to serve the physician with a subpoena.
    e. none of the above.

32. Consent is implied by law
    a. in an emergency when a patient cannot give it.
    b. when a patient reaches out an arm for the blood pressure cuff to be applied.
    c. when a patient puts on a patient gown for a physical examination.
    d. a and b only.
    e. a, b, and c.

33. If the patient does not grant consent before a medical procedure, there is a(n)
    a. libel action.
    b. arraignment.
    c. tort.
    d. case law.
    e. none of the above.

34. The punishment in a civil case is often
    a. a fine.
    b. imprisonment.
    c. death penalty.
    d. revocation of a license.
    e. all of the above.

35. The *privacy rule* of HIPAA went into effect in
    a. 1996.
    b. 2001.
    c. 2003.
    d. 2008.
    e. It has not gone into effect yet.

36. Negligent wrongs can be the result of an
    a. omission of an action.
    b. performance of an illegal action.
    c. incorrect performance of a legal action.
    d. a and c only.
    e. a, b, and c.

37. The licensure examination for a nurse is the
    a. FACP.
    b. FACS.
    c. FLEX.
    d. NCLEX.
    e. none of the above.

38. Ethics specifically refers to
    a. right and wrong.
    b. just and unjust.
    c. fair and unfair.
    d. good and bad.
    e. all of the above.

39. The medical insurance industry has
    a. no influence on the type of health care provided to a patient.
    b. increased influence during the past two decades.
    c. demanded to play a decreased role in the patient's health care.
    d. influenced a significant decrease in medical malpractice insurance costs.
    e. none of the above.

40. Physicians need to have a
    a. license in the state in which they are practicing.
    b. partner who can accept responsibility for patient care.
    c. small amount of medical insurance if they practice careful medicine.
    d. a and c.
    e. a, b, and c.

41. Individual medical personnel can
    a. provide medical advice to a patient if they are knowledgeable.
    b. advise patients to change physicians if they are dissatisfied with their current physician, even if the physician is his or her employer.
    c. be sued as well as their employer.
    d. always be protected from lawsuits under the doctrine of *respondeat superior.*
    e. a, b, and d.

42. The FDA can inspect
    a. narcotic drug records of hospitals.
    b. narcotic drug records of physicians.
    c. the distribution of drugs throughout the Unites States.
    d. a and b only.
    e. a, b, and c.

43. A living will is
    a. mandated by the Age Discrimination Act.
    b. voluntary.
    c. required for employees of the federal government.
    d. b and c.
    e. none of the above.

44. A spouse
    a. must be informed about an abortion.
    b. cannot determine when to remove life support without the written consent of the patient.
    c. has no rights in the case of a wrongful death suit brought on behalf of his or her deceased spouse.
    d. a, b, and c.
    e. none of the above.

45. The proper method for correcting an error on a medical record is to
    a. use high-quality white-out fluid.
    b. erase the error and write in the correction.
    c. draw a thick, dark line through the error and write the correction underneath it.
    d. draw a thin line through the error, write the correction above the error, and initial the change.
    e. none of the above.

46. An example of *respondeat superior* is when
    a. an employer accepts responsibility for an unintentional error made by an employee.
    b. an employer accepts partial responsibility for an intentional error made by an employee.
    c. an employee is an agent of the employer.
    d. a and b only.
    e. a, b, and c.

47. Informed consent means
    a. a physician must tell the patient about the risks of having a procedure.
    b. a physician must tell the patient about the risks of not having the procedure.
    c. giving the patient a set of instructions to read.
    d. having a knowledgeable staff member provide patient instructions.
    e. a and b only.

48. Under HIPAA, a physician can
    a. supply medical records to another physician if the patient has provided written permission.
    b. supply medical records to a consulting physician without the patient's permission as a stipulation of medical etiquette.
    c. refuse to provide an accounting of whom the health care information is given to.
    d. insist on contacting the patient only at his or her home telephone number.
    e. none of the above.

49. The medical record is privileged communication with the right of privilege belonging to the
    a. medical insurer.
    b. physician.
    c. patient.
    d. all of the above.
    e. none of the above.

50. A procedure in which donor's sperm is inserted into a woman's uterus is
    a. illegal.
    b. unethical.
    c. immoral.
    d. AID.
    e. all of the above.

51. Withholding life-sustaining treatment is often easier than
    a. signing a living will.
    b. developing a durable power of attorney for health care.
    c. withdrawing life-sustaining treatment.
    d. a and b only.
    e. a, b, and c.

52. Sympathy is the emotion of
    a. putting oneself in another's place.
    b. anger.
    c. denial.
    d. pity.
    e. fear.

53. A fetus is considered viable
    a. between the second and twelfth week after conception.
    b. during the second trimester.
    c. when it is able to survive outside of the uterus (womb).
    d. only after nine months of gestation.
    e. none of the above.

54. A viatical settlement is
    a. illegal.
    b. immoral.
    c. handled by an insurance company.
    d. not always beneficial to the patient.
    e. c and d.

55. A terminally ill patient
    a. can benefit from curative care.
    b. can benefit from palliative care.
    c. has little hope of recovery.
    d. can legally negotiate an assisted suicide in most states.
    e. b and c.

56. A procedure to test for genetic defects in which a needle is used to withdraw a small amount of the fluid surrounding the fetus is called
    a. gene therapy.
    b. eugenics.
    c. amniocentesis.
    d. a felony.
    e. a tort.

57. An example of *res judicata* is
    a. a situation in which the statute of limitations has run out.
    b. when the breach of duty is so obvious that it doesn't need further explanation, as, for example, when a surgeon leaves a surgical instrument inside a patient.
    c. when a jury decides in favor of the defendant, then the plaintiff cannot bring a new lawsuit on the same charge against the defendant.
    d. when a nursing assistant improperly connects the seat of a lift device but caused no harm to the patient.
    e. none of the above.

58. The practical application of ethics to medical dilemmas is
    a. medical law.
    b. arbitration.
    c. arraignment.
    d. acquittal.
    e. applied ethics.

59. A neglect of understanding between two parties is
    a. breach of duty.
    b. dereliction of duty.
    c. direct cause.
    d. a and b.
    e. proximate cause.

60. A term used to refer to heart and lung function is
    a. EEG.
    b. cardiopulmonary.
    c. brain death.
    d. rigor mortis.
    e. passive euthanasia.

61. Persons who specialize in the field of bioethics are
    a. lawyers.
    b. physicians.
    c. nurses.
    d. bioethicists.
    e. biologists.

62. A postmortem examination of organs and tissues to determine the cause of death is
    a. eugenics.
    b. an autopsy.
    c. genetics.
    d. rigor mortis.
    e. bioethics.

63. Legislation that states that a hospital and health care employees are not required to assist with procedures such as sterilization is called
    a. informed consent.
    b. implied consent.
    c. common law.
    d. conscience clause.
    e. none of the above.

64. Summary statements made by the attorneys for the plaintiff and the defendant are
    a. checks and balances.
    b. closing arguments.
    c. conscience clauses.
    d. covered entities.
    e. censure.

65. Numbers concerning events or facts from a person's life are called
    a. data.
    b. confidential.
    c. vital statistics.
    d. government regulated.
    e. c and d.

66. The three-step ethics model has a person ask all of the following questions except
    a. Is it ethical?
    b. Is it legal?
    c. Is it balanced?
    d. How does it make me feel if I do it?
    e. none of the above.

67. The study of rules or actions determined by an authority that have a binding effect on a person's actions is
    a. law.
    b. ethics.
    c. bioethics.
    d. a and b only.
    e. a, b, and c.

68. Adherence to one's principles is said to be an example of
    a. ethics.
    b. integrity.
    c. applied ethics.
    d. professionalism.
    e. all of the above.

69. Professional misconduct on the part of a physician might include all of the following except
    a. conviction of a felony.
    b. physical abuse of a patient.
    c. impaired ability to practice medicine.
    d. drug abuse, insufficient record keeping.
    e. all of the above are examples of professional misconduct.

70. A form of consequence-based ethics is
    a. rights-based ethics.
    b. virtue-based ethics.
    c. interpersonal ethics.
    d. utilitarianism.
    e. none of the above.

71. Sexual harassment, as defined in the Equal Employment Opportunity Commission guidelines, includes all of the following except
    a. submission to sexual advances is made an explicit condition of a person's employment.
    b. submission to sexual advances is made an implicit condition of a person's employment.
    c. sexual advances have the effect of interfering with an individual's work performance.
    d. a and c only.
    e. a, b, and c.

72. The term *bio,* as in bioethics, means
    a. biology.
    b. death.
    c. life.
    d. medicine.
    e. none of the above.

73. Illegal actions are almost always
    a. unethical.
    b. obvious.
    c. hidden.
    d. a and b only.
    e. a and c only.

74. Law that is based on decisions made by judges is called
    a. common law.
    b. constitutional law.
    c. case law.
    d. criminal law.
    e. a and c.

75. Defamation of character can result from
    a. libel.
    b. slander.
    c. gossip.
    d. making true statements about another person.
    e. all of the above.

76. An enforceable agreement between two or more persons to do or not to do something is called a
    a. conflict.
    b. contract.
    c. common law.
    d. civil law.
    e. b and d.

77. The legal term *stare decisis* means
    a. let the master answer.
    b. the thing speaks for itself.
    c. let the decision stand.
    d. the thing has been decided.
    e. none of the above.

78. Under HIPAA, *covered entities* include all of the following except
    a. life insurance companies.
    b. patients.
    c. public health authorities.
    d. universities.
    e. all of the above.

79. Inviolable rights and privileges of people are covered under
    a. constitutional law.
    b. contract law.
    c. common law.
    d. case law.
    e. administrative law.

80. A lawsuit is also called
    a. arraignment.
    b. litigation.
    c. subpoena.
    d. acquittal.
    e. indictment.

81. The highest law in the country is
    a. criminal law.
    b. administrative law.
    c. constitutional law.
    d. civil law.
    e. none of the above.

82. The term used when sperm and egg (ovum) are united in a test tube outside the mother's body is
    a. in-vitro fertilization.
    b. artificial insemination.
    c. therapeutic abortion.
    d. eugenics.
    e. none of the above.

83. The legal theory that provides that the statute of limitations begins to run at the time the injury is discovered is
    a. illegal.
    b. unethical.
    c. unfair to the physician.
    d. the discovery rule.
    e. all of the above.

84. Most states require an applicant for a medical license to
    a. pass the written USMLE.
    b. pass the oral USMLE.
    c. provide proof of the completion of a successful residency.
    d. provide information of any past drug or alcohol abuse.
    e. all of the above.

85. According to HIPAA, under what condition might a nursing home deny access to patient information?
    a. if it may endanger the physical safety of the patient.
    b. if it may endanger the life of another person.
    c. if it makes reference to another person who could then be placed in danger.
    d. a and b only.
    e. a, b, and c.

86. Laws originate in what branch of government?
    a. judicial.
    b. legislative.
    c. executive branch.
    d. administrative.
    e. none of the above.

87. The Constitution addresses relationships between all of the following *except*
    a. private businesses.
    b. private individuals.
    c. individuals and their government.
    d. a and b only.
    e. a, b, and c.

88. A medical practice that is managed by a board of directors is called a
    a. partnership.
    b. proprietorship.
    c. corporation.
    d. franchise.
    e. all of the above.

89. The continuous sequence of events that is unbroken by any intervening event is called
    a. discovery rule.
    b. dereliction.
    c. deposition.
    d. direct cause.
    e. defamation.

90. The DEA is a(n)
    a. division of the Department of Justice.
    b. enforcer for the Controlled Substances Act of 1970.
    c. diagnostic related group.
    d. a and b only.
    e. none of the above.

91. A test to measure brain activity that is used when determining brain death is
    a. EAP.
    b. CPR.
    c. EEG.
    d. DNR.
    e. none of the above.

92. A court order requiring an employer to pay a portion of the employee's paycheck directly to one of the employee's creditors is
    a. illegal.
    b. unethical.
    c. a fixed-payment plan.
    d. garnishment.
    e. all of the above.

93. A medical practitioner who, through education, training, or experience, has special knowledge about a subject and gives testimony about that subject in court is called a(n)
    a. defendant.
    b. plaintiff.
    c. expert witness.
    d. judge.
    e. grand jury.

94. The complete set of genes within the 23 pairs of human chromosomes is called the
    a. eugenics.
    b. HIPAA.
    c. HIPDB.
    d. human genome.
    e. none of the above.

95. Regulations are rules made by
    a. judges.
    b. agencies.
    c. the Constitution of the United States.
    d. lawyers.
    e. physicians.

96. A ruling in an earlier court case upon which a subsequent case result is based is called
    a. precedent.
    b. illegal.
    c. unethical.
    d. *stare decisis.*
    e. a and d.

97. Civil law includes
    a. constitutional law.
    b. tort law and contract law.
    c. criminal law.
    d. administrative law.
    e. none of the above.

98. CAAHEP accredits programs for
    a. emergency medical technicians.
    b. medical assistants.
    c. physician assistants.
    d. respiratory technicians.
    e. all of the above.

99. If a wrongful act has been committed against another person and there is no harm done, there is no
    a. tort.
    b. civil case.
    c. criminal case.
    d. *stare decisis.*
    e. *res judicata.*

100. When an action is taken to confine a person against his or her wishes, it is the tort of
    a. invasion of privacy.
    b. battery.
    c. false imprisonment.
    d. assault.
    e. none of the above.

101. The JCAHO is an accreditation agency for
    a. hospitals.
    b. all health care institutions.
    c. clinical laboratories.
    d. it is not an accreditation agency.
    e. a and c only.

102. The standard that a health care professional must provide information that a reasonable person would want before making a decision is called the
    a. *stare decisis.*
    b. *respondeat superior.*
    c. prudent person rule.
    d. privacy rule.
    e. none of the above.

103. The statute of limitations varies somewhat from state to state but is typically
    a. 5 years.
    b. 10 years.
    c. 1 to 3 years.
    d. there is no limitation.
    e. none of the above.

104. *Darling v. Charleston Community Memorial Hospital* is about
    a. the ability of the plaintiff to recover damages from the physician.
    b. the ability of the plaintiff to recover damages from the nurse.
    c. the ability of the plaintiff to recover damages from the hospital.
    d. a and b.
    e. a, b, and c.

105. An ethical theory based on traits such as integrity, trust, respect, empathy, and truthfulness is
    a. duty-based ethics.
    b. utilitarianism.
    c. virtue-based ethics.
    d. rights-based ethics.
    e. interpersonal ethics.

106. To give up the right to something is
    a. a tort.
    b. a misdemeanor.
    c. a breach.
    d. to waive it.
    e. a deposition.

107. A threat that a person believes will cause bodily harm to him or her is
    a. fraud.
    b. assault.
    c. battery.
    d. defamation of character.
    e. invasion of privacy.

108. The statute of limitations begins to run when
    a. the injury is discovered.
    b. the injury occurs.
    c. a lawsuit is instigated.
    d. all of the above.
    e. none of the above.

109. WLANs are a
    a. form of reimbursement for medical care.
    b. method for solving a civil dispute.
    c. division of the Department of Justice.
    d. system of wireless technology.
    e. form of artificial insemination.

110. A program designed to assist employees and their families with personal problems is
    a. EIN.
    b. EAP.
    c. EEG.
    d. EPO.
    e. none of the above.

111. A payment plan for medical bills that offers subscribers complete medical care in return for a monthly payment is
    a. garnishment.
    b. a sole proprietorship.
    c. corporation.
    d. fixed-payment plan.
    e. none of the above.

112. A state in which the body temperature is below a normal range is
    a. parenteral.
    b. hypothermia.
    c. a cardiopulmonary disorder.
    d. also called rigor mortis.
    e. referred to as being indigent.

113. A dispute that results in one party's suing another is called
    a. inquest.
    b. litigation.
    c. autopsy.
    d. medical etiquette.
    e. none of the above.

114. An effort by the provider of medical care to make a reasonable effort to limit the disclosure of patient information to only the minimum amount that is necessary to accomplish the purpose of the request is
    a. the minimum necessary standard.
    b. a misdemeanor.
    c. negligence.
    d. nonfeasance.
    e. b and d.

115. A medication route other than the alimentary canal
    a. intravenous.
    b. intramuscular.
    c. rectal.
    d. subcutaneous.
    e. a, b, and d.

116. Confidential information that is told by a patient to a physician or attorney is
    a. proximate cause.
    b. precedent.
    c. prudent person rule.
    d. privileged communication.
    e. public duty.

117. The emotional well-being and functional and physiological status of a person is called
    a. employee assistance.
    b. social utility method of allocation.
    c. quality of life.
    d. Dr. Kübler-Ross's stages of dying.
    e. none of the above.

118. Negligence is a(n)
    a. intentional tort.
    b. unintentional tort.
    c. type of administrative law.
    d. always a criminal action.
    e. a and d.

119. What condition(s) are necessary for *res ipsa* to have occurred?
    a. injury could not have occurred without negligence
    b. the defendant had total control over the cause of the injury
    c. the patient did not contribute to the cause of the injury
    d. a and b only
    e. a, b, and c

120. Under malpractice law, damages refer to all of the following except
    a. property damage.
    b. permanent physical disability.
    c. personal injuries.
    d. past and future loss of earnings.
    e. pain and suffering.

121. A wrongful-death lawsuit
    a. is illegal in most states.
    b. does not compensate the estate for the loss of future earnings.
    c. does not require the plaintiff to prove that he or she was totally dependent on the deceased for support.
    d. requires that the defendant's action must have been a proximate cause of death.
    e. c and d only.

122. The most common defense to a malpractice lawsuit is
    a. assumption of risk.
    b. contributory negligence.
    c. comparative negligence.
    d. denial.
    e. borrowed servant.

123. A deliberate concealment of the facts from the patient is
    a. fraud.
    b. a defense in a malpractice suit.
    c. legitimate if the statute of limitations is already "running."
    d. the same as *respondeat superior.*
    e. b, c, and d.

124. In order to have protection under the doctrine of *respondeat superior,* the health care employee should
    a. have a written job description that defines responsibilities, duties, and skills necessary for the job.
    b. use extreme care when performing the job.
    c. only carry out procedures which he or she has been assigned.
    d. be honest about any errors he or she has made.
    e. all of the above.

125. The responsibility for maintaining a safe physical environment for patients rests on
  a. the physician-owner only.
  b. physicians and nurses only.
  c. housekeeping and security personnel only.
  d. all professional staff.
  e. all professional and nonprofessional staff.

126. Arguing before the court that the negligence was unintentional
  a. cannot be used as a malpractice defense.
  b. is a legitimate argument.
  c. is a criminal offense.
  d. can result in imprisonment.
  e. none of the above.

127. A fear of lawsuits has
  a. changed nothing in the practice of health care.
  b. influenced the practice of medicine.
  c. had a positive effect on medicine.
  d. b and c.
  e. none of the above.

128. All of the following are agents of the physicians except
  a. nurses.
  b. medical assistants.
  c. physician's assistants.
  d. pharmacists.
  e. All are agents.

129. A promise to cure a patient is a consideration under
  a. constitutional law.
  b. civil law.
  c. tort law.
  d. criminal law.
  e. b and c.

130. If someone attempts to walk on a wet floor in spite of a caution sign in place,
  a. the institution owner is at risk for damages.
  b. it is at his or her own risk.
  c. the owner can be still be sued even if not at risk.
  d. b and c.
  e. none of the above.

131. The doctrine of *respondeat superior* was implemented for the benefit of the
  a. employee.
  b. physician.
  c. patient.
  d. housekeeping staff.
  e. insurance company.

132. HIPAA allows for private patient information to be conveyed to
    a. only health insurance carriers.
    b. vendors if there is an assurance through a written contract that the information will be protected.
    c. whoever asks for the information as long as the request is in writing.
    d. b and c.
    e. none of the above.

133. A physician's insurance company might settle a case even if
    a. negligence is not found.
    b. there is a charge of comparative negligence.
    c. there is a charge of contributory negligence.
    d. b and c.
    e. An insurance company will not settle in a negligence case.

134. Additional insurance coverage to protect a physician's employees is called a
    a. waiver.
    b. poor management practice.
    c. rider.
    d. creditor.
    e. none of the above.

135. Using a third party for mediation requires a
    a. binding decision.
    b. nonbinding decision.
    c. negligent action that resulted in a death.
    d. criminal case.
    e. a and c.

136. The Health Insurance Portability and Accountability Act of 1996
    a. focuses attention on issues of a patient's privacy.
    b. improves the ability to continue one's health insurance upon leaving a job.
    c. attacks fraud.
    d. promotes medical savings plans.
    e. all of the above.

137. In order to de-identify a patient, the following information must be removed from any data:
    a. e-mail address
    b. license numbers
    c. medical record number
    d. a and c only
    e. a, b, and c

138. An example of the defense of assumption of risk is
    a. to continue to smoke after receiving a warning from the physician.
    b. a medical professional who agrees to take care of a person with a communicable disease with the knowledge that the disease is communicable.
    c. drinking after being told of the danger of further liver damage.
    d. None of the above answers are legitimate defenses to assumption of risk.
    e. a, b, and c are all correct.

139. Protected health information under HIPAA consists of a patient's
    a. name.
    b. age.
    c. future mental conditions.
    d. a and b only.
    e. a, b, and c.

140. The difference between comparative negligence and contributory negligence is that
    a. the plaintiff did not contribute to negligence in any way in comparative negligence.
    b. in contributory negligence, the patient may be totally barred from recovering monetary damages if found to be negligent.
    c. in comparative negligence, the plaintiff is allowed to recover damages based on the amount of the defendant's fault.
    d. b and c.
    e. a, b, and c.

141. The costs associated with implementing HIPAA are
    a. minimal.
    b. paid for by federal taxes.
    c. entirely paid for by insurance companies.
    d. considered to be high.
    e. none of the above.

142. Joan Smith, an operating room nurse, was loaned to Dr. Brown, a surgeon, by Dr. Williams, Joan's employer. Joan and Dr. Brown are both being sued for malpractice for an injury that occurred during a surgical procedure. Who is liable for Joan's actions?
    a. Under the doctrine of *respondeat superior,* Dr. Williams is responsible for Joan's actions.
    b. Under the doctrine of *respondeat superior,* Dr. Brown is responsible for Joan's actions, since he was Joan's agent at the time of the surgery.
    c. Only Joan is responsible for her actions.
    d. There can be no case of malpractice, since the patient signed a consent for surgery.
    e. None of the above.

143. An economic decision made by Congress to contain the cost of health care is/are
    a. ADR.
    b. DEA.
    c. EIN.
    d. DRG.
    e. FDA.

144. A living will
    a. can state what patients wish to have done at the end of their life.
    b. can state what patients wish not to have done at the end of their life.
    c. is a legal document.
    d. a and c only.
    e. a, b, and c.

145. A negligent action
    a. is one in which a person fails to perform an action that a reasonable person would have performed in a similar situation.
    b. is always intentional.
    c. is one in which there is a potential for punishment by loss of licensure.
    d. is one in which there is a degree of protection under *respondeat superior*.
    e. a, c, and d.

146. Comfort measures for the terminally ill patient include all the following except
    a. frequent turning.
    b. pain medication.
    c. hydration.
    d. oxygen.
    e. intravenous fluids.

147. To overrule something is to
    a. waive it.
    b. cite precedent.
    c. preempt it.
    d. place a rider on it.
    e. provide a proxy.

148. An action so egregious that it "speaks for itself" is an example of
    a. *res judicata.*
    b. *res ipsa loquitur.*
    c. *stare decisis.*
    d. *respondeat superior.*
    e. none of the above.

149. Dr. Kübler-Ross's five stages of dying include all of the following except
    a. anger.
    b. acceptance.
    c. grief.
    d. denial.
    e. depression.

150. When an action may have two consequences, one of which is desired and one which is undesired, it is said to be
    a. immoral.
    b. illegal.
    c. recognized as morally acceptable by many people.
    d. the doctrine of double effect.
    e. c and d.

True/False Questions

1. Assumption of risk may prevent the plaintiff from recovering damages in a legal action.

2. Ethics is a branch of philosophy.

3. Common law is also called constitutional law.

4. Controlled substances should be kept in a locked cabinet.

5. A birth certificate can be completed by an office assistant any time before the child is 1 year of age.

6. Viatical settlements are handled by lawyers and insurance companies for the terminally ill patient.

7. Bioethics is that branch of ethics dealing with moral dilemmas as a result of advances in medical technology.

8. A therapeutic abortion is undertaken to save the life of the mother.

9. A preferred provider organization is a managed care concept in which patients can select any physician they wish.

10. The privacy rule is covered under HIPAA.

11. An implied contract must be written.

12. A *subpoena duces tecum* is a summons to bring something to court.

13. The borrowed servant doctrine still follows the doctrine of *respondeat superior* and holds the employer responsible for the employee's actions.

14. The AAMA has developed a code of ethics for the medical assistant.

15. Fewer people are involved in a patient's medical care due to current efficient methods of medical practice.

16. A cease and desist order gives legal protection to the physician so that he or she can continue to perform an activity.

17. The action of performing a duty is called feasance.

18. Negligence can refer to not doing something.

19. DRGs are a form of drug abuse regulation.

20. A patient's silence can indicate an implied contract.

21. The Human Genome Project is not sponsored or approved by the federal government.

22. The fixed monthly fee paid to health care providers by an HMO to provide medical care is a capitation rate.

23. Child abuse should be reported only with valid proof.

24. Comparative negligence refers only to the physician's negligence.

25. A gatekeeper is a person, such as a physician, who approves patient referrals to other physicians.

26. The Health Care Portability and Accountability Act of 1996 was initially aimed at the electronic transfer of health information.

27. Legal standards are usually higher than ethical standards.

28. The Office of Civil Rights is the investigating entity for violations of HIPAA.

29. A physician should not promise to cure a patient.

30. The plaintiff is the person who is being sued in a court of law.

31. An implied contract is commonly used in a medical practice.

32. Ethics is a branch of the study of religion.

33. An EAP can assist with an employee's family problems.

34. Narcotic record keeping is voluntary.

35. A Schedule I narcotic has the least potential for abuse.

36. Schedule III drugs can be refilled.

37. The medical record is the legal property of the patient.

38. Good Samaritan laws protect only the physician.

39. Schedule III, IV, and V drugs can be refilled up to five times.

40. It is easier to defend negligence than it is to prevent it.

41. An expressed contract is either written or oral.

42. Not all states have laws that regulate the practice of medicine.

43. Based on the principles of the AMA, a physician cannot refuse to treat a patient who wishes to have an abortion.

44. The transmission of the AIDS virus is usually through blood.

45. *Res ipsa loquitur* means "the thing has been decided."

46. If a patient does not give consent, a tort could result from taking a sample of blood, except in an emergency.

47. Brain death is often reversible.

48. To place a limit on something is to "cap" it.

49. The Bureau of Narcotics and Dangerous Drugs is responsible for enforcing laws covering statutes of addictive drugs.

50. Amniocentesis is used to detect nongenetic defects in the fetus.

51. Endorsement is the process by which one state recognizes the medical licensing procedure of another state.

52. A durable power of attorney for health care is only valid for ninety days.

53. Alternative dispute resolutions are frequently used in court.

54. Physicians do not have to be licensed where they practice except when dispensing drugs.

55. Oral testimony given in front of an officer of the court is a deposition.

56. Not all medical personnel are entitled to due process due to the nature of their profession to provide service to others.

57. The branch of law covering government regulations is administrative law.

58. A defendant is a person who sues another person or groups of people in a court of law.

59. Noncompliance is a valid reason for a physician to ask a patient to seek another physician.

60. An insurance copayment is usually around $10.

61. A physician can withdraw care from a patient as long as he or she provides sufficient notice of the withdrawal.

62. *Respondeat superior* means "the thing speaks for itself."

63. Public duties are those responsibilities that a physician can delegate to an assistant.

64. The practice of medicine is defined by state statutes.

65. A conscience clause in a person's contract allows him or her to abstain from assisting with some procedures, such as abortion.

66. Protected health information (PHI) is individually identifiable information that relates to a particular patient.

67. A censure is a written document to demonstrate approval of a person.

68. A tort is a wrongful act against another person or property that causes harm.

69. Compensatory damages are money awarded by the court to make up for emotional pain and suffering.

70. The prudent person rule means that the medical professional is thrifty.

71. An example of a clearinghouse is a billing service.

72. Misfeasance is the performance of an illegal action.

73. Punitive damages are meant to punish the offender.

74. *In loco parentis* is a person assigned by the court to act on behalf of an incapacitated adult patient.

75. Rigor mortis is one of Dr. Kübler-Ross's stages of dying.

76. Comparable worth is the ability to understand the feelings of another person without actually experiencing the pain or distress that the person is going through.

77. The closing argument is that point at the end of the testimony when the defendant has an opportunity to speak.

78. Utilitarianism is an ethical approach in which the benefit of the decision outweighs the cost.

79. The legal theory that states that the statute of limitations begins to run at the time the injury is discovered is called the privacy rule.

80. Legally, an autopsy can only be performed if a person's death is from an unknown cause.

81. Failing to perform a legal duty is referred to as a breach.

82. Good Samaritan laws protect health care professionals when providing emergency care in a hospital setting.

83. A coroner is not considered to be a public official.

84. Applied ethics is the practical application of moral standards to the conduct of individuals involved in organizations.

85. Medicaid is a federal program to assist the elderly.

86. Public duties are those responsibilities that the public owes to the physician.

87. Denial is an example of an affirmative defense.

88. A parent may appoint a *guardian ad litem* to protect his or her child.

89. Civil law does not pertain to the medical profession.

90. A cost/benefit analysis is also called a consequence-based ethical theory.

91. Claims-made insurance covers the insured party for all injuries and incidents that occurred while the policy was in effect regardless of when the claim was made.

92. Withdrawing medical care after providing sufficient notice is abandonment.

93. The employment-at-will concept means that employment is at the will of either the employer or the employee.

94. An insurance company is an example of a third-party payer.

95. A living will is the only type of document that can legally be called an advance directive.

96. Negligence is an unintentional tort.

97. State reciprocity for licensure only applies to physicians' medical licenses.

98. Consent is a voluntary agreement that allows medical personnel to touch a patient.

99. It is better for a physician not to agree to settle a malpractice suit, since this is an indication of guilt.

100. Statements in an employee handbook can form an implied contract.

101. The Equal Employment Opportunity Commission sues employers in federal court.

102. The checks and balances of the government allows elected officials to be paid.

103. Even though a minor child may be married, he or she does not have any legal rights until reaching the age of 18.

104. A nominal damage could be only $1.00.

105. Assumption of risk is a legal defense that assists the defendant.

106. A subpoena is an order from an attorney.

107. Mandatory maternity leaves violate the law, since the Pregnancy Discrimination Act of 1978 was added as an amendment to Title VII.

108. The practice to reduce or minimize the incidence of problem behavior that might result in harm to a patient is called risk maintenance.

109. Case law is also called common law.

110. The social utility method of organ allocation provides scarce organs on a first-come, first-served basis.

111. Dereliction of duty is the continuous sequence of events, unbroken by any intervening cause, that produces an injury and without which the injury would not have occurred.

112. Empathy is the same thing as pity.

113. The Age Discrimination in Employment Act of 1967 protects persons over the age of 40.

114. Fraud is a deliberate concealment of facts from another person.

115. A cease-and-desist order is a recommendation that someone should consider stopping a particular behavior.

116. An EIN is an employer identification number.

117. The doctrine of professional discretion means that licensed medical professionals, such as nurses, may determine if a patient is emotionally competent to view his or her medical record.

118. It is legal to treat patients via the Internet.

119. Standard of care refers to ordinary care given to a patient.

120. A judge determines the outcome of arbitration.

121. The HIPDB is a national data bank that reports disclosures of actions taken against health care practitioners for fraudulent activities.

122. Malpractice always refers to misconduct or an unreasonable lack of skill.

123. Eugenics is a sterilization performed to save the life of the mother.

124. A sanction is a penalty.

125. In order for a claim of defamation of character to be valid, the malicious statements about another person must be in writing.

126. *Res judicata* means "the thing has been decided."

127. The Americans with Disabilities Act applies to employers who have ten or more employees.

128. Mercy killing is another term for voluntary euthanasia.

129. The physicians in an associate practice will share responsibility for the facility, staff, and legal actions of the other members of the group.

130. Medical practice acts define the practice of medicine as well as determine the methods for licensure in a particular state.

131. With the exception of health care workers, all employees are granted the right to strike under the National Labor Relations Act.

132. A capitation rate is a fluctuating monthly fee paid to health care providers for providing medical services to patients in an HMO.

133. OSHA protects health care workers such as housekeeping personnel.

134. An expert witness is usually paid a fee for testifying in court.

135. Under the Family and Medical Leave Act of 1994, an employee may request twelve weeks off from work for a death in the family even if he or she has worked for an employer for less than a year.

136. A medical office cannot ask a patient to pay his or her unpaid medical bill once the matter has been turned over to a collection agency.

137. A person without funds is said to incompetent.

138. DRGs are used to determine patient reimbursement.

139. *Subpoena duces tecum* means "under penalty take with you."

140. An alternative dispute resolution is best handled in a court of law.

141. A group practice must have at least three physicians.

142. According to OSHA, saliva in dental procedures is potentially infectious.

143. FICA is the oldest federal act relating to compensation.

144. A prosecutor is a person who brings a civil lawsuit against another person.

145. Not all of the fifty states have developed medical practice acts.

146. Under the Fair Debt Collection Practices Act of 1978, a collection call can be made from California to a New York phone number as long as the time is before 9 P.M. in California.

147. COBRA assists people who have suffered sexual harassment in the workplace.

148. An EPO is a type of managed care that combines the concepts of an HMO and a PPO.

149. Allege means to assert or declare that something is true based on proof.

150. Practicing medicine without a license is a misdemeanor.

Answer Key

Chapter 1

1. b	8. b	15. c	22. d
2. a	9. d	16. a	23. c
3. d	10. d	17. c	24. d
4. d	11. b	18. d	25. b
5. a	12. a	19. c	
6. c	13. a	20. b	
7. a	14. a	21. c	

Chapter 2

1. b	8. d	15. b	22. c
2. d	9. b	16. b	23. b
3. d	10. c	17. d	24. c
4. d	11. d	18. d	25. d
5. b	12. b	19. a	
6. a	13. c	20. d	
7. b	14. a	21. a	

Chapter 3

1. c	8. c	15. b	22. b
2. a	9. b	16. c	23. c
3. d	10. c	17. b	24. a
4. d	11. b	18. c	25. d
5. d	12. c	19. b	
6. b	13. d	20. a	
7. a	14. b	21. c	

Chapter 4

1. c	8. a	15. c	22. d
2. b	9. d	16. b	23. b
3. d	10. c	17. a	24. d
4. d	11. b	18. c	25. b
5. c	12. a	19. a	
6. d	13. c	20. b	
7. a	14. a	21. d	

Chapter 5

1. d	8. c	15. b	22. c
2. d	9. b	16. c	23. a
3. b	10. a	17. a	24. d
4. b	11. d	18. c	25. a
5. c	12. d	19. b	
6. b	13. d	20. d	
7. a	14. a	21. d	

Chapter 6

1. b	8. a	15. b	22. d
2. c	9. c	16. a	23. c
3. c	10. d	17. c	24. d
4. b	11. b	18. d	25. b
5. c	12. b	19. b	
6. d	13. c	20. c	
7. b	14. d	21. a	

Chapter 7

1. b	8. d	15. b	22. c
2. d	9. d	16. c	23. a
3. d	10. b	17. a	24. c
4. d	11. c	18. b	25. d
5. d	12. d	19. b	
6. a	13. d	20. d	
7. c	14. c	21. a	

Chapter 8

1. b	8. c	15. c	22. b
2. c	9. c	16. d	23. b
3. c	10. a	17. b	24. b
4. a	11. c	18. a	25. b
5. d	12. a	19. d	
6. d	13. b	20. b	
7. b	14. d	21. d	

Chapter 9

1. b	8. b	15. a	22. b
2. d	9. b	16. c	23. b
3. d	10. a	17. b	24. b
4. a	11. d	18. d	25. d
5. d	12. a	19. d	
6. c	13. c	20. b	
7. c	14. b	21. c	

Chapter 10

1. b	8. d	15. b	22. b
2. c	9. b	16. c	23. d
3. d	10. b	17. d	24. b
4. a	11. d	18. d	25. d
5. c	12. d	19. b	
6. d	13. d	20. d	
7. b	14. a	21. d	

Chapter 11

1. c	8. a	15. c	22. c
2. b	9. d	16. b	23. c
3. a	10. a	17. c	24. d
4. c	11. c	18. b	25. c
5. b	12. d	19. a	
6. c	13. c	20. d	
7. d	14. a	21. b	

Chapter 12

1. a	8. b	15. c	22. d
2. c	9. d	16. d	23. c
3. b	10. b	17. c	24. c
4. b	11. d	18. b	25. b
5. d	12. d	19. b	
6. d	13. d	20. d	
7. c	14. a	21. d	

Chapter 13

1. d	8. b	15. b	22. b
2. c	9. d	16. d	23. d
3. d	10. b	17. d	24. b
4. a	11. d	18. b	25. a
5. b	12. b	19. c	
6. b	13. a	20. d	
7. d	14. c	21. a	

Comprehensive Exam

Multiple Choice Questions

1. a	11. e	21. e	31. b
2. d	12. d	22. d	32. e
3. c	13. d	23. c	33. c
4. d	14. e	24. b	34. a
5. c	15. a	25. c	35. c
6. b	16. b	26. e	36. e
7. b	17. e	27. a	37. d
8. b	18. b	28. e	38. e
9. e	19. e	29. c	39. b
10. c	20. c	30. b	40. a

41. c	69. e	97. b	125. e
42. e	70. d	98. e	126. a
43. b	71. e	99. a	127. b
44. e	72. c	100. c	128. d
45. d	73. a	101. b	129. e
46. d	74. e	102. c	130. d
47. e	75. e	103. c	131. c
48. a	76. b	104. e	132. b
49. c	77. c	105. c	133. a
50. d	78. b	106. d	134. c
51. c	79. a	107. b	135. b
52. d	80. b	108. a	136. e
53. c	81. c	109. d	137. e
54. e	82. a	110. b	138. e
55. e	83. d	111. d	139. e
56. c	84. e	112. b	140. d
57. c	85. e	113. b	141. d
58. e	86. b	114. a	142. b
59. d	87. d	115. e	143. d
60. b	88. c	116. d	144. e
61. d	89. d	117. c	145. e
62. b	90. d	118. b	146. e
63. d	91. c	119. e	147. c
64. b	92. d	120. a	148. b
65. c	93. c	121. e	149. c
66. a	94. d	122. d	150. e
67. a	95. b	123. a	
68. e	96. e	124. e	

True/False Questions

1. T	24. F	47. F	70. F
2. T	25. T	48. T	71. T
3. F	26. T	49. T	72. F
4. T	27. F	50. F	73. T
5. F	28. T	51. F	74. F
6. T	29. T	52. F	75. F
7. T	30. F	53. F	76. F
8. T	31. T	54. F	77. F
9. F	32. F	55. T	78. T
10. T	33. T	56. F	79. F
11. F	34. F	57. T	80. F
12. T	35. F	58. F	81. T
13. F	36. T	59. T	82. F
14. T	37. F	60. T	83. F
15. F	38. F	61. T	84. T
16. F	39. T	62. F	85. F
17. T	40. T	63. F	86. F
18. T	41. F	64. T	87. T
19. F	42. F	65. T	88. F
20. T	43. F	66. T	89. F
21. F	44. T	67. F	90. T
22. T	45. F	68. T	91. F
23. F	46. T	69. T	92. F

93. T	108. T	123. F	138. T
94. T	109. T	124. T	139. T
95. F	110. F	125. F	140. F
96. T	111. F	126. T	141. T
97. F	112. F	127. F	142. T
98. T	113. T	128. T	143. T
99. F	114. T	129. F	144. F
100. T	115. F	130. T	145. F
101. T	116. T	131. F	146. F
102. F	117. F	132. F	147. F
103. F	118. T	133. T	148. T
104. T	119. T	134. T	149. F
105. T	120. F	135. F	150. F
106. F	121. T	136. T	
107. T	122. T	137. F	

Chapter 1

Lecture Notes/Class Handout 1

I. Vocabulary Development

II. Introduction: Interrelatedness of Medical Law, Ethics, and Bioethics

III. Why Study Medical Law, Ethics, and Bioethics?

IV. Medical Law

Chapter 1

Lecture Notes/Class Handout 2

I. Vocabulary Development

II. Ethics—Several Categories

III. Interpersonal Ethics

IV. Three-Step Ethics Model
A test to help determine if something is ethical.

V. Bioethics
Moral dilemmas and issues prevalent in today's society as a result of advances in medicine and medical research.

VI. What Ethics Is Not

Chapter 1

Worksheet 1

Define the terms.

1. applied ethics _____
   _____

2. bioethics _____
   _____

3. ethics _____
   _____

4. laws _____
   _____

5. medical ethics _____
   _____

Answer the questions.

1. Why must a medical practitioner adhere to certain ethical standards and codes of conduct?
   _____
   _____

2. How are laws and ethics similar?
   _____
   _____

3. How are laws and ethics dissimilar?
   _____
   _____

4. Is breaking a law acceptable if the reason is justifiable?
   _____
   _____

5. Does a medical professional have any responsibility beyond the law?
   _____
   _____

6. Do we all believe we know the difference between right and wrong?

_____

_____

Chapter 1

Worksheet 2

Define the terms.

1. utilitarianism _____

_____

2. respect _____

_____

3. integrity _____

_____

4. honesty _____

_____

5. fairness _____

_____

6. empathy _____

_____

7. sympathy _____

_____

8. compassion _____

_____

9. loyalty _____

_____

10. privacy _____

_____

11. sexual harassment _____

_____

12. due process _____

_____

13. comparable worth _____

_____

Describe the three-step model for evaluating an ethical dilemma.

Step One _____

_____

_____

Step Two _____

_____

_____

Step Three _____

_____

_____

Answer the questions.

1. Are emotional responses to ethical dilemmas sufficient? Why or why not?

_____

_____

2. Are ethics just about religious beliefs? Explain your answer.

_____

_____

3. How are ethics different from bioethics?

_____

_____

4. How are ethics and feelings different?

_____

_____

Chapter 1

Test 1

Fill in the Blank

1. _____ refers to moral dilemmas and issues that are a result of advances in medicine and medical research.

2. Medical ethics is a/an _____, meaning that it is the practical application of moral standards that concern benefiting the patient.

3. _____ is moral conduct based on principles regulating the behavior of health care professionals.

4. _____ is the practical application of moral standards to the conduct of individuals involved in organizations.

5. _____ are rules or actions prescribed by a governmental authority that have binding legal force.

True or False?

_____ 6. Something is wrong, or unethical, only if the law forbids it.

_____ 7. In times of crisis, people do not always make the correct decisions.

_____ 8. What is illegal is almost always unethical.

_____ 9. Your understanding of the law will help to protect you, but not your employer, from being sued in work-related issues.

_____ 10. The medical profession adheres to ethical codes of conduct.

_____ 11. The law allows many actions that are morally offensive.

_____ 12. If the law says it is all right, then it is also ethical.

_____ 13. Medical law addresses legal rights and obligations that affect patients and protect individual rights, including the rights of health care employees.

_____ 14. Some unethical situations are difficult to handle with laws and are better handled through work policies.

_____ 15. Breaking a law is always legal if the reason is justified.

_____ 16. The study of law and ethics often overlap.

_____ 17. A medical professional has no responsibility beyond the law.

_____ **18.** The law provides a yardstick by which to measure actions and punishment.

_____ **19.** We all believe we know the difference between right and wrong.

_____ **20.** The only reason to behave ethically is to avoid a lawsuit.

Chapter 1

Test 2

Fill in the Blank

1. _____ is an ethical theory based on the principle of the greatest good for the greatest number.

2. The study of _____ is the study of a branch of philosophy related to morals and moral principles.

3. _____ is the unwavering adherence to one's principles.

4. _____ is the ability to understand another person's feelings without actually experiencing that person's pain or distress.

5. _____ is the quality of truthfulness, no matter what the situation.

Multiple Choice

Write the letter of the correct answer in the blank.

_____ 6. Anyone who carries out orders for a physician has a duty to notify the physician or any error or discrepancy in those orders. This is an example of
   a. fairness.
   b. honesty.
   c. empathy.
   d. respect.

_____ 7. Feeling sorry for or pitying someone is an example of
   a. empathy.
   b. sympathy.
   c. integrity.
   d. compassion.

_____ 8. This is a critical characteristic for those working in the health care industry because patients come from a variety of racial, ethnic, and religious backgrounds.
   a. Honesty
   b. Empathy
   c. Loyalty
   d. Respect

_____ 9. It is never appropriate to recommend that a patient seek the services of another physician unless instructed to do so by the physician. This is an example of
   a. compassion.
   b. flexibility.
   c. fairness.
   d. loyalty.

_____ **10.** Another term for *confidentiality* is
     a. due process.
     b. privacy.
     c. comparable worth.
     d. empathy.

_____ **11.** Which question is NOT part of the three-step model for evaluating an ethical dilemma?
     a. How does it make me feel?
     b. Is it balanced?
     c. Is it legal?
     d. What will others think of me?

_____ **12.** The term *bio* when combined with *ethics* refers to
     a. wise choices.
     b. life and death issues.
     c. religious beliefs.
     d. clinical issues.

_____ **13.** This is treating everyone the same.
     a. Fairness
     b. Respect
     c. Comparable worth
     d. Due process

_____ **14.** This term means focusing on performing one's duty to various people and institutions, such as parents, employers, employees, customers, and patients.
     a. Virtue-based ethics
     b. Duty-based ethics
     c. Moral responsibility
     d. Rights-based ethics

_____ **15.** *Comparable worth* is also known as
     a. due process.
     b. pay equity.
     c. payback.
     d. bioethics.

True or False?

_____ **16.** Whenever you are involved in an ethical dilemma, you analyze actions and their consequences to all concerned parties.

_____ **17.** Ethics is only about how you feel, the sincerity of your beliefs, your emotion, and your religious viewpoints.

_____ **18.** Medical ethics is moral conduct based on principles regulating the behavior of health care professionals.

_____ **19.** Ethics is not just about religious beliefs.

_____ **20.** *Bioethics* refers to moral dilemmas and issues in today's society that result from advances in medicine and medical research.

Chapter 2

Lecture Notes/Class Handout 1

I. Vocabulary Development

II. The Legal System

III. Sources of Law

IV. Classification of Laws

Chapter 2
Lecture Notes/Class Handout 2

I. Vocabulary Development

II. Contract Law

III. Public Law—Criminal Law

IV. The Court System

V. The Trial Process

VI. Subpoena—Court Order

VII. Expert Witness

Chapter 2

Worksheet 1

Define the terms.

1. case law _____
   _____

2. checks and balances _____
   _____

3. civil law _____
   _____

4. common law _____
   _____

5. consideration _____
   _____

6. constitutional law _____
   _____

7. contract law _____
   _____

8. negligence _____
   _____

9. statutes _____
   _____

10. tort _____
    _____

11. tort law _____
    _____

Answer the questions.

1. What are the two fundamental principles on which the U.S. system of government is founded?

   _____

   _____

2. What are the three branches of the U.S. government?

   _____

   _____

3. Name the two parts of the legislative branch of the U.S. government.

   _____

   _____

4. Describe the federal court structure.

   _____

   _____

5. Describe each step in the process by which a bill becomes a law.

   _____

   _____

6. What does common law explain?

   _____

   _____

7. What is the difference between assault and battery?

   _____

   _____

Chapter 2
Worksheet 2

Define the terms.

1. abandonment _____
   _____

2. administrative law _____
   _____

3. breach _____
   _____

4. breach of contract _____
   _____

5. competent _____
   _____

6. criminal case _____
   _____

7. criminal laws _____
   _____

8. defendant _____
   _____

9. deposition _____
   _____

10. discovery _____
    _____

11. expert witness _____
    _____

12. expressed agreement _____
    _____

13. felony _____
    _____

14. implied contract _____

_____

15. litigation _____

_____

16. misdemeanors _____

_____

17. plaintiff _____

_____

18. prosecutor _____

_____

19. subpoena _____

_____

20. waive _____

_____

Answer the questions.

1. What is the difference between an expressed agreement and an implied contract?

_____

_____

2. Do the laws about abandonment mean that a physician can never withdraw from a case? Explain your answer.

_____

_____

3. Criminal acts fall into two categories. Name and describe each.

_____

_____

4. What does *jurisdiction* mean?

_____

_____

5. Can a physician take a patient's delinquent account to Small Claims Court? If so, does the physician have to appear or can someone else be authorized to appear on physician's behalf?

_____

_____

6. What part of a medical record must be presented under law of subpoena?

_____

_____

Chapter 2

Test 1

Fill in the Blanks

1. The two fundamental principles on which the United States system of government is founded are _____ and _____.

2. All powers that have not been specifically delegated to the federal government by the U.S. Constitution are _____.

3. The _____ is the highest element of the federal court structure.

4. The branch of the U.S. government that is headed by the president is the _____.

5. The Senate is a part of the _____ branch of the U.S. government.

Multiple Choice

Write the letter of the correct answer in the blank.

_____ 6. Laws that are passed by federal or state legislatures are part of
   a. common law.
   b. statutory law.
   c. constitutional law.
   d. case law.

_____ 7. After a bill passes in one house of the legislature, it becomes
   a. an act.
   b. a bill.
   c. an amendment.
   d. a law.

_____ 8. The type of law that concerns relationships between individuals or between individuals and the government is called
   a. tort law.
   b. battery law.
   c. fraud law.
   d. civil law.

_____ 9. Medical professionals have a duty to report any unusual occurrence to the police, including
   a. rape.
   b. child abuse.
   c. elder abuse.
   d. all of the above.

_____ **10.** Laws are classified as
    a. private and public.
    b. case and common.
    c. intentional and unintentional.
    d. major and minor.

Matching

In the blank, write the letter of the scenario that correctly matches each term.

_____ **11.** fraud

_____ **12.** false imprisonment

_____ **13.** battery

_____ **14.** assault

_____ **15.** defamation of character

_____ **16.** invasion of privacy

a. threatening to harm a patient if he or she does not cooperate with a treatment regimen

b. not allowing a patient to leave before completing a procedure

c. saying something negative about another physician to a patient

d. promising that a miracle cure will work

e. performing a procedure without a signed consent

f. publicizing private information about a patient

True or False?

_____ **17.** Under tort law, if a wrongful act has been committed against another person and there is no harm done, then there is no tort.

_____ **18.** Civil law includes tort law and contract law.

_____ **19.** Constitutional law applies to private entities, including businesses and individuals.

_____ **20.** Legislatures sometimes authorize agencies to make laws.

Chapter 2

Test 2

Fill in the Blanks

1. Physicians may be charged with _____ of a patient if they do not give formal notice of withdrawal from a case.

2. An _____ is one where the agreement is shown through inference by signs, inaction, or silence.

3. _____ are laws that are made to protect the public as a whole from the harmful acts of others.

4. _____ handles cases involving estates of the deceased.

5. _____ is the legal process by which facts are revealed before a trial begins.

Multiple Choice

Write the letter of the correct answer in the blank.

_____ 6. When a record such as a medical record or chart is subpoenaed,
   a. the entire chart must always be presented in court.
   b. the entire chart must always be provided but it may be presented by mail.
   c. the entire original chart must be turned over to the court.
   d. only the parts of the record requested should be copied and mailed to the requesting attorney.

_____ 7. The two court systems in the United States are
   a. felony and misdemeanor courts.
   b. state and federal courts.
   c. criminal and civil courts.
   d. statutory and regulatory courts.

_____ 8. *Jurisdiction* means
   a. the power to hear a case.
   b. the power to dismiss a case.
   c. the power to dispute a case.
   d. the power to defend a case.

_____ 9. Misdemeanors
   a. are less-serious offenses.
   b. carry a punishment of up to 5 years in jail.
   c. include murder and rape.
   d. include tax evasion.

_____ **10.** How is a case tried in the court system?
   a. At the lowest level court first
   b. At the highest level court first
   c. At the level that best matches the nature of the offense
   d. In the court that is least busy

Matching

In the blank, write the letter of the description that correctly matches each term.

_____ **11.** subpoena

_____ **12.** plaintiff

_____ **13.** expert witness

_____ **14.** defendant

_____ **15.** litigation

_____ **16.** felony

a. carries a penalty of death or imprisonment

b. dispute resulting in one party suing the other party

c. person or group sued or prosecuted in court

d. person or group suing another person or group

e. court order

f. individual with special education, training or experience in a given area

True or False?

_____ **17.** It is always advisable to seek payment for all medical services that have been provided to patients.

_____ **18.** Administrative law is a branch of public law.

_____ **19.** In a criminal case, the government brings the suit against a person or group of people.

_____ **20.** The U.S. legal system is based on the premise that all persons are innocent until proven guilty. Therefore, the burden of proof is placed on the defendant.

Chapter 3
Lecture Notes/Class Handout 1

I. Vocabulary Development

II. Medical Practice Acts

III. Licensure of the Physician

IV. Licensure versus Certification

Chapter 3

Lecture Notes/Class Handout 2

I. Vocabulary Development

II. Standard of Care

III. Confidentiality

IV. Statute of Limitations

V. Good Samaritan Laws

VI. *Respondeat Superior*

VII. Risk management

Chapter 3

Worksheet 1

Define the terms.

1. endorsement _____

   _____

2. reciprocity _____

   _____

3. revoked _____

   _____

Answer the questions.

1. What is the difference between licensing and certification of a physician?

   _____

   _____

   _____

2. What does it mean to be licensed by endorsement?

   _____

   _____

   _____

3. Why does reciprocity have to exist between states for licensure to be automatic?

   _____

   _____

   _____

4. While medical practice acts vary from state to state, they generally have four things in common. List these four things.

   _____

   _____

   _____

5. What are the requirements for renewal of a physician's license?

   _____

   _____

   _____

Chapter 3

Worksheet 2

Define the terms.

1. discovery rule _____

_____

2. *respondeat superior* _____

_____

3. standard of care _____

_____

4. statute of limitations _____

_____

Answer the questions.

1. Has the standard of care stayed the same or changed over the years? Why?

_____

_____

_____

2. Why is it dangerous to discuss any patient at all in a public place? What patient right could you inadvertently violate?

_____

_____

_____

3. Is the health care employer liable for all acts of employees? Explain your answer.

_____

_____

_____

4. Legally, are health care employees supposed to interpret orders of a physician? Explain.

_____

_____

_____

5. Select one court case described in this unit and summarize it. Explain why it is important and the impact it has had on daily medical practice.

_____

_____

_____

Chapter 3

Test 1

Fill in the Blanks

1. The practice by which a state grants a license to practice medicine to a physician or nurse already licensed in another state is known as _____.

2. _____ means an approval or sanction.

3. A nationally recognized licensing examination for graduates from accredited medical schools that allows them to practice medicine is called the _____.

4. In addition to paying a fee to renew their license, physicians must complete _____ hours of continuing medical education (CME) units every _____ years to assure that they remain current in their field of practice.

5. A physician's license may be _____ or taken away.

Multiple Choice

Write the letter of the correct answer in the blank.

_____ 6. The state seeks to protect patients from harm by
   a. interviewing physicians annually.
   b. testing and licensing physicians.
   c. charging fees for physicans.
   d. none of the above.

_____ 7. Malpractice suits
   a. seldom end up in court.
   b. are not important to the consumer.
   c. are not important to the physician.
   d. are not brought against certain types of physicians.

_____ 8. If physicians continue to practice medicine without renewing their license,
   a. nothing happens if they do not practice out of their home state.
   b. they are considered to be practicing medicine without a license.
   c. nothing happens unless a patient is harmed.
   d. nothing happens unless a patient is harmed and sues.

_____ 9. A physician
   a. is the only medical professional required to be licensed by the state.
   b. may be called to give testimony in court.
   c. is never called to give testimony in court.
   d. is exempt from criminal charges for the "good of the people."

_____ **10.** Certification of a physician
  a. is involuntary.
  b. indicates an additional level of training in a specialized area.
  c. is not important to the patient.
  d. is the same as licensing.

True or False?

_____ **11.** A physician cannot legally practice medicine without certification.

_____ **12.** A physician cannot legally practice medicine without a license.

_____ **13.** A state may take away a physician's medical license for cases of severe misconduct.

_____ **14.** The Medical Practice Acts vary from state to state.

_____ **15.** Licensure by endorsement is considered for acceptance or denial on a case-by-case basis.

_____ **16.** Generally, physicians in different states may consult one another without being licensed in each other's states.

_____ **17.** Medical Practice Acts do not define the penalties for practicing without a license.

_____ **18.** Physicians do not pay licensing fees.

_____ **19.** Reciprocity is automatic if an agreement exists between the two states where licensure is being sought and if the requirements of the agreement are satisfied.

_____ **20.** It is against the law for a nurse or medical assistant to prescribe medication.

Chapter 3

Test 2

Fill in the Blanks

1. _____ refers to the ordinary skill and care that medical practitioners such as physicians, nurses, physician assistants, medical assistants, and phlebotomists must use.

2. _____ are laws that help protect health care professionals from liability while giving emergency care.

3. *Respondeat superior* is a Latin phrase that means _____.

4. *Guardian ad litem* is a Latin phrase that names _____.

5. Most physicians carry a special type of insurance that covers employees who handle money. This is called _____.

Multiple Choice

Write the letter of the correct answer in the blank.

_____ 6. What does the law require of a physician regarding treating patients?
    a. Physicians are obligated to treat everyone.
    b. Once a physician has accepted a patient for treatment, the physician has entered into a contract with the patient.
    c. Physicians must use extraordinary skill.
    d. Once a physician has accepted a patient, the physician cannot stop care under any circumstances.

_____ 7. The statute of limitations refers to the
    a. number of people who can be represented in any given lawsuit by one attorney.
    b. number of people who can sue any individual at the same time.
    c. period of time that a patient has to file a lawsuit.
    d. period of time that an attorney has for discovery.

_____ 8. The Medical Patient Rights Act
    a. states that only limited information can be shared about a patient with someone other than the patient.
    b. states that only the fact that an individual is a patient can be shared with someone other than the patient.
    c. allows information about a patient to be given to the patient's spouse if the spouse presents a valid marriage license.
    d. is a law passed by Congress.

_____ 9. No one is required to provide aid in the event of an emergency situation except
    a. a physician.
    b. a medical professional.
    c. in the state of Vermont.
    d. a state trooper.

_____ **10.** In some cases the statute of limitations is "tolled," which means it
  a. is counted.
  b. stops running.
  c. doesn't matter.
  d. runs out.

True or False?

_____ **11.** Trained health professionals are not under legal obligation to offer aid to an emergency victim.

_____ **12.** Trained health professionals are not under ethical obligation to offer aid to an emergency victim.

_____ **13.** The statute of limitations always begins when treatment starts.

_____ **14.** If a comment regarding a patient's care is overheard in an elevator, the patient's right of discovery has been violated.

_____ **15.** It is the duty of health care workers to interpret and carry out the orders of their employer/physician.

_____ **16.** If a physician delegates certain duties to employees, and they are performed incorrectly, the ultimate liability rests with the physician.

_____ **17.** Physicians/employers have a responsibility to provide a safe environment for their employees.

_____ **18.** If a patient is hospitalized, liability rests with the physician, the hospital, and the nurse.

_____ **19.** In cases of negligence, courts have consistently found the health care employee as well as the employer to be negligent.

_____ **20.** Confidentiality refers to keeping private all information about a patient and not disclosing it to a third party without the patient's written consent.

Chapter 4

Lecture Notes/Class Handout 1

I. Vocabulary Development

II. Today's Health Care Environment

III. Types of Medical Practice

IV. Medical Specialty Boards

V. Medical and Surgical Specialties

Chapter 4

Lecture Notes/Class Handout 2

I. Vocabulary Development

II. Allied Health Professions

III. Health Care Occupations

Chapter 4

Worksheet 1

Define the terms.

1. associate practice _____

   _____

2. corporation _____

   _____

3. exclusive provider organization _____

   _____

4. group practice _____

   _____

5. health maintenance organization _____

   _____

6. partnership _____

   _____

7. preferred provider organization _____

   _____

8. sole proprietorship _____

   _____

9. solo practice _____

   _____

Answer the questions.

1. In the early part of the twentieth century the main form of medical practice was the solo practice. Why has that changed? Give at least three reasons.

   a. _____

   _____

   _____

   b. _____

   _____

   _____

c. _____

_____

_____

2. Review Table 4-2 in *Fremgen's Medical Law and Ethics,* p. 78. List and describe the five most difficult medical or surgical specialties.

a. _____

_____

_____

b. _____

_____

_____

c. _____

_____

_____

d. _____

_____

_____

e. _____

_____

_____

List an advantage and a disadvantage of each type of practice.

Practice	Advantage	Disadvantage
Corporation		
Solo Practice		
Partnership		
Association Practice		
Group Practice		

Practice	Advantage	Disadvantage
Single Specialty		
Sole Proprietorship		

Fill in the blanks.

1. Professional corporation members are known as _____.

2. A corporation remains active until it is _____.

3. A group practice can be designated as an HMO or as an _____.

4. Three types of managed care providers are _____, _____, and _____.

Chapter 4

Worksheet 2

Write the meaning of each abbreviation.

1. D.C. _____

2. D.M.D. _____

3. D.D.S. _____

4. M.D. _____

5. O.D. _____

6. D.O. _____

7. Ph.D. _____

8. D.P.M. _____

9. OT _____

10. EMT _____

11. PT _____

12. RT _____

Fill in the blanks.

1. Allied professionals cannot legally function outside their _____.

2. Review Table 4-4 in *Fremgen's Medical Law and Ethics* pp. 81–82. Then describe the five health care professions that are most difficult for you to remember.

   a. _____

   _____

   b. _____

   _____

   c. _____

   _____

   d. _____

   _____

   e. _____

   _____

Complete the table with information about each health professional.

Allied Health Professional	Full Title	Level of Education	Tasks Performed
RN			
LPN			
LVN			
NP			
MT			
MLT			
PA			
CMA			
RMA			

Chapter 4

Test 1

Fill in the Blanks

1. A _____ is a managed care concept in which the patient must use a medical provider who is under contract with the insurer for an agreed-upon fee in order to receive co-payment from the insurer.

2. A _____ is a legal agreement to share in the business operation of a medical practice.

3. In a _____, a physician practices alone.

4. A _____ is managed by a board of directors.

5. _____ is the medical specialty practice that deals with the prevention and correction of disorders of the musculoskeletal system.

Multiple Choice

Write the letter of the correct answer in the blank.

_____ 6. An EPO is
  a. a managed care product that combines the HMO and PPO concepts.
  b. another name for a partnership practice.
  c. the same as a PPO.
  d. the same as an HMO.

_____ 7. The type of medical practice in which one physician may employ other physicians is called
  a. solo practice.
  b. sole proprietorship.
  c. EPO.
  d. HMO.

_____ 8. In a partnership practice,
  a. there must be at least four partners.
  b. there must be at least three partners.
  c. the partners are not responsible for the actions of the other employees.
  d. each of the partners is responsible for the actions of all other partners.

_____ 9. The most common type of health insurance covers
  a. routine physicals.
  b. office visits.
  c. hospital care.
  d. emergency care only.

_____ **10.** The managed care program that offers a range of health care services to plan members for a predetermined fee by a limited group of providers is called a
   a. PPO.
   b. HMO.
   c. EPO.
   d. partnership.

Matching

In the blank, write the letter of the advantage that correctly matches each type of practice.

_____ **11.** solo practice

_____ **12.** partnership practice

_____ **13.** associate practice

_____ **14.** group practice

_____ **15.** corporation

_____ **16.** single specialty

a. All expenses and income are shared; all equipment and facilities are shared

b. Expenses and staff are shared

c. Work is shared

d. Physician retains independence and all assets; simplicity of organization

e. Many fringe benefits are offered; protection from loss of individual assets

f. Legal responsibility, work, assets, and income are shared

In the blank, write the letter of the description that correctly matches each medical specialty.

_____ **17.** otorhinolaryngology

_____ **18.** oncology

_____ **19.** ophthalmology

_____ **20.** pathology

a. Diagnoses abnormal changes in tissues removed during surgery or autopsy

b. Treats disorders of the eye

c. Treats cancer and cancer-related tumors

d. Treats disorders of the ear, nose, and throat

Chapter 4

Test 2

Fill in the Blanks

Write the abbreviation that names each allied health professional.

1. Doctor of Chiropractic _____

2. Doctor of Philosophy _____

3. Doctor of Osteopathy _____

4. Doctor of Medicine _____

5. Doctor of Dental Medicine _____

Multiple Choice

Write the letter of the correct answer in the blank.

_____ **6.** A laboratory or medical technologist must complete
- **a.** three years of college and certification.
- **b.** four years of college and certification.
- **c.** two years of college and certification.
- **d.** one year of college and certification.

_____ **7.** An LPN can perform
- **a.** some but not all of the nursing tasks of an RN.
- **b.** all of the same tasks as an RN.
- **c.** different tasks than an RN.
- **d.** none of the above.

_____ **8.** The term *doctor* comes from the Latin word meaning
- **a.** "to care for."
- **b.** "to manage or handle."
- **c.** "to cure."
- **d.** "to teach."

_____ **9.** An NP is a
- **a.** nurse.
- **b.** physician.
- **c.** laboratory technician.
- **d.** laboratory technologist.

_____ **10.** A CMT
- **a.** works in a lab.
- **b.** cares for patients only in the hospital.
- **c.** types dictation.
- **d.** cares for patients only in a doctor's office or clinic.

Matching

In the blank, write the letter of the description that correctly matches each occupation.

_____ **11.** OT

_____ **12.** RT

_____ **13.** PT

_____ **14.** AART

_____ **15.** social worker

_____ **16.** phlebotomist

_____ **17.** radiologic technologist

_____ **18.** EMT

_____ **19.** MT

_____ **20.** EKG technologist

a. Operates nuclear medicine and radiation therapy equipment

b. Provides services and programs to meet the needs of the ill, disabled, and elderly

c. Provides exercise treatment

d. Draws blood

e. Performs laboratory analysis

f. Performs breathing treatments

g. Performs ultrasound

h. Performs evaluation of the heart

i. Provides emergency medical care

j. Provides therapy to improve management of daily living skills

Chapter 5

Lecture Notes/Class Handout 1

I. Physician–Patient Relationship

II. Physician Rights and Responsibilities

III. Patient Rights

Chapter 5

Lecture Notes/Class Handout 2

I. Confidentiality

II. Patient Self-Determination Acts

III. Patient's Responsibilities

Chapter 5

Worksheet 1

Summarize each principle in your own words.

NOTE: While the "Standards of Conduct" are developed for physicians, it is understood that all health care professionals must recognize a responsibility to patients, society, other health professionals, and to themselves.

AMA Principles of Medical Ethics	Standards of Conduct
Human dignity	
Honesty	
Responsibility to society	
Confidentiality	
Continued study	
Freedom of choice	
Responsibility to improve community	
Responsibility to the patient	
Support access to medical care for all people	

Review Table 5-2 in *Fremgen's Medical Law and Ethics,* **p. 92. For each of the seven physician duties, give one example of acceptable and unacceptable behavior**

Duty	Acceptable Behavior	Unacceptable Behavior
Accepting gifts		
Conflict of interest		
Professional courtesy		
Reporting unethical conduct of other physicians		
Second opinion		
Sexual conduct		
Treating family members		

Chapter 5

Worksheet 2

Define the terms.

1. advance directive _____
   _____

2. agent _____
   _____

3. durable power of attorney _____
   _____

4. implied consent _____
   _____

5. informed or expressed consent _____
   _____

6. living will _____
   _____

7. minor _____
   _____

8. privileged communication _____
   _____

9. Uniform Anatomical Gift Act _____
   _____

Summarize each patient right from "A Patient's Bill of Rights" in your own words.

NOTE: While the "Standards of Conduct" are developed for physicians, it is understood that all health care professionals must recognize a responsibility to patients, society, other health professionals, and to themselves.

Right	Summary
Respect	
Information	
Decisions	
Advance directive	
Privacy	
Confidentiality	
Records	
Patient request	
Business relationships	
Research	
Continuity of care	
To be informed	

Chapter 5

Test 1

Fill in the Blanks

1. In giving consent for treatment, patients reasonably expect that their physicians will use the appropriate _____ in providing care and treatment.

2. The patient has the right to approve or _____ for all treatment.

3. A physician has the right to _____ the patients he or she wishes to treat or enter into a contract with.

4. The patient's right to _____ prohibits the presence of unauthorized persons during physical examination or treatment.

5. Historically, there is a customary practice among many physicians to not charge each other for professional services. This practice is called _____.

Multiple Choice

Write the letter of the correct answer in the blank.

_____ 6. Which is NOT a patient right?
   a. To be informed of the advantages and potential risks of treatment
   b. To refuse treatment
   c. To not pay a bill if they feel they have not been treated satisfactorily
   d. To be informed of the risk of not having a treatment

_____ 7. Is it considered ethical behavior for a physician to accept gifts from medical companies?
   a. Sometimes, under certain circumstances
   b. Never
   c. Yes
   d. Only if they give the gifts away

_____ 8. What is considered the acceptable policy for vacations for physicians?
   a. They may not take a vacation if any of their patients are near death.
   b. They may not take a vacation without giving advanced written notice to all patients.
   c. They may take a vacation at any time they choose.
   d. They may take vacations after arranging for other qualified physicians to cover their practice in their absence.

_____ 9. When a physician places financial interest above patient welfare, this is called
   a. illegal.
   b. professional discourtesy.
   c. freedom of choice.
   d. conflict of interest.

_____ **10.** If the patient does not confide critical information truthfully to the physician, the physician
  a. is not liable for the outcome.
  b. remains liable for the outcome.
  c. is not hindered because he or she can understand without having all information from the patient.
  d. can ask the family.

True or False?

_____ **11.** Physicians should not treat family members except in an emergency.

_____ **12.** Physicians should never recommend a second opinion for a patient.

_____ **13.** Physicians have a responsibility to participate in activities contributing to an improved community.

_____ **14.** A physician has a responsibility to society to respect the law.

_____ **15.** A physician has a right to choose the environment in which to provide services.

Chapter 5

Test 2

Fill in the Blanks

1. A patient may decide to have no extraordinary medical treatment, such as being placed on a respirator. After the patient makes this request in writing, the physician must issue a _____ order for the patient.

2. When signed by the patient, a _____ allows an agent or representative to act on behalf of the patient.

3. According to "A Patient's Bill of Rights," the patient has the right to have an _____, such as a living will, health care proxy, or durable power of attorney for health care, concerning treatment or designating a surrogate decision maker with the expectation that the hospital will honor the intent of that directive to the extent permitted by law and hospital policy.

4. _____ refers to confidential information told to a physician (or attorney) by the patient.

5. Documents executed by the patient stating the patient's intentions for health care decisions and in some cases naming another person to make decisions for the patient are called _____ documents.

Multiple Choice

Write the letter of the correct answer in the blank.

_____ 6. A durable power of attorney is
   a. in effect until canceled by the patient.
   b. valid even if the patient does not sign.
   c. always covers medical and business decisions for someone who is unable to make his or her own decisions.
   d. valid in very few states.

_____ 7. Consent is
   a. a voluntary agreement that a patient gives to allow a medically trained person the permission to touch, examine, and perform a treatment.
   b. an involuntary agreement that a patient gives to allow a medically trained person the permission to touch, examine, and perform a treatment.
   c. not necessary if the patient trusts the physician.
   d. only valid if legally witnessed.

_____ 8. Who is solely responsible for providing informed consent?
   a. The nurse
   b. The hospital admission staff
   c. The patient's family
   d. The physician

_____   **9.** This occurs when patients indicate by their behavior that they are accepting of a procedure.
   a. Implied consent
   b. Informed consent
   c. Consent
   d. Durable power of attorney

_____   **10.** This is assumed in medical emergencies when the patient cannot respond to give consent for care.
   a. Implied consent
   b. Informed consent
   c. Consent
   d. Durable power of attorney

True or False?

_____   **11.** It is very difficult to fully inform a patient about all the things that can go wrong with a treatment.

_____   **12.** In most states, minors are unable to give consent for treatment except in special cases.

_____   **13.** Patients have rights, but they also have certain obligations.

_____   **14.** The Uniformed Anatomical Gift Act allows all persons of sound mind to make a gift of any or all body parts for purposes of organ transplantation or medical research.

_____   **15.** If a patient has not indicated a desire to be a donor, the family may consent on the patient's behalf.

Chapter 6

Lecture Notes/Class Handout 1

I. Vocabulary Development

II. Professional Negligence and Medical Malpractice

III. Defense to Malpractice Suits

Chapter 6

Lecture Notes/Class Handout 2

I. Vocabulary Development

II. Professional Liability

III. Arbitration

IV. Liability of Other Health Professions

V. Malpractice Prevention

Chapter 6

Worksheet 1

Define the terms.

1. cap _____

_____

2. compensatory damages _____

_____

3. dereliction _____

_____

4. direct cause _____

_____

5. duty _____

_____

6. feasance _____

_____

7. malfeasance _____

_____

8. misfeasance _____

_____

9. nominal damages _____

_____

10. nonfeasance _____

_____

11. proximate _____

_____

12. punitive damages _____

_____

13. *res ipsa loquitur* _____

_____

14. *res judicata* _____

_____

15. tort _____

_____

Fill in the Blanks

According to the law, in a malpractice suit, the burden of proof is on the _____, who must prove that the defendant did a _____. Therefore, the most common defense on the part of a physician in a malpractice suit is _____.

Answer the questions.

1. What are the "four Ds" of negligence? Give an example of each.

a. _____

_____

_____

_____

b. _____

_____

_____

_____

c. _____

_____

_____

_____

d. _____

_____

_____

_____

2. A health care professional must have an understanding of what is right and wrong under the law. What does this mean to you?

_____

_____

_____

3. What is the difference between *res ipsa loquitur* and *res judicata*?

_____

_____

_____

4. Is ignorance of the law a reasonable defense? Why or why not?

_____

_____

_____

Chapter 6

Worksheet 2

Define the terms.

1. alternative dispute resolution (ADR) _____

   _____

2. arbitration _____

   _____

3. arbitrator _____

   _____

4. liable _____

   _____

5. mediation _____

   _____

6. rider _____

   _____

7. settle _____

   _____

Answer the questions.

1. An exception to the statute of limitations is the rule of discovery. What does this mean?

   _____

   _____

   _____

2. Why is a promise to cure a patient considered unlawful under contract law?

   _____

   _____

   _____

3. A fear of lawsuits has influenced the practice of medicine. Is this good or bad? Explain your answer and give examples.

_____

_____

_____

Chapter 6

Test 1

Fill in the Blanks

1. A _____ is the same thing as a civil wrong of negligence and malpractice.

2. _____ refers to the responsibility established by the physician–patient relationship.

3. _____ is the failure to perform a necessary action.

4. _____ is the improper performance of an otherwise proper or lawful act.

5. The doctrine of _____, meaning "the thing speaks for itself," applies to the law of negligence.

6. The _____ is responsible for explaining the risks of a treatment or procedure.

7. _____ refers to a slight or token payment to a patient to demonstrate that, while there may not have been any physical harm done, the patient's legal rights were violated.

8. _____ refers to a monetary award by a court to a person who has been harmed in an especially malicious or willful way.

9. _____ means "the thing has been decided" or "a matter decided by judgment."

10. The _____ doctrine is a special application of *respondeat superior* that occurs when an employer lends an employee to someone else.

Multiple Choice

Write the letter of the correct answer in the blank.

_____ 11. Ignorance of the law
   a. means you are not responsible.
   b. is a valid argument in court.
   c. is not a defense.
   d. is a valid argument only before a case goes to court.

_____ 12. Comparative negligence is
   a. unlike contributory negligence.
   b. very similar to contributory negligence in that the plaintiff's own negligence helped cause the injury.
   c. means an employer lends an employee to someone else.
   d. means one side of the case must demonstrate a greater weight of evidence than the other side.

_____ **13.** If a patient's death has been caused by the physician's negligence, then the patient's family and heirs
    a. can sue for murder.
    b. can sue for wrongful death.
    c. cannot sue for five years.
    d. can sue for pain and suffering.

_____ **14.** A person with special knowledge or experience who is allowed to testify in court about facts and professional conclusions is called
    a. a plaintiff.
    b. a witness.
    c. a rider.
    d. an expert witness.

_____ **15.** Which is NOT one of the "four Ds" of negligence?
    a. Duty
    b. Denial
    c. Dereliction of duty
    d. Damages

Chapter 6

Test 2

Fill in the Blanks

1. Under the doctrine of _____ or "let the master answer," the employer is liable for the consequences of the employee's actions committed in the scope of employment.

2. _____ is a contract by which one person promises to compensate or reimburse another if he or she suffers a loss from a specific cause or a negligent act.

3. The process of _____ involves submitting a dispute to a person other than a judge.

4. Using methods other than going to court to solve civil disputes is called _____.

5. _____ means that one has legal responsibility for one's own actions.

Multiple Choice

Write the letter of the correct answer in the blank.

_____ 6. Does the doctrine of "let the master answer" apply to a pharmacist who is dispensing medication ordered by a physician?
   a. No
   b. Yes
   c. Sometimes
   d. Only if the drug is experimental

_____ 7. If treatment continues after it has been refused by the patient, the health care provider could be liable for
   a. assault.
   b. battery.
   c. nothing.
   d. detaining the patient.

_____ 8. The two basic types of malpractice insurance are
   a. claims-made insurance and occurrence insurance.
   b. major and minor.
   c. with injury or damage and without injury or damage.
   d. professional and nonprofessional.

_____ 9. Is a hospital liable for injury if someone falls on a wet floor despite clearly posted caution signs?
   a. Yes
   b. No
   c. Yes, but only if the individual is handicapped

_____ **10.** An insurance company may "settle" a case, which means that the company
  a. comes to an agreement.
  b. is admitting guilt.
  c. is dismissing the case with no action.

True or False?

_____ **11.** Malpractice insurance can be very expensive.

_____ **12.** A rider is an addition to an insurance policy that may cover negligence on the part of employees.

_____ **13.** A promise to cure a patient with a certain procedure or form of treatment is considered under civil law rather than contract law.

_____ **14.** In the largest sense of the term, everyone is legally responsible or liable for his or her own actions.

_____ **15.** It is easier to prevent negligence than it is to defend it in court.

Chapter 7

Lecture Notes/Class Handout 1

I. Vocabulary Development

II. Public Health Records and Vital Statistics

Chapter 7

Lecture Notes/Class Handout 2

I. Vocabulary Development

II. Communicable Diseases

III. Child Abuse

IV. Elder Abuse

V. Spousal Abuse

VI. Substance Abuse

VII. Gathering of Evidence

VIII. Other Reportable Conditions

Chapter 7

Lecture Notes/Class Handout 3

I. Vocabulary Development

II. Other Reportable Conditions

III. Controlled Substances Act and Regulations

IV. Prescriptions of Controlled Drugs

Chapter 7

Lecture Notes/Class Handout 4

I. Vocabulary Development

II. Schedule Controlled Substances

III. Protection of the Employee and the Environment

Chapter 7

Worksheet 1

Define the terms.

1. autopsy _____

   _____

2. coroner _____

   _____

3. data _____

   _____

4. inquest _____

   _____

5. postmortem _____

   _____

6. public duties _____

   _____

7. vital statistics _____

   _____

Answer the questions.

1. What are the things that must be reported by physicians as part of their public duties?

   _____

   _____

   _____

2. Name the reporting agencies that collect vital statistics.

   _____

   _____

   _____

3. What are the nine recommendations for completing legal records and certificates?

_____

_____

_____

Chapter 7

Worksheet 2

Define the terms.

1. elder abuse _____

_____

2. communicable disease _____

_____

3. STD _____

_____

Answer the questions.

1. List the childhood vaccines and toxoids that are required by law for all children.

_____

_____

_____

2. Explain the courts' position on "battered child syndrome."

_____

_____

_____

3. What act defines elder abuse?

_____

_____

_____

4. What does the Child Abuse and Prevention and Treatment Act of 1974 require in all child abuse cases?

_____

_____

_____

Chapter 7

Worksheet 3

Define the terms.

1. addiction _____

_____

2. BNDD _____

_____

3. DEA _____

_____

4. FDA _____

_____

5. Controlled Substances Act of 1970 _____

_____

6. habituation _____

_____

Answer the questions.

1. Who may administer drugs in most states?

_____

_____

_____

2. Both the federal and the state governments have laws regulating the control of drugs. Can a state government choose to be less restrictive than the federal law requires? Explain your answer.

_____

_____

_____

3. What must be recorded in a narcotics record according to federal law?

_____

_____

_____

4. By law, what procedure must be followed if a controlled substance must be "wasted"?

_____

_____

_____

5. How can medical assistants help a physician in maintaining compliance with the laws regarding controlled substances?

_____

_____

_____

Chapter 7

Worksheet 4

Define the terms.

1. schedule _____

_____

2. chemical waste _____

_____

3. solid waste _____

_____

4. radioactive waste _____

_____

5. infectious waste _____

_____

Answer the questions.

1. What and who is protected by the proper disposal of medical waste?

_____

_____

_____

2. Where is infectious waste first separated from other solid and chemical waste?

_____

_____

_____

Chapter 7

Test 1

Fill in the Blanks

1. An _____ is an investigation held by a public official, such as a coroner, to determine the cause of death.

2. A physician must sign a _____ indicating the cause of a natural death.

3. The _____ is a public officer who holds an investigation if a person's death is from an unknown or violent cause.

4. _____ is postmortem examination of organs and tissues to determine the cause of death.

5. _____ are major events from a person's life including births, deaths, induced abortions, marriages, and divorces.

Multiple Choice

Write the letter of the correct answer in the blank.

_____ 6. Physicians have a responsibility to report certain events, including
   a. rapes and births.
   b. antibiotic therapy and abortion.
   c. accidents and drug abuse.

_____ 7. What does NOT have to be listed on a death certificate?
   a. Presence or absence of a pregnancy
   b. Time of death
   c. Age of the patient

_____ 8. Which situation does NOT require a health official's evaluation?
   a. Death in a hospital of nonviolent cause, treated for the last three days
   b. Death of a person whose body is not claimed by friends or relatives
   c. Death in jail or prison

_____ 9. Why is it important for a physician to sign a death certificate as soon after death as possible?
   a. Because the family cannot be notified that the patient is dead until it is signed
   b. Because funeral arrangements and burial cannot take place until it is signed
   c. Because the patient cannot be touched or moved until it is signed

_____ 10. What is NOT recommended for completing legal records and certificates?
   a. Keeping a copy in the patient's record
   b. Using abbreviations
   c. Typing or printing

Chapter 7

Test 2

Fill in the Blanks

1. The _____ passed by Congress in 1986 requires a physician or health care administrator to report all vaccine administration and adverse reactions to vaccines and toxoids.

2. The _____ of 1974 requires reporting of all child abuse cases.

3. _____ is defined in the amendment to the Older Americans Act of 1987.

4. Many states require reporting of certain medical conditions in order to maintain accurate pubic health statistics. Because testing for many of these conditions occurs in the hospital, the reporting responsibility rests with _____.

5. A violation of controlled substances laws is a _____ offense.

True or False?

_____   6. A report of communicable disease can be made only in writing.

_____   7. Laws governing the reporting of spousal abuse vary from state to state.

_____   8. Any person who suspects that child abuse is taking place can report the abuse to local authorities without fear of liability.

_____   9. Physicians have been held liable if they do not report cases of child abuse.

_____   10. Gathering evidence from abuse victims usually takes place in a hospital or emergency room setting.

Chapter 7

Test 3

Fill in the Blanks

1. The _____, an agency within the Department of Health and Human Resources, ultimately enforces drug prescription (and over-the-counter) sales and distribution.

2. _____ is an acquired physical or psychological dependence on a drug.

3. The _____ of the Department of Justice controls drugs by enforcing the law.

4. By law, all narcotic records must be kept for _____ years.

5. The _____ is the agency of the federal government authorized to enforce drug control.

True or False?

_____ 6. Only those persons with a DEA registration number may legally issue a prescription for narcotics.

_____ 7. Because there is a high potential for abuse of and addiction to narcotics, such prescriptions may not be refilled.

_____ 8. Controlled drugs are classified into four schedules based on the potential for abuse.

_____ 9. Cocaine is not legal for consumption in the United States under any conditions.

_____ 10. Marijuana is not legal for consumption in the United States under any conditions.

Chapter 7

Test 4

Fill in the Blanks

1. Schedule _____ controlled substances have low potential for addiction and abuse.

2. Schedule _____ controlled substances have high potential for addiction and abuse.

3. The four major types of medical waste are _____, _____, _____, and _____.

4. _____ is any medical waste that has the potential to carry disease.

True or False?

_____ 5. In some states, lay persons are not covered by law that protects them from liability when administering emergency care.

_____ 6. Medical waste is first separated from other solid and chemical waste at the waste management facility.

_____ 7. Chemical wastes must be documented on the MSDS.

Chapter 8

Lecture Notes/Class Handout 1

I. Vocabulary Development

II. Employer–Employee Relationship

III. Equal Employment Opportunity and Employment Discrimination

Chapter 8

Lecture Notes/Class Handout 2

I. Vocabulary Development

II. Rehabilitation Act of 1973

III. Americans with Disabilities Act of 1990

IV. Occupational Safety and Health Act of 1970

V. Clinical Laboratory Improvement Act (CLIA)

VI. Health Maintenance Organization Act of 1973 (HMO)

VII. COBRA (1985)

VIII. Drug-Free Workplace Act of 1988

IX. Compensation and Benefits Regulations

Chapter 8

Lecture Notes/Class Handout 3

I. Vocabulary Development

II. Worker's Compensation Act

III. Employee Retirement Income Security Act

IV. Family and Medical Leave Act of 1994

V. Consumer Protection and Collection Practices

Chapter 8

Lecture Notes/Class Handout 4

I. Vocabulary Development

II. Consumer Protection and Collection Practices (continued)

III. Antitrust Law

IV. Federal Labor Law

Chapter 8

Worksheet 1

Define the terms.

1. preempt _____

   _____

2. EEOC _____

   _____

3. employment-at-will _____

   _____

4. employer _____

   _____

5. employee _____

   _____

6. Title VII _____

   _____

Answer the questions.

1. Name an exception to Title VII law.

   _____

   _____

   _____

2. What agency monitors Title VII? What agency enforces the statute?

   _____

   _____

   _____

3. Why is it important to examine employee handbooks carefully for errors or misleading statements?

_____

_____

_____

4. What does the EEOA of 1972 authorize?

_____

_____

_____

5. What does the Pregnancy Discrimination Act of 1978 require?

_____

_____

_____

Chapter 8

Worksheet 2

Define the terms.

1. parenteral _____

   _____

2. bloodborne pathogens _____

   _____

3. ADA _____

   _____

4. OSHA _____

   _____

5. HMO _____

   _____

6. COBRA _____

   _____

7. FLSA _____

   _____

8. FICA _____

   _____

Answer the questions.

1. What act prohibits discrimination based on disability in any institution that receives federal financial assistance?

   _____

   _____

   _____

2. What act requires any company with at least 25 employees to provide an HMO alternative to regular group insurance for their employees, if an HMO is available in the area?

   _____

   _____

   _____

3. To whom do the OSHA regulations apply?

_____

_____

_____

4. What does OSHA require regarding hepatitis B vaccination?

_____

_____

_____

5. Describe an exception to the Fair Labor Standards Act.

_____

_____

_____

Chapter 8

Worksheet 3

Define the terms.

1. creditor _____

   _____

2. ERISA _____

   _____

3. vesting _____

   _____

4. FMLA _____

   _____

5. discrimination _____

   _____

6. collection agency _____

   _____

7. bankruptcy _____

   _____

8. debtor _____

   _____

9. FCC _____

   _____

Answer the questions.

1. What is the goal of worker's compensation?

   _____

   _____

   _____

2. If an employee who is covered by worker's compensation is injured due to the actions of nonemployees, what legal options does the employee have to recover damages for the injurty?

   _____

   _____

   _____

3. What act is also referred to as Regulation Z?

_____

_____

_____

4. Select three guidelines for collection efforts and explain why they are important. Include what could be the possible consequences of NOT following each guideline.

_____

_____

_____

Chapter 8

Worksheet 4

Define the terms.

1. statute of limitations _____

   _____

2. antitrust laws _____

   _____

3. cease and desist order _____

   _____

4. NLRA _____

   _____

Fill in the Blanks

1. _____ is the primary antitrust law that affects the medical industry.

2. The _____ is also called the Wagner Act.

True or False

_____   1. Under the NLRA an employer can refuse to bargain.

_____   2. The time limit for a medical practice to file suit to collect on a past-due account varies from state to state.

_____   3. Debt collection should be put off as long as possible.

_____   4. The Sherman Antitrust Act was enacted to prevent the formation of monopolies.

_____   5. Union activity in the healthcare field has become more active since 1950.

_____   6. An employer cannot discriminate due to an employee's union activity.

Chapter 8

Test 1

Fill in the Blanks

1. In most situations, federal laws _____ or overrule state laws.

2. _____ means that employment takes place at the will of either the employer or the employee.

3. Title _____ of the Civil Rights Act of 1964 prohibits discrimination in employment based on race, color, religion, sex, or national origin.

4. The _____ monitors the Civil Rights Act of 1964.

5. Under the _____ Act of 1978, employers must treat pregnant women as they would any other employee, providing they can still do the job.

True or False?

_____   6. The government regulates many aspects of the employment relationship, including laws affecting recruitment, placement, pay plans, benefits, penalties, and terminations.

_____   7. Employee handbooks should be examined for any erroneous or misleading statements because many courts have ruled they constitute an employee contract.

_____   8. If an employer withholds employment taxes from a person's income, then that person is considered an employee.

_____   9. A person who employs the services of another and provides payment for those services is considered an employer.

_____   10. The employer–employee relationship is regulated by state law only.

Chapter 8

Test 2

Fill in the Blanks

1. The _____ of 1973 prohibits discrimination based on disability in any institution that receives federal financial assistance.

2. Under _____, an employer is required to provide a safe and healthy work environment.

3. The OSHA standards that develop rules to protect employees from bloodborne diseases are the _____.

4. The _____ of 1973 requires any company with at least 25 employees to provide an HMO alternative to regular group insurance for their employees, if an HMO is available in the area.

5. The _____ of 1935 was the origin of the current unemployment insurance program.

True or False?

_____ 6. Under COBRA (1985), employers contracting to provide goods or services to the federal government must certify that they maintain a drug-free workplace.

_____ 7. The main statute regulating benefits is the Fair Labor Standards Act of 1938.

_____ 8. In order to receive unemployment insurance, the employee must have worked for an employer who has paid or was required to pay unemployment compensation taxes.

_____ 9. The Equal Pay Act of 1963 is the oldest act relating to compensation.

_____ 10. To prevent drug abuse, some organizations, such as hospitals, require drug testing as a condition of employment.

Chapter 8

Test 3

Fill in the Blanks

1. ERISA stands for _____.

2. The goal of worker's compensation is to get the employee back to work _____.

3. For any fee to be collected in more than four payments, the Truth in Lending Act requires _____.

4. _____ is a legal method for providing some protection to debtors and establishing a fair method for distribution of debtors' assets to creditors.

5. FMLA stands for _____.

True or False?

_____ 6. If an employee is covered by worker's compensation, the employee may not sue and recover for injuries caused by nonemployees.

_____ 7. FMLA guarantees paid leave for up to twelve weeks due to family emergency.

_____ 8. Collection calls can be made between 7:00 A.M. and 10:00 P.M.

_____ 9. A creditor who fails to comply with bankruptcy laws can be cited for contempt of court.

_____ 10. A good guideline for collection is to request payment, whenever possible, before the patient leaves the office.

Chapter 9
Lecture Notes/Class Handout 1

I. Vocabulary Development

II. The Medical Record

III. Purpose of the Medical Record

IV. Contents of the Medical Record

Chapter 9

Lecture Notes/Class Handout 2

I. Vocabulary Development

II. Problem-Oriented Medical Record

III. SOAP Charting

IV. Guidelines for Charting

V. Medical Record Contents

Chapter 9

Lecture Notes/Class Handout 3

I. Vocabulary Development

II. Ownership of Medical Records

III. Retention and Storage of Medical Records

Chapter 9

Lecture Notes/Class Handout 4

I. Vocabulary Development

II. Computerized Medical Records

III. Reporting and Disclosing Requirements

Chapter 9

Worksheet 1

Define the terms.

1. JCAHO _____

_____

2. POMR _____

_____

Fill in the Blanks

1. List the 7 features that each medical record must include.

a. _____
b. _____
c. _____
d. _____
e. _____
f. _____
g. _____

2. List at least six purposes of the medical record.

a. _____
b. _____
c. _____
d. _____
e. _____
f. _____

True or False?

_____ 1. Medical records serve multiple purposes.

_____ 2. The medical record is a legal document.

_____ 3. Different medical specialties will have different formats for medical records.

_____ 4. All patient records are formatted exactly alike.

_____ 5. Medical records consist of all written documentation relating to a patient.

_____ 6. Chronological charting is superior to POMR charting.

Chapter 9

Worksheet 2

Define the terms.

1. late entry _____

_____

2. POMR _____

_____

3. SOAP _____

_____

Fill in the Blanks

1. List the 11 guidelines for charting.

a. _____

b. _____

c. _____

d. _____

e. _____

f. _____

g. _____

h. _____

i. _____

j. _____

k. _____

2. List 8 tips for maintaining patient confidentiality when using fax machines, copy machines, e-mail, or the computer.

a. _____

b. _____

c. _____

d. _____

e. _____

f. _____

g. _____

h. _____

Chapter 9

Worksheet 3

Define the terms.

1. disclosed _____

   _____

2. Privacy Act of 1974 _____

   _____

3. open records laws _____

   _____

4. Public Health Services Act _____

   _____

5. AHIMA _____

   _____

Fill in the Blanks

1. A/An _____ copy of a medical record should never be sent to a patient.

2. The Privacy Act applies only to _____.

3. Freedom of information laws grant public access to records maintained by _____.

4. Records should not be released to patients without _____.

5. The time period for retaining fetal heart monitor records is _____.

6. The time period for retaining adult patient records is _____.

7. The time period for retaining a register of birth is _____.

8. The time period for retaining a register of death is _____.

9. Physicians may keep older medical records by storing them in _____, in _____, and on _____.

10. An exception to disclosure of information law would occur when _____.

Chapter 9

Worksheet 4

Define the terms.

1. need-to-know basis _____

   _____

2. subpoenaed _____

   _____

3. *subpoena duces tecum* _____

   _____

Fill in the Blanks

1. The name for a court order is a _____.

2. Legal confidentiality obligations apply to all methods of _____.

3. A timely response to a subpoena is a response that is submitted _____.

4. When responding to a subpoena, the _____, the _____, and the _____ should be notified.

5. When responding to a subpoena, the costs for photocopying a court-requested document should be billed to _____.

Chapter 9

Test 1

Multiple Choice

Write the letter of the correct answer in the blank.

_____ 1. Medical records serve
   a. only one purpose: to record care of the patient.
   b. only one purpose: to provide a legal document for the physician.
   c. multiple purposes.

_____ 2. As a legal document, the medical record can be used by
   a. the defendant only.
   b. the plaintiff only.
   c. both the defendant and the plaintiff.

_____ 3. Which statement is true?
   a. Some states have passed statutes that define what must be contained in a medical record.
   b. No states have passed statutes that define what must be contained in a medical record.
   c. All states have passed statutes that define what must be contained in a medical record.

_____ 4. You should not enter flippant or unprofessional comments into a medical record because
   a. it could be read by the patient and such comments would hurt his or her feelings.
   b. it is a legal document.
   c. medical assistants cannot write in a medical chart.

_____ 5. The format of the medical record
   a. is always in the exact same format because the law requires it.
   b. can include as little or as much information as the physician chooses.
   c. reflects the physician's specialty.

_____ 6. Under Medicare requirements, which item is NOT required in a medical chart?
   a. Admitting diagnosis
   b. Names of all the patient's children
   c. Discharge summary

Fill in the Blanks

7. POMR stands for _____.

8. Two common forms of medical charting are _____ and _____.

9. A particular diagnosis such as high blood pressure would be more easily charted using the _____ form of medical charting.

10. JCAHO stands for _____.

Chapter 9

Test 2

Multiple Choice

Write the letter of the correct answer in the blank.

_____ 1. Problem-oriented medical records
   a. frequently use SOAP charting.
   b. address one problem per patient visit.
   c. address only medical problems.

_____ 2. SOAP stands for
   a. Serious, Objective, Assessment, Pain.
   b. Subjective, Objective, Assessment, Pain.
   c. Subjective, Objective, Assessment, Plan.

_____ 3. Federal reimbursement guidelines mandate that all medical records be completed within how many days following the patient's discharge from the hospital?
   a. 10 days
   b. 30 days
   c. 60 days

_____ 4. Which statement is true?
   a. Falsification of medical records is grounds for civil indictment.
   b. Falsification of medical records is grounds for criminal indictment.
   c. Falsification of medical records is a matter that is handled within an individual medical practice.

_____ 5. In the eyes of the court, if something is not documented, it
   a. is probably illegal.
   b. is probably insignificant.
   c. wasn't done.

_____ 6. If a physician is not able to produce a medical record or documentation about treatment of a patient, the court
   a. may make an inference of guilt.
   b. will rely instead on testimony, which is just as valid and helpful in court.
   c. will dismiss all charges.

_____ 7. If a patient complains of feeling tired all the time, under which letter in SOAP charting will you accurately document this?
   a. S
   b. O
   c. A
   d. P

_____ **8.** Under which letter in SOAP charting is it accurate to chart a patient's temperature?
   a. S
   b. O
   c. A
   d. P

_____ **9.** Under which letter in SOAP charting is it accurate to chart that a medication regime was or was not effective?
   a. S
   b. O
   c. A
   d. P

_____ **10.** The patient is scheduled to return to the office for a follow-up appointment in two weeks. Under which letter in SOAP charting is it accurate to chart this?
   a. S
   b. O
   c. A
   d. P

Chapter 9

Test 3

Multiple Choice

Write the letter of the correct answer in the blank.

_____ 1. Records should not be released to the patient without the permission of
   a. the insurance company.
   b. the physician.
   c. the patient.

_____ 2. In most states, the general rule for ownership of medical records is that
   a. the patient owns them.
   b. the insurance company owns them.
   c. the physician owns them.

_____ 3. The Privacy Act of 1974 provides
   a. private citizens some control over information that the federal government collects about them.
   b. private citizens complete control over information that the federal government collects about them.
   c. private citizens no control over information that the federal government collects about them.

_____ 4. Open records laws
   a. are required in all states.
   b. grant public access to records maintained by state agencies.
   c. are federal laws.

_____ 5. Older records of former patients
   a. must be kept in the medical office for ten years.
   b. may be warehoused.
   c. may be shredded after one year.

_____ 6. Legally, how long should all medical records be stored from the time of the last entry?
   a. Two years
   b. Five years
   c. Ten years

_____ 7. The Public Health Services Act
   a. protects only minor patients.
   b. protects patients who are receiving treatment for drug and alcohol abuse.
   c. protects the physician treating patients receiving treatment for drug and alcohol abuse.

_____ 8. A register of birth must be retained
   a. for five years.
   b. for ten years.
   c. permanently.

_____   **9.** A register of death must be retained
     a. for five years.
     b. for ten years.
     c. permanently.

_____   **10.** A register of surgical procedures must be retained
     a. for five years.
     b. for ten years.
     c. permanently.

Chapter 9

Test 4

Multiple Choice

Write the letter of the correct answer in the blank.

_____ 1. Which statement is true?
   a. Legal confidentiality obligations apply to all methods of record keeping.
   b. Legal confidentiality obligations apply to written methods of record keeping only.
   c. Legal confidentiality obligations apply to computerized methods of record keeping only.

_____ 2. Which statement is true?
   a. All health care employees should be able to access all patient records in the computer.
   b. All health care employees should not be able to access all patient records in the computer.
   c. To be able to see all patient records is a right of every health care worker.

_____ 3. What kind of liability may health care providers and institutions such as hospitals and clinics face for releasing medical records without the proper patient authorization?
   a. Civil
   b. Criminal
   c. Both a and b

_____ 4. If a court requires certain records that document patient care and billing, it can issue
   a. an injunction.
   b. an edict.
   c. a subpoena.

_____ 5. Which is NOT a guideline to follow regarding court-requested material?
   a. Always turn over the entire medical chart.
   b. Notify the physician that a request has been made.
   c. Notify the physician's attorney that a request has been received.

_____ 6. Which statement is true?
   a. The patient should be billed for copying costs of a court-requested document.
   b. The court should be billed for copying costs of a court-requested document.
   c. The requesting attorney should be billed for copying costs of a court-requested document.

_____ 7. A health care worker must respond to a court order for medical records
   a. within 24 hours.
   b. within one week.
   c. by the due date on the order.

_____ 8. "Need-to-know" means
   a. all health care workers need to know the law.
   b. no health care worker should know any more personal information about a patient than is necessary to meet his or her needs.
   c. all health care workers should have full access to all elements of patients' records because they need to know everything to treat the patients.

Chapter 10
Lecture Notes/Class Handout

I. Vocabulary Development

II. Confidentiality

III. Health Insurance Portability and Accountability Act (HIPAA) of 1996

IV. Ethical Concerns with Information Technology (Informatics)

Chapter 10
Worksheet

Define the terms.

1. clearinghouse _____

_____

2. covered entities _____

_____

3. Employer Identification Number _____

_____

4. Employer Identifier Standard _____

_____

5. health care plan _____

_____

6. Healthcare Integrity and Protection Data Bank (HIPDB) _____

_____

7. Health Insurance Portability and Accountability Act (HIPPAA) of 1996 _____

_____

8. HIPAA-defined permissions _____

_____

9. Medical Informatics _____

_____

10. minimum necessary standard _____

_____

11. Notice of Privacy Practices (NPP) _____

_____

12. Office of Civil Rights ()CR) _____

_____

13. Privacy Rule _____

_____

14. Protected Health Information _____

_____

15. sanctions _____

_____

16. State's Preemption _____

_____

17. Telemedicine _____

_____

18. Treatment, Payment, and Healthcare Operations (TPO) _____

_____

19. Wireless Local Area Networks (WLANs) _____

_____

Answer the questions.

1. What has become of a patient sharing his or her medical information with just one physician?

    _____

    _____

    _____

2. Can physicians run a practice in today's world if they are unable to share patient's medical informa-
    tion with other entities?

    _____

    _____

    _____

3. Why might a nursing home wish to deny access to a patient's medical information?

    _____

    _____

    _____

4. When do patients *not* have the right to access their medical information?

    _____

    _____

    _____

Chapter 10

Test

Fill in the Blanks

1. HIPAA stands for the _____ _____ _____ and _____ Act of 1996.

2. The _____ _____ _____ is a number assigned to an employer for purposes of identification.

3. _____ are penalties or fines.

4. _____ is the use of communications and information technologies to provide health care services to people at a distance.

5. The _____ _____ _____ Networks are a communication system used by physicians and nurses to access patient information.

Multiple Choice

Write the letter of the correct answer in the blank.

_____   6. Protected Health Information is
     a. the same as WLANs.
     b. nonconfidential.
     c. a health care plan.
     d. individual identifiable information.

_____   7. Under HIPAA patients
     a. own their medical record.
     b. can complain to a covered entity.
     c. have no rights.
     d. cannot be de-identified.

_____   8. A state's preemption occurs when
     a. federal law takes precedence.
     b. there is no evidence of an infectious disease outbreak.
     c. state privacy laws are stricter than federal laws.
     d. a physician requests it.

_____   9. Unique identifiers for health care providers include
     a. passport photos.
     b. birthmarks.
     c. telephone numbers.
     d. tax ID numbers.

_____ **10.** A patient's right to privacy is covered in the Constitution under the
    a. First Amendment.
    b. Fourth Amendment.
    c. Fourteenth Amendment.
    d. all of the above.

Matching

In the blank, write the letter of the term that correctly matches the definition.

_____ **11.** HIPAA   **a.** privacy notice

_____ **12.** EIN   **b.** national data bank

_____ **13.** HIDPB   **c.** identifiable patient information

_____ **14.** NPP   **d.** employer identification

_____ **15.** PHI   **e.** law regulating information

True or False?

_____ **16.** WLANs are used by patients when searching the Internet.

_____ **17.** The Office of Civil Rights investigates violations of HIPAA.

_____ **18.** Patients' rights under HIPAA allows them to deny access to their medical records to others, including physicians.

_____ **19.** Public Health Information cannot be de-identified.

_____ **20.** Sanctions for violations of HIPPA can be as much as $50,000.

Chapter 11
Lecture Notes/Class Handout 1

I. Vocabulary Development

II. Introduction

III. Early History

IV. Ethical Standards and Behavior

V. Code of Ethics

Chapter 11

Lecture Notes/Class Handout 2

I. Vocabulary Development

II. Summary of the Opinions of the Council on Ethical and Judicial Affairs of the AMA

III. Nurses' Code of Ethics

IV. Biomedicine and Bioethical Issues

V. Genetic Engineering

VI. Health Care Reform

Chapter 11

Worksheet 1

Define the terms.

1. AMA _____
_____

2. AAMA _____
_____

3. allege _____
_____

4. censure _____
_____

5. expulsion _____
_____

Answer the questions.

1. What does "applied ethics" mean?
_____
_____
_____

2. Describe how ethics is more than just "common sense."
_____
_____
_____

3. Is the Hippocratic Oath used today? Explain your answer.
_____
_____
_____

4. What is the AMA required to do if someone alleges that a physician has committed a criminal act?
_____
_____
_____

5. What is the theme of the Nuremberg Code?

_____

_____

_____

6. What is the function of the Judicial Council on Ethical and Judicial Affairs?

_____

_____

_____

7. How are the principles of the AMA and the AAMA similar? How are they different?

_____

_____

_____

Chapter 11

Worksheet 2

Define the terms.

1. euthanasia _____

_____

2. gene therapy _____

_____

3. creed _____

_____

4. nontherapeutic research _____

_____

5. therapeutic research _____

_____

6. double-blind research _____

_____

Answer the questions.

1. What is fee splitting?

_____

_____

_____

2. Why do many ethicists believe that it is unethical to use a control group when conducting medical experiments?

_____

_____

_____

3. Who is responsible for explaining to the patient all the risks involved in a research project?

_____

_____

_____

4. If a health care provider has a personal, religious, or ethical reason for not wishing to be involved in a particular procedure, what should he or she do?

_____

_____

_____

5. There are still many areas of medical ethics for which there are no conclusive answers. What does this statement mean to you and why?

_____

_____

_____

Chapter 11

Test 1

Multiple Choice

Write the letter of the correct answer in the blank.

_____ **1.** Health care ethics
  a. is nothing more than common sense.
  b. has become important only since very recent technological advances in science.
  c. is applied ethics.

_____ **2.** An unethical act
  a. may or may not be illegal.
  b. is always illegal.
  c. is never illegal.

_____ **3.** A warning or criticism by the AMA is called
  a. a tort.
  b. expulsion.
  c. censure.

_____ **4.** Unethical behavior as defined by the AMA refers to
  a. moral principles or practices.
  b. the customs of the medical profession and matters of medical policy.
  c. both a and b.

_____ **5.** When you declare something without proof, you are
  a. censuring.
  b. alleging.
  c. expelling.

_____ **6.** Applied ethics means
  a. health care professionals must talk about their values.
  b. health care professionals' behavior must match their set of values.
  c. codes have been written to describe medical ethics.

_____ **7.** The abbreviation AAMA stands for
  a. American Medical Association.
  b. American Association of Medical Assistants.
  c. American Association of Moral Actions.

_____ **8.** The Council on Ethical and Judicial Affairs is part of the
  a. AMA.
  b. AAMA.
  c. neither a nor b.

_____ **9.** Which statement is true?
      a. Physicians have developed modern codes of ethics that serve as a moral guide for health care professionals.
      b. Concern for patient privacy is the theme of the Nuremberg Code.
      c. The Hippocratic Oath is no longer a part of medical codes of ethics.

Chapter 11

Test 2

Multiple Choice

Write the letter of the correct answer in the blank.

_____ 1. Euthanasia is
   a. replacement of a defective or malfunctioning gene.
   b. administration of a lethal agent by another person to cause death.
   c. the practice of a physician's accepting payment from another physician for referring a patient.

_____ 2. The Council's position on gene therapy is that the replacement of a defective or malfunctioning gene is
   a. unacceptable except under extraordinary circumstances.
   b. acceptable under all conditions.
   c. acceptable as long as it is for therapeutic purposes and not for altering human traits.

_____ 3. Which statement is true?
   a. The AMA is the only medical professional organization that has a code of ethics.
   b. Many medical organizations have developed codes of ethics.
   c. There are no areas of medical ethics for which there are no conclusive answers.

_____ 4. When making ethical decisions, the decision maker must always be
   a. subjective.
   b. objective.
   c. sympathetic.

_____ 5. In a double-blind test
   a. neither the experimenter nor the patient knows who is getting the research treatment.
   b. only the experimenter knows who is getting the research treatment.
   c. only the patient knows who is getting the research treatment.

_____ 6. Many ethicists believe that it is unethical to use a control group when conducting medical experiments because this group
   a. has no hope of benefiting from the experiment.
   b. is in danger of being injured from the experiment.
   c. is too ill to benefit from the experiment.

_____ 7. The person responsible for explaining to the patient all the risks involved in a research project is the
   a. physician.
   b. physician assistant (PA).
   c. nurse.

_____ 8. The form of medical research that may directly benefit the research subject is called
   a. randomized test trials.
   b. therapeutic research.
   c. nontherapeutic research.

_____ **9.** If health care providers have personal, religious, or ethical reasons for not wishing to be involved in a particular procedure, they should
  a. state their preferences before being hired.
  b. keep this information to themselves.
  c. simply refuse to carry out the procedure when instructed to do so.

Chapter 12

Lecture Notes/Class Handout 1

I. Vocabulary Development

II. Fetal Development

III. Assisted or Artificial Conception

Chapter 12

Lecture Notes/Class Handout 2

I. Vocabulary Development

II. Abortion

III. Genetic Counseling and Testing

Chapter 12

Worksheet 1

Define the terms.

1. artificial insemination _____

   _____

2. artificial insemination donor (AID) _____

   _____

3. artificial insemination husband (AIH) _____

   _____

4. contraception _____

   _____

5. embryo _____

   _____

6. eugenic (involuntary) sterilization _____

   _____

7. eugenics _____

   _____

8. fetus _____

   _____

9. gestational period _____

   _____

10. in-vitro fertilization _____

    _____

11. sterilization _____

    _____

12. surrogate mother _____

    _____

13. therapeutic sterilization _____

    _____

Answer the questions

1. When does life begin in your opinion? Identify and describe the stage of fetal development and explain your position.

   _____

   _____

   _____

2. Describe the Baby M case. Do you agree or disagree with the court decision? Why?

   _____

   _____

   _____

3. What is "harvesting"? What is your position regarding this controversial procedure?

   _____

   _____

   _____

Chapter 12
Worksheet 2

Define the terms.

1. viable _____

_____

2. spontaneous abortion _____

_____

3. induced abortion _____

_____

4. genetics _____

_____

5. genetic counseling _____

_____

6. amniocentesis _____

_____

Answer the questions.

1. *Roe v. Wade* legalized abortion during certain stages of pregnancy. What are those stages? When is abortion not authorized?

_____

_____

_____

2. Describe the positions U.S. society has taken on abortion from the nineteenth century through the present.

_____

_____

_____

3. What was the result of the 1992 *Planned Parenthood v. Casey* case? Do you agree with this ruling? Why or why not?

_____

_____

_____

Chapter 12

Test 1

Multiple Choice

Write the letter of the correct answer in the blank.

_____ 1. The term used for an unborn child between the second and twelfth weeks after conception is
  a. gestation.
  b. embryo.
  c. fetus.

_____ 2. In-vitro fertilization is
  a. illegal except under extraordinary circumstances.
  b. a process where ovum and sperm are combined outside the body.
  c. the same thing as artificial insemination.

_____ 3. The Baby M case
  a. resulted from a surrogate parenting contract between a woman and a married couple.
  b. resulted in the courts' awarding continuing custody rights to the natural mother.
  c. resulted from a gay couple seeking custody of an infant.

_____ 4. The process of medically altering reproductive organs so as to terminate the ability to produce offspring is
  a. contraception.
  b. birth control.
  c. sterilization.

_____ 5. The science that studies methods for controlling certain characteristics in offspring is
  a. voluntary sterilization.
  b. involuntary sterilization.
  c. eugenics.

True or False?

_____ 6. For most surgical operations, the patient's written consent is all that is necessary.

_____ 7. Eugenic or involuntary sterilization may be necessary if the mother's life is threatened.

_____ 8. In some cases, negligence occurs during the sterilization process.

_____ 9. Currently, no federal law requires consent from one spouse for the other spouse's sterilization.

_____ 10. Not all people hold the same views on the ethics of using contraception.

Chapter 12

Test 2

Multiple Choice

Write the letter of the correct answer in the blank.

_____ **1.** *Viable* means
  a. abortion.
  b. spontaneous abortion.
  c. able to survive outside the uterus.

_____ **2.** Which statement is true?
  a. A spontaneous abortion is the same as an induced abortion.
  b. The case of *Roe v. Wade* legalized abortion in all three trimesters.
  c. The AMA adopted an anti-abortion position in 1859.

_____ **3.** The study of heredity and its variations is called
  a. eugenics.
  b. genetics.
  c. bionomics.

_____ **4.** Wrongful-life suits are
  a. illegal.
  b. generally rejected by courts as it is impossible to assess a dollar amount of damages.
  c. applicable only when there is a birth defect.

True or False?

_____ **5.** Hospital employees have the right to refuse to participate in performing an abortion, and the hospital cannot dismiss the employee for insubordination.

_____ **6.** The law says that a husband cannot prevent his wife from having an abortion.

_____ **7.** Since *Roe v. Wade,* no other abortion cases have reached the Supreme Court to challenge the ruling.

_____ **8.** The most common means of genetic testing during pregnancy is through blood testing.

_____ **9.** Spina bifida is a bleeding disorder.

Chapter 13

Lecture Notes/Class Handout 1

I. Vocabulary Development

II. The Dying Process

Chapter 13

Lecture Notes/Class Handout 2

I. Vocabulary Development

II. Cardiac Death (continued)

III. Brain-Oriented Death—Irreversible Coma

Chapter 13

Lecture Notes/Class Handout 3

I. Vocabulary Development

II. Euthanasia

III. Arguments in Support of and Opposed to Euthanasia

Chapter 13

Lecture Notes/Class Handout 4

I. Vocabulary Development

II. Stages of Dying

III. Advance Directives

IV. Choices in Life and Death

Chapter 13

Worksheet 1

Define the terms.

1. expired _____

   _____

2. comatose _____

   _____

3. EEG _____

   _____

4. rigor mortis _____

   _____

Answer the questions.

1. Why was the Karen Ann Quinlan case "groundbreaking" in terms of the law?

   _____

   _____

   _____

2. What is a permanently vegetative condition?

   _____

   _____

   _____

3. What do you think is the correct position regarding the dying process and respect for human dignity? Support your position.

   _____

   _____

   _____

Chapter 13

Worksheet 2

Define the terms.

1. hypothermia _____

   _____

2. cardiopulmonary _____

   _____

3. brain death _____

   _____

4. UDDA _____

   _____

5. withdrawing life-sustaining treatment _____

   _____

6. withholding life-sustaining treatment _____

   _____

Answer the questions.

1. Why is a cardiac-oriented definition of death not enough when considering organ transplantation?

   _____

   _____

   _____

2. Describe the "whole-brain-oriented" definition of death.

   _____

   _____

   _____

3. Describe the Harvard Criteria for a Definition of Irreversible Coma.

   _____

   _____

   _____

Chapter 13

Worksheet 3

Define the terms

1. active euthanasia _____

   _____

2. passive euthanasia _____

   _____

3. PAS _____

   _____

4. "allow to die" _____

   _____

5. ordinary means _____

   _____

6. extraordinary means _____

   _____

Answer the questions.

1. List four major arguments in favor of euthanasia.

   _____

   _____

   _____

2. List nine major arguments in opposition to euthanasia.

   _____

   _____

   _____

3. Describe your position on euthanasia and why you feel as you do.

   _____

   _____

   _____

Chapter 13
Worksheet 4

Define the terms.

1. advance directive _____

   _____

2. living will _____

   _____

3. CPR _____

   _____

4. DNR _____

   _____

5. proxy _____

   _____

6. mercy killing _____

   _____

7. durable power of attorney _____

   _____

Answer the questions.

1. According to *Issues in Health Care Ethics,* what are the four situations in which a person cannot exercise the fundamental right of self-determination?

   _____

   _____

   _____

2. Name the treatments that might be ordered for a patient failing in one of the rights of self-determination.

   _____

   _____

   _____

Chapter 13

Test 1

Multiple Choice

Write the letter of the correct answer in the blank.

_____ 1. The Quinlan case was groundbreaking because it represented the first time a family had requested that a court approve the removal of
a. a respirator from a permanently comatose patient and won the case.
b. a feeding tube from a permanently comatose patient and won the case.
c. intravenous fluids from a permanently comatose patient and won the case.

_____ 2. Traditionally, death was defined as
a. brain death.
b. cardiac death.
c. both.

_____ 3. An EEG measures
a. brain activity.
b. heart activity.
c. body temperature.

_____ 4. When in a permanently vegetative condition, a person
a. is dead.
b. is considered comatose.
c. has no brain activity.

_____ 5. Which statement is true?
a. Neither the AMA code nor the International Code of Nursing addresses human dignity.
b. Once a person is dead, human dignity no longer is a concern.
c. Both the AMA Code and the International Code of Nursing address human dignity.

True or False?

_____ 6. People who are sustained on life support are, in the eyes of the law, alive.

_____ 7. Using only the cardiac definition of death is no longer enough to determine death.

_____ 8. Modern medicine has enabled people to live longer and survive diseases such as pneumonia that once caused death.

_____ 9. Rigor mortis is the loss of body temperature after death.

_____ 10. A cardiac death is considered a legal death.

Chapter 13

Test 2

Multiple Choice

Write the letter of the correct answer in the blank.

_____ **1.** Hypothermia is
   a. irreversible loss of cardiac function.
   b. low body temperature.
   c. high body temperature.

_____ **2.** Irreversible coma according to the Harvard Criteria is known as
   a. brain death.
   b. cardiac death.
   c. neither.

_____ **3.** Modern technology has made it possible to maintain heart and lung function
   a. for hours.
   b. for days.
   c. indefinitely.

_____ **4.** What criteria is NOT part of the Harvard Criteria for a Definition of Irreversible Coma?
   a. Unreceptive and unresponsive
   b. Receptive and responsive
   c. No reflexes

_____ **5.** Which statement is true?
   a. The UDDA was approved by the American Bar Association in the 1980s.
   b. All groups of faith agree on the brain-death criterion as described in the UDDA.
   c. Withdrawing life-sustaining treatment means never starting life support.

True or False?

_____ **6.** The terms *cardiac* and *cardiopulmonary*, referring to the heart and the lung function, are inter-changeable in a legal definition of death.

_____ **7.** To protect against malpractice suit, a physician should seek an outside medical opinion before terminating a life-support system.

_____ **8.** Patients have the right to refuse treatment as well as food, even if they are not terminally ill.

_____ **9.** In most states, if the whole brain is dead, then the person is considered deceased.

_____ **10.** A problem with using only the cardiac-oriented definition of death involves organ transplantation.

Chapter 13

Test 3

Multiple Choice

Write the letter of the correct answer in the blank.

_____ 1. Passive euthanasia is
   a. legal in all states.
   b. legal in some states.
   c. illegal in all states.

_____ 2. Active euthanasia is
   a. legal everywhere.
   b. legal in some states.
   c. illegal in all states.

_____ 3. A treatment or procedure that is morally required, such as fluids and comfort measures, is called
   a. ordinary measures.
   b. extraordinary measures.
   c. euthanasia.

_____ 4. Dr. Jack Kevorkian is known for
   a. conducting assisted suicides.
   b. opposing euthanasia.
   c. treating Nancy Cruzan in 1983.

_____ 5. Which statement is true?
   a. Many people oppose euthanasia in any form.
   b. The term "passive euthanasia" is endorsed by the Roman Catholic Church.
   c. A terminal patient does not have the right to refuse life-sustaining treatment.

True or False?

_____ 6. Passive euthanasia includes withholding basic needs such as hydration and nutrition.

_____ 7. Hospice offers supportive care to both the young and old terminal patient, in the home and in hospital-like settings.

_____ 8. The double-effect doctrine states that an action may have two desired consequences.

_____ 9. With PAS, a physician provides a patient with the medical know-how or the means to take his or her own life.

_____ 10. Patients will often ask a health care worker what course to take with a dying loved one.

Chapter 13

Test 4

Multiple Choice

Write the letter of the correct answer in the blank.

_____ 1. The term that does NOT describe a stage of dying is
   a. acceptance.
   b. anger.
   c. vulnerability.

_____ 2. The five stages of dying were developed by
   a. the Patient Self-Determination Act of 1991.
   b. Dr. Elisabeth Kübler-Ross.
   c. Eileen Flynn in *Issues in Health Care Ethics.*

_____ 3. How are suicide and voluntary euthanasia different?
   a. Suicide is illegal in all states. Voluntary euthanasia is legal in all states.
   b. Suicide does not take as long as voluntary euthanasia.
   c. Suicide involves the actions of a single person. Voluntary euthanasia involves a second person.

True or False?

_____ 6. Voluntary euthanasia is also called mercy killing.

_____ 7. A DNR order is an advance directive.

_____ 8. The general practice in hospitals and nursing homes is to feed patients via tubes if they are unable to eat normally.

_____ 9. Current opinions of the Council on Ethical and Judicial Affairs of the American Medical Association include guidelines on do not resuscitate orders.

_____ 10. Advance directives are not the same as living wills.

Worksheet and Test Answer Keys
Chapter 1

Worksheet 1

Define the terms.

1. Medical ethics is an applied ethics, meaning that it is the practical application of moral standards that concern benefiting the patient.
2. Moral dilemmas and issues that are a result of advances in medicine and medical research.
3. The branch of philosophy relating to morals or moral principles.
4. Rules or actions prescribed by a governmental authority that have a binding legal force.
5. Moral conduct based on principles regulating the behavior of health care professionals.

Answer the questions.

1. Because medical ethics is applied ethics, meaning that it is the practical application of moral standards that concern benefiting the patient
2. Both are rules for behavior, both are required for medical professionals.
3. Laws are required by national, state, or local governmental bodies. When laws are broken, there are direct consequences as directed by government authorities. Ethics do not have governmental requirements.
4. It may or may not be acceptable based on the decision of the officials of the court system (district attorney) and the jury.
5. Yes, absolutely. Medical ethics require a higher standard.
6. Yes, but we all do not agree with each other. The law represents the consensus of most of the people of a society.

Worksheet 2

Define the terms.

1. An ethical theory based on the principle of the greatest good for the greatest number.
2. The ability to have consideration for and honor another person's beliefs and opinions.
3. Unwavering adherence to one's principles.
4. Quality of truthfulness.
5. Treating everyone the same.
6. The ability to understand another person's feelings without actually experiencing that person's pain or distress.
7. Feeling sorry for or pitying another.
8. The ability to have a gentle, caring attitude toward others.
9. Faithfulness and commitment to a person or commitment.
10. Confidentiality.
11. Unwelcome sexual advances when submission to such conduct is made either explicitly or implicitly a term or condition of an individual's employment, or submission to or rejection of such conduct is used as the basis for employment decisions, or conduct has the purpose or effect of interfering with work performance or creating an intimidating, hostile, or offensive working environment.

12. Entitlement of all employees to certain procedures to be followed when they believe their rights are in jeopardy.

13. Pay equity or a theory that extends equal pay requirements to all persons who are doing equal work.

Describe the three-step model for evaluating an ethical dilemma.

Is it legal? If the issue is illegal, then it is clearly unethical.

Is it balanced? (This step is to be followed only if answer to Step One is "yes.") Balance means determining if someone is negatively impacted or will suffer as a result of the issue.

How does it make me feel? How would I feel if everyone knew about my position on this issue? If I would feel good, then the decision is likely to be ethical.

Answer the questions.

1. No. Emotions may affect how we behave, but they do not necessarily justify the behavior.

2. No. Ethics are about "right and wrong." Ethics may overlap religious beliefs, but a person can hold ethical beliefs and not have a faith in a higher being or God or profess to be a "believer" or practitioner of any religion.

3. Ethics is the study of a branch of philosophy related to morals and moral principles. Bioethics refers to the moral dilemmas and issues prevalent in today's society as a result of advances in medicine and medical research.

4. Ethics is the study of a branch of philosophy related to morals and moral principles. Feelings and beliefs are emotional reactions to situations. Feelings are very personal and are sometimes difficult to justify, whereas an ethical position is more easily justifiable.

Test 1

Fill in the Blank

1. Bioethics
2. applied ethics
3. Medical ethics
4. Applied ethics
5. Laws

True or False?

6. F	10. T	14. T	18. T
7. T	11. T	15. F	19. T
8. T	12. F	16. T	20. F
9. F	13. T	17. F	

Test 2

Fill in the Blank

1. Utilitarianism
2. ethics
3. Integrity
4. Empathy
5. Honesty

Multiple Choice

Write the letter of the correct answer in the blank.

6. b	**9.** d	**12.** b	**15.** b
7. b	**10.** b	**13.** a	
8. d	**11.** d	**14.** a	

True or False?

16. T	**18.** T	**20.** T
17. F	**19.** T	

Chapter 2

Worksheet 1

Define the terms.

1. Common law, based on the decisions made by judges.

2. Designed by the framers of the Constitution so that no single branch of government could control the entire government, and so that each branch of government is scrutinized by other branches of government.

3. Concerns relationships between individuals or between individuals and the government that are not criminal.

4. Case law that is based on decisions made by judges.

5. In contract law, this refers to something of value given as part of the agreement.

6. Rights, privileges, or immunities secured and protected for each citizen by the U.S. Constitution or the state constitutions.

7. The division of law that includes enforceable promises and agreements between two or more persons to do or not do a particular thing.

8. Failure to perform professional duties to an accepted standard of care.

9. Laws enacted by state and federal legislatures

10. Wrongful act, defined by law, that is committed against another person or property and that results in harm

11. Division of law that covers acts that result in harm to another

Answer the questions.

1. Federalism; checks and balances.

2. Legislative, executive, and judicial branches.

3. Senate and House of Representatives.

4. The U.S. Supreme Court is the highest court. Below the Supreme Court are two courts: the Court of Appeals for the Federal Circuit, and the Circuit Courts of Appeals. Each of these courts receives appeals from three separate bodies. The Court of Appeals hears appeals from the Court of Claims, the Merit Systems Protection Board, and the Court of International Trade. The Circuit Courts hear appeals from the Tax Court, administrative agencies, and federal District Courts.

5. (1) A statute begins as a bill submitted by legislators at the state or federal level. (2) The bill is then submitted into one of the two legislature houses. It may "die" at any stage. It may go to committee, and the committee may choose to call hearings to gather more information for review and discussion. This first committee will issue a recommendation to pass or fail the bill. If it fails, all further action is dismissed. (3) If it passes, the bill then goes to the second legislative body for review and vote. (4) If it passes in both houses, it is signed by both the Speaker of the House and the VP of the Senate. (5) The approved act is then sent to the president (federal) or the governor (state), who either approve or veto the bill. A veto must occur within 10 days. (6) If approved, the bill becomes law and is issued a public law number.

6. It is law established from a court decision, which may explain or interpret the other sources of law. It may explain what constitutional law, a statute, or a regulation means.

7. Assault is the *threat* of bodily harm to another. Battery is *actual* bodily harm to another without permission.

Worksheet 2

Define the terms.

1. Withdrawing medical care from a patient without providing sufficient notice to the patient.
2. Regulation set by government agencies.
3. Neglect of an understanding between two parties.
4. Failure, without legal excuse, to perform any promise or to carry out any of the terms of an agreement.
5. Capable of making a decision without mental confusion.
6. Court action brought by the government against an individual or a group that could result in imprisonment or fine.
7. Laws set up by the government to protect the public from harm.
8. Person or group sued civilly or prosecuted criminally in a court of law.
9. Oral testimony.
10. Legal process by which facts are revealed before a trial.
11. An individual with special education, training, or experience in a given area who testifies in a court of law for a fee.
12. An oral or written agreement.
13. A serious crime that carries a punishment of death or imprisonment for more than 1 year.
14. An agreement that is made through inference by signs, inaction, or silence.
15. A dispute resulting in one party suing another.
16. Offenses less serious than felonies, punishable by fine or imprisonment of up to 1 year.
17. Person or group bringing suit against another person or group.
18. A person who brings a criminal suit on behalf of the government.
19. Court order.
20. Give up the right to something.

Answer the questions.

1. An expressed agreement is an oral or written agreement. An implied contract is an agreement that is made through inference by signs, inaction, or silence.
2. No, but the physician must give sufficient notice to a patient, or refer the patient to another competent source of care before withdrawing medical care.
3. Felonies: Serious crimes that carry a punishment of death or imprisonment for more than 1 year. Misdemeanors: Offenses less serious than felonies, punishable by fine or imprisonment of up to 1 year.
4. The power to hear a case.
5. Yes. The office manager or other assistant of the physician may appear on the physician's behalf.
6. Only the parts of the medical record requested should be copied and delivered to the requesting attorney.

Test 1

Fill in the Blanks

1. federalism checks and balances
2. retained by the states
3. U.S. Supreme Court
4. executive branch
5. legislative

Multiple Choice

Write the letter of the correct answer in the blank.

6. b   **8.** d   **10.** a
7. a   **9.** d

Matching

In the blank, write the letter of the scenario that correctly matches each term.

11. d   **13.** e   **15.** c
12. b   **14.** a   **16.** f

True or False?

17. T   **18.** T   **19.** F   **20.** T

Test 2

Fill in the Blanks

1. abandonment   **4.** Probate court (or estate court)
2. implied contract
3. Criminal laws   **5.** Discovery

Multiple Choice

Write the letter of the correct answer in the blank.

6. d   **8.** a   **10.** a
7. b   **9.** a

Matching

In the blank, write the letter of the description that correctly matches each term.

11. e   **13.** f   **15.** b
12. d   **14.** c   **16.** a

True or False?

17. T   **18.** T   **19.** T   **20.** F

Chapter 3

Worksheet 1

Define the terms.

1. An approval or sanction.

2. The cooperation of one state in granting a license to practice medicine to a physician already licensed in another state.

3. Taken away, as in *revoked license.*

Answer the questions.

1. *Licensure* is granted through one of three ways: examination, endorsement, or reciprocity. A physician must have a valid license to legally practice medicine. *Certification* is voluntary additional training for a physician.

2. A state will grant a license by endorsement to applicants who pay a fee and successfully complete the NBME. Most physicians in the United States are licensed by endorsement, meaning they sat for and passed their national board exam. They are then recommended for licensure. Licensure is recommended and does not happen automatically.

3. Different states have different requirements for medical licensing. Some states require a physician to be licensed for a certain number of years before qualifying.

4. They all: (1) Establish the baseline for the practice of medicine in the state. (2) Determine the prerequisites for licensure. (3) Forbid the practice of medicine without a license. (4) Specify the conditions for license renewal, suspension, and revocation.

5. Renewal fee, either annually or biannually, and 75 CEUs in a three-year period.

Worksheet 2

Define the terms.

1. Legal theory that provides that the statute of limitations begins to run at the time the injury is discovered or when the patient should have known of the injury.
2. "Let the master answer" means the employer is responsible for the actions of the employee.
3. The ordinary skill and care that medical practitioners use and that is commonly used by other medical practitioners in the same locality when caring for patients.
4. The period of time that a patient has to file a lawsuit.

Answer the questions.

1. It has changed. Court cases change the standard of care and give new interpretations.
2. This is dangerous because you can never be sure that your voice doesn't carry to someone who should not hear. All patient information is confidential. The patient's right to confidentiality could easily be violated under such circumstances.
3. The employer is liable for acts of employees within the scope of employment, meaning the employer or physician is liable for negligent acts of employees while working for the employer.
4. Yes, health care workers have a duty to interpret and carry out the orders of their employer/physician. If something is not clear, they have an obligation to seek clarification before carrying out the order.
5. Answers will vary. Use this question for class discussion.

Test 1

Fill in the Blanks

1. reciprocity
2. Endorsement
3. U.S. Medical Licensing Examination (USMLE)
4. 75 3
5. revoked

Multiple Choice

Write the letter of the correct answer in the blank.

6. b
7. a
8. b
9. b
10. b

True or False?

11. F
12. T
13. T
14. T
15. T
16. T
17. F
18. F
19. T
20. T

Test 2

Fill in the Blanks

1. Standard of care
2. Good Samaritan laws
3. "let the master answer"

4. an adult who acts in court on behalf of a child in litigation.
5. bonding

Multiple Choice

Write the letter of the correct answer in the blank.

6. b
7. c

8. d
9. c

10. b

True or False?

11. T
12. F
13. F

14. F
15. T
16. T

17. T
18. T
19. T

20. T

Chapter 4

Worksheet 1

Define the terms.

1. A legal agreement in which physicians agree to share a eacility and staff but do not, as a rule, share legal responsibility for the actions of each other.
2. A type of medical practice, as established by law, that is managed by a board of directors.
3. EPO: A type of managed care that combines the concepts of HMO and PPO.
4. Three or more physicians who share the same facility and practice medicine together.
5. HMO: A type of managed care plan that offers a range of health care services to plan members for a predetermined fee per member by a limited group of providers.
6. A legal agreement in which physicians share in the operation of a medical practice and become responsible for the actions of the other partners.
7. PPO: A managed care concept in which the patient must use a medical provider who is under contract with the insurer for an agreed-upon fee in order to receive co-payment from the insurer.
8. A type of medical practice in which one physician may employ other physicians.
9. A medical practice in which the physician works alone.

Answer the questions.

1. a. Specialties in medicine have developed, making it impossible for one physician to learn it all, so physicians have started coming together in other forms of practice to better treat patients.

   b. Insurance costs and lawsuits have increased, making it more important to function in groups. The managed care industry is driving the development of group practice for the best reimbursement.

   c. In general, medical offices function more as businesses now than ever before. They require business personnel, and the costs of these expensive employees can be shared within physician groups of various types.

2. a. Answers will vary.

   b.

   c.

List an advantage and a disadvantage of each type of practice.

Practice	Advantage	Disadvantage
Corporation	Protection from loss of individual assets	Low income
Solo Practice	Independence	Capital necessary; death or illness of the physician
Partnership	Shared legal responsibility	Personal differences

Practice	Advantage	Disadvantage
Association Practice	Shared work	Legal responsibility not shared
Group Practice	Shared expenses	Personality differences
Single Specialty	Shared expenses and staff	Competition among specialists
Sole Proprietorship	Physician retains all asset	Physician bears all expenses

Fill in the blanks.
1. shareholders
2. dissolved
3. IPA or independent practice association
4. HMO; PPO; EPO

Worksheet 2

Write the meaning of each abbreviation.
1. Doctor of Chiropractic
2. Doctor of Dental Medicine
3. Doctor of Dental Surgery
4. Doctor of Medicine
5. Doctor of Optometry
6. Doctor of Osteopathy
7. Doctor of Philosophy
8. Doctor of Podiatric Medicine
9. Occupational Therapist
10. Emergency Medical Technician
11. Physical Therapist
12. Respiratory Therapist

Fill in the blanks.
1. scope of practice
2. a. Answers will vary.
   b.
   c.
   d.
   e.

Complete the table with information about each health professional.

Allied Health Professional	Full Title	Level of Education	Tasks Performed
RN	Registered Nurse	AD: 2-year program BSN: 4-year program State license	All nursing tasks
LPN	Licensed Practical Nurse	1-year program State license	Limited nursing tasks
LVN	Licensed Vocational Nurse	1-year program State license	Limited nursing tasks
NP	Nurse Practitioner	RN with BSN and additional training in specialty area Masters in nursing	Specialty nursing tasks
MT	Laboratory or Medical Technologist	4-year program Certification	All variety of lab tests
MLT	Medical Laboratory Technician	2-year program Certification	Limited lab tests
PA	Physician Assistant	Masters level training with internship	Assist physician in primary care Can function independently

Allied Health Professional	Full Title	Level of Education	Tasks Performed
CMA	Certified Medical Assistant	Diploma: 6- to 9-month program AD: 2-year program Certification	Assist physician in ambulatory care setting

Test 1

Fill in the Blanks

1. preferred provider organization (PPO)
2. partnership
3. solo practice
4. corporation
5. Orthopedics

Multiple Choice

Write the letter of the correct answer in the blank.

6. a
7. b
8. d
9. c
10. b

Matching

In the blank, write the letter of the advantage that correctly matches each type of practice.

11. d
12. f
13. c
14. a
15. e
16. b

In the blank, write the letter of the description that correctly matches each medical specialty.

17. d
18. c
19. b
20. a

Test 2

Fill in the Blanks

Write the abbreviation that names each allied health professional.

1. D.C.
2. Ph.D.
3. D.O.
4. M.D.
5. D.M.D.

Multiple Choice

Write the letter of the correct answer in the blank.

6. b
7. a
8. d
9. a
10. c

Matching

In the blank, write the letter of the description that correctly matches each occupation.

11. j
12. f
13. c
14. g
15. b
16. d
17. a
18. i
19. e
20. h

Chapter 5

Worksheet 1

Summarize each principle in your own words. Possible answers are given. NOTE: While the "Standards of Conduct" are developed for physicians, it is understood that all health care professionals must recognize a responsibility to patients, society, other health professionals, and to themselves.

AMA Principles of Medical Ethics	Standards of Conduct
Human dignity	Dedication to providing competent medical services with compassion and respect for all human dignity.
Honesty	Honesty in all dealings, including a responsibility to expose other physicians who are not honest.
Responsibility to society	While always seeking the best interest of the patient, the physician will respect the law.
Confidentiality	Safeguard the confidentiality (all private matters) within the constraints of the law.
Continued study	A physician makes a commitment to continue his or her own education, keeping up with medical research and advances, consulting with other physicians as needed for the good of the patient.
Freedom of choice	A physician is free, except in emergency, to choose whom to serve and associate with and the environment for that work.
Responsibility to improve community	A physician has a responsibility to participate and contribute in improving the community.

(continued)

AMA Principles of Medical Ethics	Standards of Conduct
Responsibility to the patient	A physician shall, while caring for a patient, regard responsibility to the patient as paramount.
Support access to medical care for all people	A physician, to the best of his or her ability, shall attempt to provide access to medical care for all patients.

Review Table 5-2 in *Fremgen's Medical Law and Ethics*, p. 92. For each of the seven physician duties, give one example of acceptable and unacceptable behavior.

Duty	Acceptable Behavior	Unacceptable Behavior
Accepting gifts	Answers will vary. Use for class discussion.	
Conflict of interest		
Professional courtesy		
Reporting unethical conduct of another physician		
Second opinion		
Sexual conduct		
Treating family members		

Worksheet 2

Define the terms.

1. The various methods by which a patient exercises the right to self-determination prior to a medical necessity; includes living wills, health care proxies, and durable power of attorney.
2. Person authorized to act on behalf of patient.
3. Legal agreement that allows an agent or representative of the patient to act on behalf of the patient.
4. Consent inferred by signs, inaction, or silence of a patient.
5. Consent granted by a patient after the patient has received knowledge and understanding of potential risks and benefits.
6. Legal document in which a person states that life-sustaining treatments and nutritional support should not be used to prolong life.
7. Person who has not reached the age of maturity, which in most states is 18.
8. Confidential information that has been told to a physician for attorney by the patient.
9. State statute allowing persons 18 years of age or older and of sound mind to make a gift of any or all body parts for purposes of organ transplantations or medical research.

Summarize each patient right from "A Patient's Bill of Rights" in your own words.

Right	Summary
Respect	The patient has the right to consideration from health care personnel.
Information	The patient has the right to information concerning diagnosis, treatment, and prognosis from any reliable source in understandable language.
Decisions	Patients have the right to make their own decisions about their treatment and have the right to refuse treatment.
Advance directive	Patients have the right to make their desires known and honored.
Privacy	Privacy is a basic human right of dignity.
Confidentiality	A patient can expect to have personal information protected and not disclosed without reason.

(continued)

Right	Summary
Records	The patient has the right to see his or her own records and have them explained in plain language.
Patient request	The patient has the right to expect reasonable response to his or her health requests.
Business relationships	The patient has the right to be informed of all business relationships of his or her medical providers.
Research	The patient has the right to consent or decline medical research activities with full knowledge of that research.
Continuity of care	The patient has the right to reasonable continuity of care, or to be notified if care is not available.
To be informed	The patient has the right to know of medical facility policy and practices that relate to his or her care.

Test 1

Fill in the Blanks

1. standard of care
2. give permission or consent
3. select
4. privacy
5. professional courtesy

Multiple Choice

Write the letter of the correct answer in the blank.

6. c
7. a
8. d
9. d
10. a

True or False?

11. T
12. F
13. T
14. T
15. T

Test 2

Fill in the Blanks

1. Do Not Resuscitate (DNR)
2. durable power of attorney
3. advance directive,
4. Privileged communication
5. self-determination

Multiple Choice

Write the letter of the correct answer in the blank.

1. a
2. a
3. d
4. a
5. a

True or False?

11. T
12. T
13. T
14. F
15. T

Chapter 6

Worksheet 1

Define the terms.

1. limit
2. court-awarded payment to compensate a patient for an injury
3. neglect, as in neglect of duty
4. the continuous sequence of events, unbroken by any intervening cause, that produces an injury and without which the injury would not have occurred
5. obligation or responsibility
6. doing an act or performing a duty
7. performing an illegal act
8. the improper performance of an otherwise proper or lawful act
9. slight or token payment awarded by the court
10. the failure to perform an action when it is necessary
11. the injury was closely related to the physician's neglect
12. monetary award by a court to a person who has been harmed in an especially malicious and willful way
13. Latin phrase meaning "the thing speaks for itself"
14. Latin phrase meaning "the thing has been decided"
15. a civil wrong

Fill in the blanks.

plaintiff wrongful or negligent act denial

Answer the questions.

1. a.   Duty: Once a physician–patient relationship has been established, the physician has a duty to assist the patient with his or her medical care. Example: Physician refused to give care to established patient without giving a reason or an appropriate alternative for care in writing.

   b.   Dereliction of duty: Neglect. The physician's performance did not comply with the acceptable standard of care. Example: Once a diagnosis of pneumonia was made, the physician did not prescribe antibiotics.

   c.   Direct cause: There are no intervening forces between a patient's injury and the physician's action. This must be proven. Example: If a patient claims treatment given by physician caused back and neck damage later in the day, patient could not establish direct cause if he or she was involved in a traffic accident on the way home from the doctor's office.

   d.   Damages: Injuries caused by the defendant. Example: The patient must prove there was an injury of some kind to the plaintiff. The patient cannot prove damages if the physician is running late in the office.

2. Answers will vary. Use this question for class discussion.

3. *Res ipsa loquitur* means "the thing speaks for itself," or the matter is so obvious that no further explanation is needed. *Res judicata* means "the thing has been decided," or that the case has been decided by the court and may not be the subject of another lawsuit.

4. No. If it were a legitimate defense, everyone would use it. Medical professionals must know the law and abide by it.

Worksheet 2

Define the terms.

1. using methods other than going to court to solve civil disputes
2. submitting a dispute for resolution to a person other than a judge
3. a person chosen to decide a disagreement between two parties
4. legal responsibility for one's own actions
5. using the opinion of a third party to resolve a civil dispute in a nonbinding decision
6. additional component to an insurance policy
7. the act of determining the outcome of a case outside a courtroom; not an indication of legal wrongdoing

Answer the questions.

1. The "clock" does not start to run counting down the period of the statute of limitations until the injury is discovered. It also does not run if fraud is involved.
2. Because there is a breach of a promise or a contract violation. This does not involve negligence in the care of the patient or injury to the patient.
3. Good: (a) Some believe that fear of law suit will keep poorly prepared physicians from practicing or will motivate them to seek more training. (b) Those who are injured deserve compensation for their loss.

   Bad: (a) Many physicians cannot afford the high cost of liability and malpractice insurance and are not selecting careers, such as OB/GYN, because of that. Consumers need these services. (b) Many physicians are ordering more expensive tests for patients than they need in an effort to "cover themselves" legally. This is adding to the high cost of health care.

Test 1

Fill in the Blanks

1. tort
2. Duty
3. Nonfeasance
4. Misfeasance
5. *res ipsa loquitur*
6. physician
7. Nominal damages
8. Punitive damages
9. *Res judicata*
10. borrowed servant

Multiple Choice

Write the letter of the correct answer in the blank.

11. c
12. b
13. b
14. d
15. b

Test 2

Fill in the Blanks

1. *respondeat superior*
2. Liability insurance
3. arbitration
4. Alternative Dispute Resolution (ADR)
5. Liable

Multiple Choice

Write the letter of the correct answer in the blank.

6. a
7. b
8. a
9. b
10. a

True or False?

11. T
12. T
13. F
14. T
15. T

Chapter 7

Worksheet 1

Define the terms.

1. a postmortem examination of organs and tissues to determine the cause of death
2. a public health officer who holds an investigation (inquest) if a person's death is from an unknown or violent cause
3. statistics, figures, or information
4. an investigation held by a public official such as a coroner to determine the cause of death
5. after death
6. responsibilities the physician owes to the public
7. major events or facts from a person's life, such as live births, deaths, induced termination of pregnancy, and marriages

Answer the questions.

1. Births; stillbirths; deaths; communicable illnesses or diseases; drug abuse; certain injuries such as rape, gunshots, knife wounds, and animal bites; abuse of children, spouses, and elders; marriages, divorces and terminations of pregnancy
2. Department of Health and Human Services, Centers for Disease Control and Prevention, National Health Center for Health Statistics, Public Health Service
3. (1) Request information from the state registrar for specific requirements on completing certificates. (2) Type or print. (3) Complete all blanks. (4) Verify spellings. (5) Do not use rubber stamps. (6) File originals with appropriate registrar. (7) Avoid abbreviations. (8) Do not alter certificate or erase. (9) Keep a copy in patient file.

Worksheet 2

Define the terms.

1. physical abuse, neglect, exploitation, and abandonment of adults 60 years and older
2. disease that can be easily be transmitted from one person to another and that is a general threat to the public
3. sexually transmitted disease

Answer the questions.

1. diphtheria, tetanus toxoid, pertussis vaccine (DPT), measles, mumps, rubella (MMR), polio live, polio inactive, hepatitis B vaccine, tuberculosis
2. It is a legitimate medical diagnosis, and a physician cannot return a child into a situation if there is suspicion of abuse or neglect.
3. the amendment to the Older Americans Act of 1987
4. reporting of all child abuse cases as defined by the state

Worksheet 3

Define the terms.

1. acquired physical or psychological dependence on a drug
2. Bureau of Narcotics and Dangerous Drugs—agency of the federal government responsible for enforcing laws covering statutes of addictive drugs
3. Drug Enforcement Administration—division of the Department of Justice that enforces the Controlled Substances Act of 1970
4. Food and Drug Administration—agency within the Department of Health and Human Services that ultimately enforces drug sales and other distribution
5. federal statute regulating the manufacture and distribution of drugs that are capable of causing dependency
6. development of an emotional dependence on a drug due to repeated use

Answer the questions.

1. Physicians and nurses only may administer drugs.
2. No. A state government may be more restrictive but not less restrictive regarding the handling of controlled substances and their records
3. date of distribution, patient name, signature of person administering the drug
4. It must be poured down a drain or flushed down a toilet with two people witnessing. This must be recorded in the narcotics log signed by both witnesses.
5. Alert the physician to license renewal dates. Maintain accurate inventory records. Keep all controlled substances in a secure and locked cabinet. Keep prescription blanks and pads in a secure and locked cabinet.

Worksheet 4

Define the terms.

1. a grading or ranking system for controlled substances (from Schedule I to Schedule V)
2. germicides, cleaning solvents, and pharmaceuticals that can create a hazardous situation
3. trash, including paper goods, bottles, cardboard, and cans
4. any waste that contains or is contaminated with liquid or solid radioactive material
5. any waste that has the potential to carry disease

Answer the questions.

1. The environment, the employee, the patient, and other people are protected.
2. It is separated at the point of origin.

Test 1

Fill in the Blanks

1. inquest
2. death certificate
3. coroner
4. Autopsy
5. Vital statistics

Multiple Choice

Write the letter of the correct answer in the blank.

6. a   **8.** a   **10.** b
7. c   **9.** b

Test 2

Fill in the Blanks

1. National Childhood   **3.** Elder abuse
Vaccine Injury Act
                                  4. the hospital.
2. Child Abuse Prevention and
Treatment Act   **5.** criminal

True or False?

6. F   **8.** T   **10.** T
7. T   **9.** T

Test 3

Fill in the Blanks

1. Food and Drug   **3.** Drug Enforcement   **5.** Bureau of Narcotics and
Administration (FDA)   Administration (DEA)   Dangerous Drugs (BNDD)

2. Addiction   **4.** two

True or False?

6. T   **8.** F   **10.** F
7. T   **9.** F

Test 4

Fill in the Blanks

1. V

2. II

3. solid chemical radioactive infectious

4. Infectious waste

True or False?

5. F

6. T

Chapter 8

Worksheet 1

Define the terms.

1. overrule
2. Equal Employment Opportunity Commission
3. employment takes place at the will of either the employer or the employee
4. person who employs the services of another and provides payment for those services
5. If an employer withholds employment taxes from a person's income, then that person is considered an employee.
6. Title VII of the Civil Rights Act of 1964 prohibits discrimination in employment based on race, color, religion, sex, or national origin.

Answer the questions.

1. Religious discrimination is allowed in certain religious institutions.
2. EEOC monitors Title VII, and the Justice Department enforces the statute.
3. Many courts have ruled employee handbooks constitute an employee contract.
4. It authorizes the EEOC to sue employers in federal court on behalf of a class of people or an individual whose Title VII rights have been violated.
5. Employers must treat pregnant women as they would any other employee, providing they can still do the job.

Worksheet 2

Define the terms.

1. medication route other than the alimentary canal (oral and rectal), including subcutaneous, intravenous, and intramuscular routes
2. disease-producing microorganisms transmitted by means of blood and body fluids containing blood
3. Americans with Disabilities Act of 1990
4. Occupational Safety and Health Act of 1970
5. Health Maintenance Organization Act of 1973
6. Consolidated Omnibus Budget Reconciliation Act of 1985
7. Fair Labor Standards Act of 1938
8. Federal Insurance Contribution Act of 1935

Answer the questions.

1. Rehabilitation Act of 1973
2. Health Maintenance Organization Act
3. Any employee who has occupational exposure (defined as reasonable anticipation that the employee's duties will result in skin, mucous membrane, eye, or parenteral contact with bloodborne pathogens or other potential infectious material)

4. Each employee with occupational exposure must be offered the hepatitis B vaccination at the expense of the employer.

5. Hospitals can negotiate an agreement with their employees to establish a work period of 14 days.

Worksheet 3

Define the terms.

1. person or institution to whom a debt is owed
2. Employee Retirement Income Security Act
3. point in time, such as after ten years of employment, when an employee's rights to receive benefits from a retirement plan cannot be withdrawn
4. Family and Medical Leave Act
5. unfair or unequal treatment
6. agency that is contracted to collect debt
7. legal method for providing some protection to debtors and establishing a fair method for distribution of the debtor's assets to creditors
8. one who is in debt or owes money to another person or institution
9. Federal Communications Commission

Answer the questions.

1. to get the employee back to work as soon as possible
2. The employee may sue and recover damages for injuries caused by non-employees.
3. Truth in Lending Act of 1969
4. Responses will vary. Use this question for classroom discussion.

Worksheet 4

Define the terms.

1. how long a medical practice has to file suit to collect on a past-due account
2. laws that seek to preserve the private competitive market system by prohibiting activities that are anticompetitive
3. court order to immediately stop an activity and not attempt any further violation
4. National Labor Relations Act

Fill in the Blanks

1. The Sherman Antitrust Act
2. National Labor Relations Act

True or False?

1. F	3. F	5. T
2. T	4. T	6. T

Test 1

Fill in the Blanks

1. preempt
2. Employment-at-will
3. VII
4. Equal Employment Opportunity Commission (EEOC)
5. Pregnancy Discrimination

True or False?

6. T
7. T
8. T
9. T
10. F

Test 2

Fill in the Blanks

1. Rehabilitation Act
2. OSHA
3. Occupational Exposure to Bloodborne Pathogen Standards
4. Health Maintenance Organization Act
5. Social Security Act

True or False?

6. F
7. T
8. T
9. F
10. T

Test 3

Fill in the Blanks

1. Employee Retirement Income Security Act
2. as soon as possible
3. full written disclosure about interest rates and finance charges
4. Bankruptcy
5. Family and Medical Leave Act

True or False?

6. F
7. F
8. F
9. T
10. T

Chapter 9

Worksheet 1

Define the terms.

1. Joint Commission on Accreditation of Healthcare Organizations
2. Problem-Oriented Medical Record

Fill in the blanks.

1. a. admitting diagnosis
   b. physician exam and history
   c. complications
   d. consents
   e. consultations
   f. clinical notes and reports
   g. discharge summary

2. a. medical record of patient from birth to death
   b. continuous management of a patient's health care
   c. data and statistics
   d. track ongoing patterns of patient's health
   e. documentation of patient condition and treatment
   f. legal document

True or False?

1. T
2. T
3. T
4. F
5. T
6. F

Worksheet 2

Define the terms.

1. Even for a brief period of time the medical record is incomplete.
2. Problem-Oriented Medical Record
3. Subjective, Objective, Assessment, Plan

Fill in the Blanks

1. a. double-check that you have the correct chart
   b. legible writing
   c. patient's name on every page
   d. all entries signed and dated
   e. brief and complete
   f. correct spelling and accepted abbreviations
   g. no erasing
   h. all phone calls and correspondence noted
   i. all actions taken as result of telephone conversations documented
   j. all missed appointments documented
   k. no derogatory or defensive language

2. (a) Shred. (b) Do not fax unless you know the intended receiver is aware of your action. (c) Fax cover sheet marked "Confidential." (d) Use fax for patient information only when

absolutely necessary. (d) Fax only necessary documents. (e) Do not email confidential material. (f) Guard the computer screen from being viewed by unauthorized viewers, (g) Do not leave confidential material unattended on a fax machine.

Worksheet 3

Define the terms.

1. made known
2. provides private citizens some control over information that the federal government collects about them
3. freedom of information laws
4. protects patients who are receiving treatment for drug and alcohol abuse
5. American Health Information Management Association

Fill in the Blanks

1. original
2. federal agencies and government contractors.
3. state agencies.
4. physician's permission.
5. ten years after infant reaches maturity.
6. ten years after the most recent encounter.
7. permanently.
8. permanently.
9. the office, a warehouse, microfilm (CD, DVD, etc.).
10. emergency care necessitates divulging information for the sake of the patient.

Worksheet 4

Define the terms.

1. No health care worker should know any more personal information about a patient than is necessary to meet their needs.
2. when something is ordered by the court
3. a written order requiring a person to appear in court, give testimony, and bring particular records, files, books, or information

Fill in the Blanks

1. subpoena.
2. record keeping.
3. on the due date.
4. patient, physician, physician's attorney.
5. the requesting attorney.

Test 1

Multiple Choice

Write the letter of the correct answer in the blank.

1. c   **3.** a   **5.** c
2. c   **4.** b   **6.** b

Fill in the Blanks

7. problem-oriented medical record.

8. chronological POMR

9. POMR

10. Joint Commission on Accreditation of Healthcare Organizations

Test 2

Multiple Choice

Write the letter of the correct answer in the blank.

1. a   **4.** b   **7.** a   **10.** d
2. c   **5.** c   **8.** b
3. b   **6.** a   **9.** c

Test 3

Multiple Choice

Write the letter of the correct answer in the blank.

1. b   **4.** b   **7.** b   **10.** c
2. c   **5.** b   **8.** c
3. a   **6.** c   **9.** c

Test 4

Multiple Choice

Write the letter of the correct answer in the blank.

1. a   **3.** c   **5.** a   **7.** c
2. b   **4.** c   **6.** c   **8.** b

Chapter 10

Worksheet

Define the terms.

1. A private or public health care entity that facilitates the processing of nonstandard electronic transactions into HIPAA transactions (e.g., a billing service).

2. Health care organizations covered under HIPAA regulations such as public health authorities, health care clearinghouses, self-insured employers, life insurers, information systems vendors, and universities.

3. A number assigned to an employer for purposes of identification.

4. A standard number based on an employer's tax ID number or EIN that is used in all electronic transmissions.

5. An individual or group plan that provides or pays for medical care.

6. A national data bank that collects and reports disclosures of actions taken against health care practitioners, providers, and vendors for noncompliance and fraudulent activities.

7. Regulates the privacy of patient's health information.

8. Permission to use information based on the reason for knowing, or use of, the information.

9. The application of communication and information to medical practice, research, and education.

10. The provider must make a reasonable effort to limit the disclosure of patient information to only the minimum amount that is necessary to accomplish the purpose of the request.

11. A written statement which details the provider's privacy practices.

12. The federal office that investigates violations of HIPAA.

13. A requirement that all covered entities under HIPAA must be in compliance with the privacy, security, and electronic data provisions by April 14, 2003.

14. Any individually identifiable information that relates to the physical or mental condition or the provision of health care to an individual.

15. Penalties or fines.

16. Occurs when the state privacy laws are stricter than the privacy standards established by HIPAA.

17. The use of communications and information technologies to provide health care services to people at a distance.

18. Functions that a health care provider can perform.

19. A wireless system that is used by physicians and nurses to access patient information.

Answer the question.

1. In today's world it is becoming increasingly uncommon for a patient to see only one physician. Many patients are referred to other health care professionals, including physicians, by their primary care physician (PCP). This has happened mainly with the advent of the DRG system to minimize costs. This system required that Medicare patients have a PCP who would then act as a "gatekeeper." (See Chapter 4 in *Fremgen's Medical Law and Ethics*).

2. HIPAA was originally meant to control the *electronic* transfer of patient information. Electronic means are necessary for billing purpose including charges to patients' insurance companies. It would be extremely difficult for any physician to practice without the use of any electronic equipment. Currently, HIPAA has been used by health care professionals and institutions to limit the access to any patient information without the patient's written authority.

3. In many cases, a nursing home assumes full responsibility for the care of its residents. When this happens, then the nursing home may have to deny a person or entity access to medical and personal information if it believes that the resident may be injured as a result of divulging this information.

4. a.   When it is psychotherapy notes

  b.   Results of certain laboratory test that are only divulged to the physician who ordered the tests

  c.   If they are prison inmates

  d.   For certain research projects in which limited access has been granted in advance

  e.   If the PHI is part of a government record

  f.   If the PHI was obtained under the promise of confidentiality

Test

Fill in the Blanks

1. Health Insurance Portability and Accountability

2. Employer Identification Number

3. Sanctions

4. Telemedicine

5. Wireless Local Area

Multiple Choice

Write the letter of the correct answer in the blank.

6. d

7. b

8. c

9. d

10. d

Matching

In the blank, write the letter of the term that correctly matches the definition.

11. e

12. d

13. b

14. a

15. c

True of False?

16. F

17. T

18. T

19. F

20. T

Chapter 11

Worksheet 1

Define the terms.

1. American Medical Association
2. American Association of Medical Assistants
3. declare without proof
4. to find fault with
5. the act of forcing out

Answer the questions.

1. Health care professionals must take their moral and value systems and the codes of their profession and apply them in daily work.
2. It is a critical thinking approach that examines important considerations such as fairness, the impact of the decisions on society, and the future implications of decisions.
3. Yes, the principles, if not the exact language, are found in many of the professional codes of today.
4. The AMA is required to report the allegation to the state licensing board.
5. The theme is concern for the subject in medical experimentation.
6. Its function is to interpret the Principles of Medical Ethics for the AMA.
7. Both deal with decisions of right and wrong. They differ in that they deal with slightly different topics in the care of the patient. Whereas the AMA is written for physicians who may make life-and-death decisions, the AAMA is written for medical assistants who deal with the daily care and management of patients.

Worksheet 2

Define the terms.

1. the administration of a lethal agent by another person to a patient for the purpose of relieving intolerable and incurable suffering
2. the replacement of a defective or malfunctioning gene
3. statement of intent
4. a form of research that will not directly benefit the research subject
5. a form of research that might directly benefit the research subject
6. research in which neither the experimenter nor the patient knows who is getting the research treatment

Answer the questions.

1. Fee splitting is the practice of a physician's accepting payment from another physician for the referral of a patient.
2. This group has no hope of benefiting from the experiment.
3. The physician is responsible.
4. Ideally, the preference should be stated before the individual is hired. The employee should go directly to the employer and explain how he or she feels and try to reach an agreement respecting the wishes and needs of both parties.
5. Answers will vary. Use this question for class discussion.

Test 1

Multiple Choice

Write the letter of the correct answer in the blank.

1. c	**4.** c	**7.** b
2. a	**5.** b	**8.** a
3. c	**6.** b	**9.** a

Test 2

Multiple Choice

Write the letter of the correct answer in the blank.

1. b	**4.** b	**7.** a
2. c	**5.** a	**8.** b
3. b	**6.** a	**9.** a

Chapter 12

Worksheet 1

Define the terms.

1. the injection of seminal fluid that contains male sperm into the female's vagina from her husband, partner, or donor by some means other that sexual intercourse
2. a procedure in which a donor's sperm is used
3. a procedure in which sperm from the woman's husband or partner is used
4. birth control
5. the name given to an unborn child between the second and twelfth weeks after conception
6. sterilization of certain categories of persons, such as the insane and mentally retarded, in order to prevent them from passing on defective genes to their children
7. the science that studies methods for controlling certain characteristics in offspring
8. unborn child from the third month after conception until birth
9. time before birth during which the fetus is developing
10. the process of combing ovum and sperm outside of a woman's body
11. the process of medically altering reproductive organs so as to terminate the ability to produce offspring
12. a woman who agrees to bear a child for another couple
13. sterilization undertaken to save the mother's life or protect her health

Answer the questions.

1. Each student will express his or her own opinion. May be used for class discussion and debate
2. A surrogate parenting contract was drawn up between Ms. Mary Beth Whitehead and Mr. and Mrs. Stern. Ms. Whitehead was artificially inseminated with Mr. Stern's sperm, and a baby girl was born. Ms. Whitehead took the child and went into hiding. She was discovered, and the New Jersey courts eventually granted parental rights to her, but granted custody to the Sterns, citing the best interests of the child. (Each student should describe the case and state his or her own personal comment.)
3. Entering the uterus and removing embryos, leaving only two or three. The embryos are then destroyed. (Students' positions will vary.)

Worksheet 2

Define the terms.

1. able to survive outside the uterus
2. termination of a pregnancy that occurs naturally before the fetus is viable
3. an abortion caused by artificial, means including medications and surgical procedures
4. the science describing the biological influence that parents have on their offspring
5. investigation and counsel by interview and conferencing to determine prospective parents' potential for passing on genetic traits to offspring
6. surgical procedure to withdraw amniotic fluid from the pregnant uterus for testing; most common means of genetic testing during pregnancy

Answer the questions.

1. Abortions can be performed during the first two trimesters of pregnancy. During the third trimester, they can be performed only to save the life of the mother or to protect maternal health.

2. (a) Nineteenth century common law—Abortion performed prior to six weeks gestation not illegal. (b) 1859—AMA adopts anti-abortion position. (c) States begin passing statutes against abortion unless performed to same a mother's life. (d) 1960s–1970s—Various states amend laws to allow abortion under certain circumstances. (e) *Roe v. Wade* legalizes abortion in first and second trimester, and in third trimester only to save the life of the mother.

3. The ruling states that a husband cannot prevent the mother from having an abortion. Students opinions about the ruling will vary. (You may use this question for class discussion.)

Test 1

Multiple Choice

Write the letter of the correct answer in the blank.

1. b	**3.** a	**5.** c
2. b	**4.** c	

True or False?

6. T	**8.** T	**10.** T
7. F	**9.** T	

Test 2

Multiple Choice

Write the letter of the correct answer in the blank.

1. c	**3.** b
2. c	**4.** b

True or False?

6. T	**8.** F	**10.** F
7. T	**9.** F	

Chapter 13

Worksheet 1

Define the terms.

1. died
2. vegetative condition
3. electroencephalogram—test that measures activity of the brain
4. stiffness that occurs in a dead body

Answer the questions.

1. It represented the first time a family had requested a court to approve the removal of a respirator from a permanently comatose patient and won the case.
2. This is a condition of coma in which the patient will remain permanently.
3. Answers will vary. You may use this question for class discussion. Be aware that this may be a sensitive issue for some students.

Worksheet 2

Define the terms.

1. low body temperature
2. referring to the heart and lung function
3. irreversible coma
4. Uniform Determination of Death Act
5. to discontinue after initiated
6. never starting treatment

Answer the questions.

1. If the surgeon waits until all cardiac function has ceased, many of the potential donor's organs are useless as transplants.
2. Death occurs when there is an irreversible cessation of all brain function. It is based on the premise that the brain is responsible for all bodily functions and once the brain stops functioning, all other bodily functions will stop.
3. The criteria include consideration of whether the patient (a) is unreceptive and unresponsive with a total unawareness of externally applied, and even painful, stimuli; (b) has no spontaneous movements or breathing, as well as an absence of response to stimuli such as pain, touch, sound, or light; and (c) has no reflexes with fixed dilated pupils, lack of eye movement, and lack of deep tendon reflexes.

Worksheet 3

Define the terms
1. the intentional killing of a terminally ill patient — illegal in all states
2. allowing a patient to die naturally; includes withholding fluids and nutrition
3. physician-assisted suicide
4. statement favored by the Catholic Church over the term "passive euthanasia"
5. treatment or procedure that is morally required, such as fluids and comfort measures
6. treatment and procedure that is morally expendable, not serving any useful purpose

Answer the questions.
1. a. Respect for patient self–determination
   b. Means for harvesting viable organs for transplant
   c. Relief for family
   d. Means to end suffering
2. a. We can't know for sure that a person is terminal
   b. May find a cure
   c. May be misused by a family who does not want to spend any more money
   d. May be used indiscriminately
   e. It is just not a good practice for society
   f. There is value and dignity in every human life
   g. Euthanasia will erode the very basis of the medical profession
   h. The sick and dying may have a fear of involuntary euthanasia
   i. Only God has dominion over life and death
3. Unique and personal for each student

Worksheet 4

Define the terms.
1. a written statement in which a person states the type and amount of care he or she wishes to receive during a terminal illness and as death approaches
2. popular name for an advance directive
3. cardiopulmonary resuscitation
4. do not resuscitate
5. another person who makes health care decisions for an incompetent person
6. voluntary euthanasia
7. a legal document that empowers another person to make health care decisions for an incompetent patient

Answer the questions.

1. (a) Persons with head injury who are conscious but incoherent or in coma from which they may not recover; (b) persons in irreversible coma; (c) persons with brain damage; (d) persons with degenerative brain disease and a terminal disease.

2. CPR, respirator, tube feeding, kidney dialysis, chemotherapy, IVs, surgery, diagnostic tests, antibiotics, transfusion, medication for pain

Test 1

Multiple Choice

Write the letter of the correct answer in the blank.

1. a
2. b

3. a
4. b

5. c

True or False?

6. F
7. T

8. T
9. F

10. T

Test 2

Multiple Choice

Write the letter of the correct answer in the blank.

1. b
2. a

3. c
4. b

5. a

True or False?

6. T
7. T

8. T
9. T

10. T

Test 3

Multiple Choice

Write the letter of the correct answer in the blank.

1. a
2. c

3. a
4. a

5. a

True or False?

6. T   8. F   10. T
7. T   9. T

Test 4

Multiple Choice

Write the letter of the correct answer in the blank.

1. c   3. c
2. b

True or False?

6. T   8. T   10. F
7. T   9. T